Krishna's

Analytical

SOLID GEOMETRY

(Analytical Geometry of Three Dimensions)

(For Honours & Post-Graduate Students of all Indian Universities)

By

A.R. Vasishtha
Ex. Head,
Department of Mathematics
Meerut College, Meerut (U.P.)
(C.C.S. University, Meerut)

D.C. Agarwal
Retd. Principal & Head,
Department of Mathematics
S.S.V. College, Hapur (U.P.)
(C.C.S. University, Meerut)

[redacted] [redacted]

KRISHNA Prakashan Media (P) Ltd.
KRISHNA HOUSE, 11, Shivaji Road, Meerut-250 001 (U.P.), India

Krishna's

Analytical

SOLID GEOMETRY

(Analytical Geometry of Three Dimensions)

First Edition : 1980

Fifteenth Edition : 2021

Edition : 2023

Revision and Proof Reading done by: **Dr. A. K. Vasishtha**

Book Code No. : 211–15 (D)

[redacted] [redacted]

Published by : **Sugam Rastogi & Kanupriya Rastogi**
for **KRISHNA** Prakashan Media (P) Ltd.
11, Shivaji Road, Meerut – 250 001 (U.P.) India.
Phones : 91.121.2644766, 2642946, 4026111, 4026112 Fax : 91.121.2645855
Website : www.krishnaprakashan.com
E-mail : info@krishnaprakashan.com

Printed at : Vimal Offset Printers, Meerut.

PREFACE

This book has been written to meet the requirements of the Honours and Post-graduate students of various Indian Universities, and is so written as to cover the courses commonly prescribed for these examinations. In this book only those topics have been given which are generally prescribed in the Post-graduate syllabi of many universities. The topics including plane, straight line, sphere and cone have been discussed in our book on 'Analytical Geometry of three dimensions' for degree classes and the reader is advised to consult the book if needed.

The book has been written in a very simple and lucid style so that both students and teachers will find it an interesting study. Care has been taken to explain the fundamental principles fully and rigorously. Each article is illustrated by means of typical examples fully solved, so as to give the student a clear idea of the type of examples he has to solve.

Any suggestions for the improvement of the book will be thankfully received.

Finally, our thanks are due to the publishers and the printers who have taken great pains in producing the book in the present nice form.

— The Authors

PREFACE TO THE REVISED EDITION

In this edition the book has been thoroughly revised. Many more questions asked in various university examinations have been added to enhance the utility of the book. Suggestions for the further improvement of the book will be gratefully received.

— The Authors

CONTENTS

Chapters *Pages*

1
Central Conicoids

§ 1. Introduction.

While studying 'The Plane' in Analytical Geometry of three dimensions we learn that the general equation of first degree in x, y and z represents a plane surface. In a similar way the general equation of second degree in x, y and z namely

$$ax^2+by^2+cz^2+2fyz+2gzx+2hxy+2ux+2vy+2wz+d=0 \quad \ldots(1)$$

always represents a **conicoid** or a **quadratic surface.**

The equation (1) by a proper transformation of axes can be reduced to the following **standard form**

$$ax^2+by^2+cz^2=1. \quad \ldots(2)$$

The standard form (2) is called the **central conicoid.**

Now we shall discuss below some important properties of the central conicoid given by (2).

(a) *The origin is the centre of the conicoid*

$$ax^2+by^2+cz^2=1.$$

Let $P(x_1, y_1, z_1)$ be any point on the central conicoid (2), so that we have

$$ax_1^2+by_1^2+cz_1^2=1$$

which can also be written as

$$a(-x_1)^2+b(-y_1)^2+c(-z_1)^2=1. \quad \ldots(3)$$

The relation (3) shows that the point $Q(-x_1, -y_1, -z_1)$ will also lie on (2) if $P(x_1, y_1, z_1)$ lies on (2). The middle point of the chord PQ is $(0, 0, 0)$. This shows that all chords of the surface (2) which pass through the origin are bisected at the origin. Therefore the surface (2) has a centre and it is at the origin. Thus origin is the centre of the central conicoid (2) and due to this property the surface (2) is called a central conicoid.

(b) *To prove that the co-ordinate planes bisect all chords perpendicular to them.*

Let $P(x_1, y_1, z_1)$ be a point on the central conicoid (2), then clearly the point $Q(-x_1, y_1, z_1)$ also lies on it. The middle point of the chord PQ is $(0, y_1, z_1)$ which clearly lies on the YOZ plane *i.e.* the plane $x=0$. The d.r.'s of the chord PQ are $2x_1, 0, 0$ *i.e.* 1, 0, 0 showing that the chord PQ is perpendicular to the plane YOZ. Hence we conclude that the co-ordinate plane YOZ bisects all chords perpendicular to it. Similarly we can prove that the co-ordinate planes ZOX and XOY also bisect all chords perpendicuar to them respectively.

Hence the central conicoid (2) is symmetrical with respect to all the three co-ordinate planes and these planes are called the **principal planes of thc central conicoid.**

The three principal planes (*i.e.* the co-ordinate planes in this case) taken in pairs intersect in three lines (*i.e.* the co-ordinate axes in this case) which are called the **principal axes** of the central conicoid.

(c) The standard form (2) of the central conicoid can take the following three forms each of which represents a surface with a definite name assigned to it :

(i) $\frac{x^2}{a^2}+\frac{y^2}{b^2}+\frac{z^2}{c^2}=1$ **(Ellipsoid)**

(ii) $\frac{x^2}{a^2}+\frac{y^2}{b^2}-\frac{z^2}{c^2}=1$ **(Hyperboloid of one sheet)**

(iii) $\frac{x^2}{a^2}-\frac{y^2}{b^2}-\frac{z^2}{c^2}=1.$ **(Hyperboloid of two sheets)**

Now in the following articles we shall discuss the above three surfaces (*i.e.* central conicoids) in details.

§ 2. The Ellipsoid.

The standard equation of the ellipsoid is given by

$$x^2/a^2+y^2/b^2+z^2/c^2=1. \qquad ...(1)$$

(i) The origin is the centre of the ellipsoid given by (1). Proceeding exactly as in § 1(a) we see that all the chords passing through the origin are bisected at the origin. Therefore the surface (1) has the origin as its centre.

(ii) *The co-ordinate planes bisect all chords perpendicular to them.* Proceeding exactly as in § 1 (b), we see that the co-ordinate planes biscet all chords perpendicular to them. Hence the ellipsoid (1) is symmetrical with respect to all the three co-ordinate planes and these planes are called the **principal planes** of the ellipsoid.

The three principal planes taken in pairs intersect in three lines (*i.e.* the co-ordinate axes in this case) which are called the **principal axes** of the ellipsoid.

(iii) *The ellipsoid is a closed surface.* The equation (1) may be rewritten as

$$y^2/b^2+z^2/c^2=1-x^2/a^2. \quad \ldots(2)$$

If x is numerically greater than a, then from the equation (2) we find that $y^2/b^2+z^2/c^2=$a $-$ve quantity *i.e.* the sum of two perfect squares is a negative quantity which shows that at least one of y and z should be imaginary. Hence it follows that x cannot be numerically greater than a and therefore, the surface exists between the two parallel planes $x=a$ and $x=-a$. In a similar manner it follows that the surface (1) lies only between the parallel planes $y=b$, $y=-b$ and $z=c$, $z=-c$.

Thus the ellipsoid (1) is a closed surface.

(iv) *The intercepts on the co-ordinate axes.* The equations of the x-axis are $y=0, z=0$. It meets the surface (1) in the points $A(a, 0, 0)$ and $A'(-a, 0, 0)$. Therefore, the surface (1) intercepts a length $2a$ on the x-axis. In a similar manner the surface (1) intercepts lengths $2b$ and $2c$ on the y and z axes respectively. These intercepts $2a$, $2b$ and $2c$ are called *the lengths of the principal axes of the ellipsoid.*

(v) *The sections of the ellipsoid by the planes parallel to the co-ordinate planes.* Consider a plane $z=\lambda$ parallel to the XOY plane.

The section of the ellipsoid (1) by the plane $z=\lambda$ is the ellipse given by

$$x^2/a^2+y^2/b^2=1-\lambda^2/c^2, \; z=\lambda. \quad \ldots(3)$$

The lengths of the semi-axes of the ellipse (3) are

$$a\sqrt{(1-\lambda^2/c^2)} \text{ and } b\sqrt{(1-\lambda^2/c^2)}.$$

Now the **following cases arise :**

Case I. *If λ is numerically greater than* c. We have proved in (iii) of this article that the ellipsoid is a closed surface bounded by the planes $x=a$, $x=-a$; $y=b$, $y=-b$ and $z=c$, $z=-c$. Hence λ cannot be numerically greater than c otherwise the section will not be real *i.e.* the plane $z=\lambda$ will not cut the ellipsoid.

Case II. *If $\lambda=c$ or $\lambda=-c$.* In this case (3) becomes

$$x^2/a^2+y^2/b^2=0,$$

showing that $x=0$, $y=0$. Therefore, the section is an infinitesimally small ellipse or in other words the section reduces to the points $(0, 0, c)$ and $(0, 0, -c)$ and both the planes $z=c$ and $z=-c$ are the tangent planes to the ellipsoid (1) at these points.

Case III. *If* $\lambda=0$. In this case (3) becomes

$$x^2/a^2+y^2/b^2=1, \ z=0$$

which is an ellipse in the *XOY* plane.

Case IV. *If* λ *increases from* 0 *to c.* When λ increases from 0 to c, the quantity $(1-\lambda^2/c^2)$ becomes smaller and smaller and vanishes at $\lambda=c$. Hence the lengths $a\sqrt{(1-\lambda^2/c^2)}$ and $b\sqrt{(1-\lambda^2/c^2)}$ of the semi-axes of the ellipse (3) become smaller and smaller and vanish at $\lambda=c$. Hence the ellipses (3) diminish in size as we go away from the *XOY* plane.

Now if we consider the section of the ellipsoid (1) by the plane $z=-\lambda$, all the above arguments hold good.

Similarly the sections of the ellipsoid (1) by the planes parallel to the planes *YOZ* and *ZOX* can be considered.

(vi) **Sketch.** From the above discussion it is possible to draw a rough sketch of the ellipsoid (1) and is given below :

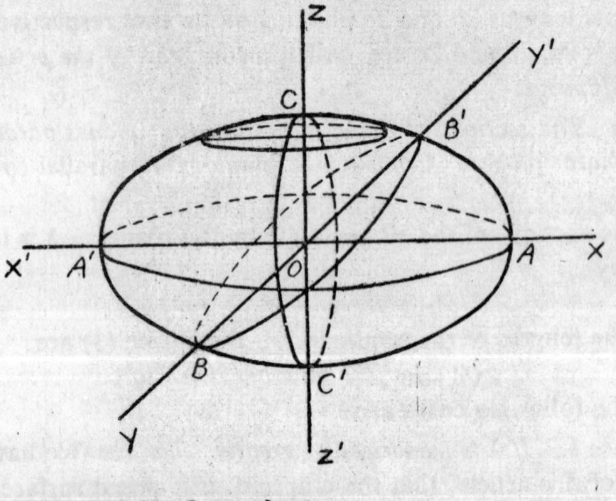

§ 3. The Hyperboloid of one sheet.

The standard equation of the hyperboloid of one sheet is given by

$$x^2/a^2+y^2/b^2-z^2/c^2=1. \qquad \ldots(1)$$

(i) Proceeding exactly as in § 1(a) we find that all the chords passing through the origin are bisected at the origin. Therefore, the surface (1) has the origin as its centre.

(ii) Proceeding exactly as in § 1(b) we observe that the co-ordinate planes bisect all chords perpendicular to them. Hence we conclude that the hyperboloid of one sheet (1) is symmetrical with respect to all the three co-ordinate planes and these planes are called the principal planes of the surface (1).

The three principal planes taken in pairs intersect in three lines (*i.e.* the co-ordrinate axes in the present case) which are called the principal axes of the surface (1).

(iii) *The intercepts on the co-ordinate axes.* The equations of the x-axis are $y=0,\ z=0$. It meets the surface (1) in the points $A(a, 0, 0)$ and $A'(-a, 0, 0)$. Therefore, the surface (1) intercepts a length $2a$ on the x-axis. In a similar manner the surface (1) intercepts a length $2b$ on the y-axis. The z-axis *i.e.* $x=0, y=0$ meets the surface (1) in imaginary points $[z=\pm\sqrt{(-c)}]$ *i.e.* the z-axis does not meet the surface (1) in real points.

(iv) *The section of the hyperboloid of one sheet by the planes parallel to the co-ordinate planes.* The equation of any plane parallel to XOY plane is given by $z=\lambda$. The section of the surface (1) by the plane $z=\lambda$ is the ellipse given by

$$x^2/a^2+y^2/b^2=1+\lambda^2/c^2,\ z=\lambda. \qquad \text{...(2)}$$

The lengths of the semi-axes of the ellipse (2) are

$$a\sqrt{(1+\lambda^2/c^2)} \quad \text{and} \quad b\sqrt{(1+\lambda^2/c^2)}$$

and its centre is $(0, 0, \lambda)$ *i.e.* centre lies on the z-axis at a distance λ from the origin. Since the quantity $\sqrt{(1+\lambda^2/c^2)}$ remains real for all real values of λ, we get an infinite number of elliptical sections as λ increases numerically from 0 to ∞. Also the sizes of these ellipses increase as the value of λ increases *i.e.* as we go away from the XOY plane.

In a similar way the sections of the surface (1) by the planes $z=-\lambda$ are the ellipses on the other side of the plane XOY.

The section of the surface (1) by the plane $x=\lambda$ [*i.e.* plane parallel to YOZ plane) is the hyperbola given by

$$y^2/b^2-z^2/c^2=1-\lambda^2/a^2,\ x=\lambda.$$

Similarly the section of the surface (1) by the plane $y=\lambda$ (*i.e.* a plane parallel to ZOX plane) is the hyperbola given by

$$x^2/a^2-z^2/c^2=1-\lambda^2/b^2,\ y=\lambda.$$

(v) **Sketch.** From the above discussion it is possible to draw a rough sketch of the hyperboloid of one sheet and is given below :

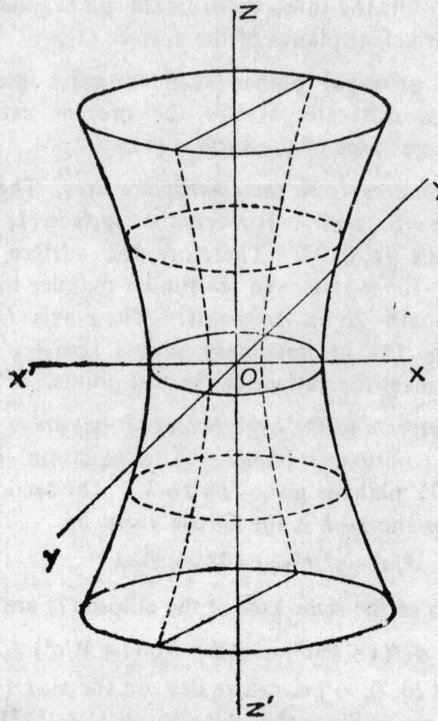

§ 4. The Hyperboloid of two sheets.

Its standard equation is given by

$$x^2/a^2-y^2/b^2-z^2/c^2=1. \quad \ldots(1)$$

(i) Proceeding exactly as in § 1 (a), we find that all the chords passing through the origin are bisected at the origin. Therefore, the surface (1) has the origin as its centre.

(ii) Proceeding exactly as in § 1 (b) we observe that the co-ordinate planes bisect all chords perpendicular to them. Hence we couclude that the hyperboloid of two sheets given by the equation (1) is symmetrical with respect to all the three co-ordinate planes and these planes are called the principal planes of the surface (1).

The three principal planes taken in pairs intersect in three lines (*i.e.* the co-ordinate axes in the present case) which are called the principal axes of the surface (1).

(iii) *The intercepts on the co-ordinate axes.* The x-axis ($y=0$, $z=0$) meets the surface (1) in the points $A(a, 0, 0)$ and $A'(-a, 0, 0)$. Therefore, the surface (1) intercepts a length $2a$ on the x-axis. But the y and z axes do not meet the surface (1) in real points.

(iv) *The sections of the hyperboloid of two sheets by the planes parallel to the co-ordinate planes.* The equation of any plane parallel to YOZ plane is given by $x=\lambda$. The section of the surface (1) by the plane $x=\lambda$ is the ellipse given by

$$y^2/b^2+z^2/c^2=\lambda^2/a^2-1,\ x=\lambda. \quad ...(1)$$

The lengths of the semi-axes of the ellipse (2) are

$$b\sqrt{(\lambda^2/a^2-1)} \quad \text{and} \quad c\sqrt{(\lambda^2/a^2-1)}$$

and its centre is $(\lambda, 0, 0)$ *i.e.* the centre lies on the x-axis at a distance λ from the origin. The ellipses (2) are real when λ is numerically greater than a and increase in size as λ increases beyond a. If λ is numerically less than a, then the ellipses given by (2) become imaginary and hence no portion of the surface lies between the planes $x=a$ and $x=-a$.

The sections of the surface (1) by the planes $y=\lambda$ and $z=\lambda$ are hyperbolas given by the equations

$$x^2/a^2-z^2/c^2=1+\lambda^2/b^2,\ y=\lambda$$

and

$$x^2/a^2-y^2/b^2=1+\lambda^2/c^2,\ z=\lambda$$

respectively.

(v) **Sketch.** From the above discussion it is possible to draw a rough sketch of the hyperboloid of two sheets and is given ahead.

Remark. From the articles 1 to 4 discussed above it follows that the standard equation $ax^2+by^2+cz^2=1$ of the central conicoid represents

(i) an ellipsoid if a, b, c are all positive,

(ii) a hyperboloid of one sheet if any two of a, b, c are positive and the remaining third is negative, and

(iii) a hyperboloid of two sheets if any two of a, b and c are negative and the remaining third is positive.

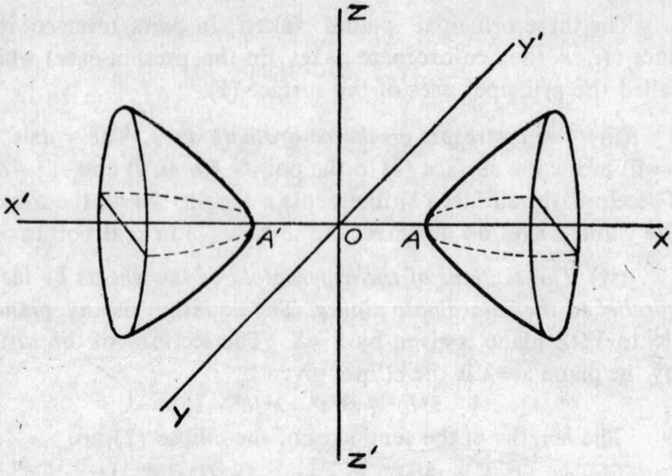

§ 5. The tangent plane.

(A) *To find the equation of the tangent plane to the central conicoid* $ax^2+by+cz^2=1$ *at the point* (x_1, y_1, z_1).

(Kanpur 1979, 81, Lucknow 78, 80)

The equation of the central conicoid is

$$ax^2+by^2+cz^2=1. \quad \text{..(1)}$$

Let (x_1, y_1, z_1) be any given point on the surface (1).

The equations of any line through (x_1, y_1, z_1) and having d.c.'s l, m, n are given by

$$\frac{x-x_1}{l}=\frac{y-y_1}{m}=\frac{z-z_1}{n}=r \text{ (say)}. \quad \text{...(2)}$$

The co-ordinates of any point on the line (2) are $(lr+x_1, mr+y_1, nr+z_1)$. Let the line (2) meet the conicoid (1) at this point, then this point will satisfy the equation (1) and so we have

$$a(lr+x_1)^2+b(mr+y_1)^2+c(nr+z_1)^2=1$$

or $r^2(al^2+bm^2+cn^2)+2r(alx_1+bmy_1+cnz_1)$

$$+(ax_1^2+by_1^2+cz_1^2-1)=0. \quad \text{...(3)}$$

Since the point (x_1, y_1, z_1) lies on the conicoid (1), we have

$$ax_1^2+by_1^2+cz_1^2=1. \quad \text{...(4)}$$

Using (4), the equation (3) becomes

$$r^2(al^2+bm^2+cn^2)+2r(alx_1+bmy_1+cnz_1)=0. \quad \text{..(5)}$$

The equation (5) is a quadratic equation in r and hence gives two values of r *i.e.* the line (2) meets the surface (1) in two points.

If the line (2) is a tangent line to the conicoid (1) at the point (x_1, y_1, z_1) then the two values of r should be coincident. Clearly one value of r given by (5) is zero and hence in order that the line (2) is a tangent line to the conicoid at (x_1, x_1, z_1), the other value of r should also be zero the condition for which is

$$alx_1+bmy_1+cnz_1=0. \qquad ...(6)$$

The tangent plane to the conicoid at (x_1, y_1, z) is the locus of such lines through (x_1, y_1, z_1) that satisfy the condition (6) and so its equation is obtained by eliminating l, m, n between the equations (2) and (6). Hence the required equation of the tangent plane to the conicoid (1) at the point (x_1, y_1, z_1) is given by

$$a(x-x_1)\,x_1+b\,(y-y_1)\,y_1+c\,(z-z_1)\,z_1=0$$

or $$axx_1+byy_1+czz_1=ax_1^2+by_1^2+cz_1^2$$

or $$axx_1+byy_1+czz_1=1, \qquad \text{using (4).}$$

Rule. To write the tangent plane to the conicoid at the point (x_1, y_1, z_1) replace x^2 by xx_1, y^2 by yy_1 and z^2 by zz_1.

(B) *To find the equation of the tangent plane to the ellipsoid* $x^2/a^2+y^2/b^2+z^2/c^2=1$ *at the point* (x_1, y_1, z_1).

Proceeding exactly as in § 5 (A) and replacing a by $1/a^2$, b by $1/b^2$ and c by $1/c^2$ everywhere, the required equation of the tangent plane is given by

$$xx_1/a^2+yy_1/b^2+zz_1/c^2=1.$$

§ 6. The condition of tangency.

(A) *To find the condition that the plane* $lx+my+nz=p$ *may touch the central conicoid* $ax^2+by^2+cz^2=1$.

(Agra 1980, 82; Allahabad 78; Lucknow 82; Kanpur 78; Meerut 71; Rohilkhand 77; Punjab 78; Rajasthan 71)

The equation of the given plane is

$$lx+my+nz=p \qquad ...(1)$$

and the equation of the given conicoid is

$$ax^2+by^2+cz^2=1. \qquad ...(2)$$

Let the plane (1) touch the conicoid (2) at the point (x_1, y_1, z_1). The equation of the tangent plane to the conicoid (2) at the point (x_1, y_1, z_1) is

$$axx_1+byy_1+czz_1=1. \qquad ...(3)$$

If the plane (1) touches the conicoid (2) at the point (x_1, y_1, z_1), then the equations (1) and (3) represent the same plane and hence comparing their coefficients, we have

$$\frac{l}{ax_1}=\frac{m}{by_1}=\frac{c}{cz_1}=\frac{p}{1} \text{ or } x_1=\frac{l}{ap}, y_1=\frac{m}{bp}, z_1=\frac{n}{cp} \qquad ...(4)$$

Again since (x_1, y_1, z_1) lies on (2), we have

$$ax_1^2+by_1^2+cz_1^2=1$$

or $$a\,(l/ap)^2+b\,(m/bp)^2+c\,(n/cp)^2=1, \qquad \text{using (4)}$$

or $$l^2/a+m^2/b+n^2/c=p^2. \qquad ...(5)$$

This is the required condition that the plane (1) touches the conicoid (2).

The co-ordinates of the point of contact of the plane (1) with the conicoid (2) are given by (4) *i.e.* are $(l/ap, m/bp, n/cp)$ where p is given by (5).

Note. Substituting the value of p from (5) in (1), it immediately follows that the planes

$$lx+my+nz=\pm\sqrt{\left(\frac{l^2}{a}+\frac{m^2}{b}+\frac{n^2}{c}\right)}$$

always touch the central conicoid (2).

(B) *To find the condition that the plane* $lx+my+nz=p$ *may touch the ellipsoid* $x^2/a^2+y^2/b^2+z^2/c^2=1$.

(Rajasthan 1974, 76, 78; Kurukshetra 77, Burdwan 76, 80)

Proceeding exactly as in § 6(A) above and replacing a by $1/a^2$, b by $1/b^2$ and c by $1/c^2$ everywhere, the required condition of tangency is given by

$$a^2l^2+b^2m^2+c^2n^2=p^2. \qquad ...(1)$$

Note. From (1), we get

$$p=\pm\sqrt{(a^2l^2+b^2m^2+c^2n^2)}.$$

Using these values of p, we observe that the planes

$$lx+my+nz=\pm\sqrt{(a^2l^2+b^2m^2+c^2n^2)}$$

always touch the ellipsoid $x^2/a^2+y^2/b^2+z^2/c^2=1$.

§ 7. The Director Sphere.

Definition. *The director sphere is the locus of the point of intersection of three mutually perpendicular tangent planes to a central conicoid.* **(Rohilkhand 1979; Allahabad 79)**

The equation of the director sphere. *To find the equation of the director sphere of the central conicoid* $ax^2+by^2+cz^2=1$.

(Rohilkhand 1981; Lucknow 79; Kanpur 66)

The equation of the central conicoid is

$$ax^2+by^2+cz^2=1. \qquad ...(1)$$

Let the equations of three tangent planes to (1) be

$$l_1x+m_1y+n_1z=\sqrt{\{l_1^2/a+m_1^2/b+n_1^2/c\}} \quad ...(2)$$
$$l_2x+m_2y+n_2z=\sqrt{\{l_2^2/a+m_2^2/b+n_2^2/c\}} \quad ...(3)$$
and
$$l_3x+m_3y+n_3z=\sqrt{\{l_3^2/a+m_3^2/b+n_3^2/c\}} \quad ...(4)$$
where l_1, m_1, n_1; l_2, m_2, n_2 and l_3, m_3, n_3 are the actual direction cosines of the normals to the above three tangent planes respectively. If these tangent planes are mutually perpendicular, then we have

$$l_1^2+l_2^2+l_3^2=1,\ m_1^2+m_2^2+m_3^2=1,\ n_1^2+n_2^2+n_3^2=1 \quad ...(5)$$
$$l_1m_1+l_2m_2+l_3m_3=0,\ m_1n_1+m_2n_2+m_3n_3=0,\ n_1l_1+n_2l_2+n_3l_3=0 \quad ...(6)$$

The director sphere of the surface (1), being the locus of the point of intersection of the three tangent planes (2), (3) and (4) is obtained by eliminating l_1, m_1, n_1; l_2, m_2, n_2 and l_3, m_3, n_3 between the equations (2), (3) and (4) with the help of the relations (5) and (6). Squaring and adding (2), (3) and (4), we get

$$(l_1x+m_1y+n_1z)^2+(l_2x+m_2y+n_2z)^2+(l_3x+m_3y+n_3z)^2$$
$$=(1/a)\ \Sigma\ l_1^2+(1/b)\ \Sigma\ m_1^2+(1/c)\ \Sigma\ n_1^2$$
or
$$x^2\ \Sigma\ l_1^2+y^2\ \Sigma\ m_1^2+z^2\ \Sigma\ n_1^2+2yz\ \Sigma\ m_1n_1+2zx\ \Sigma\ n_1l_1$$
$$+2xy\ \Sigma\ l_1m_1=(1/a)+(1/b)+(1/c), \quad \text{using (5)}$$
or
$$x^2+y^2+z^2=(1/a)+(1/b)+(1/c), \quad \text{using (5) and (6).}$$

This is the required equation of the director sphere of the central conicoid (1).

Corollary. If the central conicoid be the ellipsoid

$$x^2/a^2+y^2/b^2+z^2/c^2=1,$$

then proceeding exactly as above, the equation of its director sphere is given by

$$x^2+y^2+z^2=a^2+b^2+c^2.$$

(Punjab 1977; Rajasthan 77; Gurunanakdev 75)

SOLVED EXAMPLES (A)

Ex. 1. *Find the equation of the tangent plane to the central conicoid* $3x^2-5y^2+z^2+2=0$ *at the point* (1, 1, 0).

Solution. The equation of the given conicoid is

$$3x^2-5y^2+z^2+2=0. \quad ...(1)$$

The equation of the tangent plane to the conicoid (1) at the point (1, 1, 0) [See Rule to § 5] is given by

$$3x.1-5y.1+z.0+2=0 \text{ or } 3x-5y+2=0. \quad \textbf{Ans.}$$

Ex. 2(a). *Find the equations to the tangent planes to the ellipsoid* $x^2/a^2+y^2/b^2+z^2/c^2=1$ *which are parallel to the plane*

$lx+my+nz=0$. **(Punjab 1971; Rohilkhand 80)**

Solution. The equation of the given ellipsoid is

$$x^2/a^2+y^2/b^2+z^2/c^2=1. \qquad ...(1)$$

Let the equation of a tangent plane parallel to the plane $lx+my+nz=0$ be given by

$$lx+my+nz=p. \qquad ...(2)$$

If the plane (2) touches the ellipsoid (1) then we have [See § 6(B), given complete proof]

$$a^2l^2+b^2m^2+c^2n^2=p^2 \text{ or } p=\pm\sqrt{(a^2l^2+b^2m^2+c^2n^2)}. \qquad ...(3)$$

Putting the values of p from (3) in (2), the required equations of the tangent planes are

$$lx+my+nz=\pm\sqrt{(a^2l^2+b^2m^2+c^2n^2)}.$$

Ex. 2(b). *Show that the plane* $x+2y+3z=2$ *touches the conicoid* $x^2-2y^2+3z^2=2.$ **(Gurunanakdev 1976)**

Solution. The equation of the given conicoid is

$$x^2-2y^2+3z^2=2 \text{ or } (1/2)\, x^2-y^2+(3/2)\, z^2=1. \qquad ...(1)$$

The equation of the given plane is

$$x+2y+3z=2. \qquad ...(2)$$

If the plane (2) touches the conicoid (1), then applying the condition $l^2/a+m^2/b+n^2/c=p^2$ [See § 6(A)], we have

$$\frac{1}{1/2}+\frac{4}{-1}+\frac{9}{3/2}=4 \text{ or } 2-4+6=4 \text{ or } 4=4$$

which is true. Hence the given plane (2) touches the given conicoid.

Ex. 3(a). *Find the equations to the tangent planes to the hyperboloid* $2x^2-6y^2+3z^2=5$ *which pass through the line*

$3x-3y+6z-5=0=x+9y-3z.$ **(Agra 1976; Rajasthan 74)**

Solution. The equation of the given hyperboloid is

$$2x^2-6y^2+3z^2=5 \text{ or } (2/5)\, x^2-(6/5)\, y^2+(3/5)\, z^2=1. \qquad ...(1)$$

The equations of the given line are

$$3x-3y+6z-5=0,\ x+9y-3z=0. \qquad ...(2)$$

The equation of any plane through the line (2) is

$$3x-3y+6z-5+\lambda\,(x+9y-3z)=0$$

or $$(3+\lambda)\, x+(-3+9\lambda)\, y+(6-3\lambda)\, z=5. \qquad ...(3)$$

If the plane (3) touches the hyperboloid (1), then applying the condition $l^2/a+m^2/b+n^2/c=p^2$ [See § 6(A)], we have

$$(5/2)\,(3+\lambda)^2+(-5/6)\,(-3+9\lambda)^2+(5/3)\,(6-3\lambda)^2=(5)^2$$

or $$15\,(9+6\lambda+\lambda^2)-5\,(9-54\lambda+81\lambda^2)+10\,(36-36\lambda+9\lambda^2)=150$$

or $$3\,(9+6\lambda+\lambda^2)-(9-54\lambda+81\lambda^2)+2\,(36-36\lambda+9\lambda^2)=30$$

or $$-60\lambda^2+60=0 \text{ or } \lambda^2=1 \text{ or } \lambda=\pm 1.$$

When $\lambda=1$, from (3) the equation of the tangent plane is

$$4x+6y+3z=5.$$

When $\lambda=-1$, from (3) the equation of the tangent plane is

$$2x-12y+9z=5.$$

Ex. 3(b). *Find the equation of the tangent plane to the ellipsoid* $7x^2+5y^2+3z^2=60$ *which pass through the line*

$$5y-3z=0=7x+10y-30.$$ **(Kanpur 1974)**

Solution. Proceeding exactly as in Ex. 3(a) the required equations of the tangent planes to the given ellipsoid are

$$7x+5y+3z=30,\ 14x+10y+9z=50.$$

Ex. 4(a). *A tangent plane to the ellipsoid* $x^2/a^2+y^2/b^2+z^2/c^2=1$ *meets the co-ordinates axes in points P, Q and R. Prove that the centroid of the triangle PQR lies on the surface*

$a^2/x^2+b^2/y^2+c^2/z^2=9$. **(Rohilkhand 1978; Kanpur 77; Agra 75)**

Solution. The equation of the given ellipsoid is

$$x^2/a^2+y^2/b^2+z^2/c^2=1. \quad ...(1)$$

Let the co-ordinates of any point on the ellipsoid (1) be (x_1, y_1, z_1).

The equation of the tangent plane to the ellipsoid (1) at the point (x_1, y_1, z_1) is

$$xx_1/a^2+yy_1/b^2+zz_1/c^2=1. \quad ...(2)$$

The plane (2) meets the co-ordinate axes in the points given by $\quad P\ (a^2/x_1, 0, 0)$; $Q\ (0, b^2/y_1, 0)$ and $R\ (0, 0, c^2/z_1)$.

Let (α, β, γ) be the co-ordinates of the centroid of the triangle PQR, then

$$\alpha=\frac{(a^2/x_1)+0+0}{3}=\frac{a^2}{3x_1},\ \beta=\frac{b^2}{3y_1},\ \gamma=\frac{c^2}{3z_1}.$$

$$\therefore\ x_1=\frac{a^2}{3\alpha},\ y_1=\frac{b^2}{3\beta},\ z_1=\frac{c^2}{3\gamma}. \quad ...(3)$$

We are to find the locus of (α, β, γ) for varying values of x_1, y_1, z_1. Since the point (x_1, y_1, z_1) lies on the ellipsoid (1), therefore

$$\frac{x_1^2}{a^2}+\frac{y_1^2}{b^2}+\frac{z_1^2}{c^2}=1. \quad ...(4)$$

Substituting for x_1, y_1, z_1 from (3) in (4), we have

$$\frac{a^4}{9\alpha^2a^2}+\frac{b^4}{9\beta^2b^2}+\frac{c^4}{9\gamma^2c^2}=1$$

or

$$a^2/\alpha^2+b^2/\beta^2+c^2/\gamma^2=9.$$

Hence the locus of the centroid (α, β, γ) is

$$a^2/x^2+b^2/y^2+c^2/z^2=9.$$ **Proved.**

Ex. 4(b). *A tangent plane to the conicoid* $ax^2+by^2+cz^2=1$ *meets the co-ordinate axes in P, Q and R. Prove that the centroid of the triangle PQR lies on the locus*

$$1/(ax^2)+1/(ay^2)+1/(az^2)=9.$$

Solution. Proceed exactly as in Ex. 4(a) above.

Ex. 5(a). *Tangent planes are drawn to the ellipsoid* $x^2/a^2+y^2/b^2+z^2/c^2=1$ *through the point* (α, β, γ). *Prove that the perpendiculars to them from the origin generate the cone*

$$(\alpha x+\beta y+\gamma z)^2=(a^2x^2+b^2y^2+c^2z^2). \qquad \textbf{(Allahabad 1980)}$$

Solution. The equation of the ellipsoid is

$$x^2/a^2+y^2/b^2+z^2/c^2=1. \qquad ...(1)$$

The equation of any plane through the point (α, β, γ) is

$$l(x-\alpha)+m(y-\beta)+n(z-\gamma)=0$$

or
$$lx+my+nz=l\alpha+m\beta+n\gamma. \qquad ...(2)$$

If the plane (2) touches the ellipsoid (1), then we know that $a^2l^2+b^2m^2+c^2n^2=(l\alpha+m\beta+n\gamma)^2$. [See § 6(B)]. ...(3)

Also the equations of the perpendicular from the origin to the plane (2) are given by $x/l=y/m=z/n$. ...(4)

Eliminating l, m, n between (3) and (4), the required equation of the cone generated by the line (4) is given by

$$a^2x^2+b^2y^2+c^2z^2=(lx+my+nz)^2. \qquad \textbf{Proved.}$$

Ex. 5(b). *Tangent planes are drawn to the ellipsoid* $x^2/a^2+y^2/b^2+z^2/c^2=1$ *through the point* (α, β, γ). *Prove that the perpendiculars to them through* (α, β, γ) *generate the cone*

$$\{\alpha(x-\alpha)+\beta(y-\beta)+\gamma(z-\gamma)\}^2=a^2(x-\alpha)^2+b^2(y-\beta)^2+c^2(z-\gamma)^2.$$

Solution. Rewrite all steps of Ex. 5(a) upto the equation (3).

Also the equations of the perpendicular to the plane (2) from the point (α, β, γ) are given by

$$\frac{x-\alpha}{l}=\frac{y-\beta}{m}=\frac{z-\gamma}{n}.$$

Eliminating l, m, n between (3) and (4), the required equation of the cone generated by (4) is given by

$$a^2(x-\alpha)^2+b^2(y-\beta)^2+c^2(z-\gamma)^2=\{\alpha(x-\alpha)+\beta(y-\beta)+\gamma(z-\gamma)\}^2$$

Proved.

Ex. 5(c). *Tangent planes are drawn to the conicoid* $ax^2+by^2+cz^2=1$ *through the point* (α, β, γ). *Prove that the perpendiculars to them from the origin generate the cone*

$$(\alpha x+\beta y+\gamma z)^2=(x^2/a)+(y^2/b)+(z^2/c). \qquad \textbf{(Kanpur 1976)}$$

Also show that the reciprocal cone of the above cone is

$$(ax^2+by^2+cz^2)\ (a\alpha^2\quad b\beta^2+c\gamma^2-1)-(a\alpha x+b\beta y+c\gamma z)^2=0$$

and hence show that the tangent planes envelop the cone

$$(ax^2+by^2+cz^2-1)\ (a\alpha^2+b\beta^2+c\gamma^2-1)=(a\alpha x+b\beta y+c\gamma z-1)^2.$$

Solution. I Part. Proceeding exactly as in Ex. 5(a) above and replacing a^2 by $1/a$, b^2 by $1/b$ and c^2 by $1/c$, the equation of the required cone is given by

$$(\alpha x+\beta y+\gamma z)^2=(x^2/a)+(y^2/b)+z^2/c). \qquad ..(1)$$

Proved.

II Part. *To find the equation of the Reciprocal cone to* (1).

The equation (1) may be rewritten as

$$x^2\ (\alpha^2-1/a)+y^2\ (\beta^2-1/b)+z^2\ (\gamma^2-1/c)+2\beta\gamma yz+2\gamma\alpha zx+2\alpha\beta xy=0. \qquad ..(2)$$

Let the equation of the cone reciprocal to the cone (2) be

$$Ax^2+By^2+Cz^2+2Fyz+2Gzx+2Hxy=0. \qquad ...(3)$$

Then $A=bc-f^2=\left(\beta^2-\dfrac{1}{b}\right)\left(\gamma^2-\dfrac{1}{c}\right)-(\beta\gamma)^2$

$$=-\left(\frac{\beta^2}{c}+\frac{\gamma^2}{b}-\frac{1}{bc}\right)=-\frac{a\ (b\beta^2+c\gamma^2-1)}{abc}$$

$$\therefore\quad Ax^2=-\frac{ax^2\ (b\beta^2+c\gamma^2-1)}{abc}=-\frac{ax^2\ (a\alpha^2+b\beta^2+c\gamma^2-1)-a^2\alpha^2x^2}{abc},$$

with similar expressions for By^2 and Cz^2.

Also $F=gh-af=(\gamma\alpha).(\alpha\beta)-\left(\alpha^2-\dfrac{1}{a}\right)(\beta\gamma)=\dfrac{\beta\gamma}{a}$,

$$G=\frac{\gamma\alpha}{b},\ H=\frac{\alpha\beta}{c}.$$

Putting these values in (3), the required equation of the reciprocal cone is given by

$$-\frac{1}{abc}\ [\{ax^2\ (a\alpha^2+b\beta^2+c\gamma^2-1)-a^2\alpha^2x^2\}$$
$$+\{by^2\ (a\alpha^2+b\beta^2+c\gamma^2-1)-b^2\beta^2y^2\}$$
$$+\{cz^2\ (a\alpha^2+b\beta^2+c\gamma^2-1)-c^2\gamma^2z^2)\}]$$
$$+\frac{2\beta\gamma yz}{a}+\frac{2\gamma\alpha zx}{b}+\frac{2\alpha\beta}{c}\,xy=0$$

or $(ax^2+by^2+cz^2)\ (a\alpha^2+b\beta^2+c\gamma^2-1)-\{a^2\alpha^2x^2+b^2\beta^2y^2+c^2\gamma^2z^2$
$$-2bc\beta\gamma yz-2ca\gamma\alpha zx-2ab\alpha\beta xy\}=0$$

or $(ax^2+by^2+cz^2)\ (a\alpha^2+b\beta^2+c\gamma^2-1)=(a\alpha x+b\beta y+c\gamma z)^2.$

Proved.

III Part. To find the equation of the enveloping cone.

The equation of the enveloping cone is given by $SS_1=T^2$.

Here $S=ax^2+by^2+cz^2-1$. The point is (α, β, γ).

$$\therefore \quad S_1=a\alpha^2+b\beta^2+c\gamma^2-1$$

and
$$T=a\alpha x+b\beta y+c\gamma z-1.$$

Hence required equation of the enveloping cone is

$$(ax^2+by^2+cz^2-1)(a\alpha^2+b\beta^2+c\gamma^2-1)=(a\alpha x+b\beta y+c\gamma z-1)^2.$$

Ex. 5(d). *Tangent planes are drawn to the central conicoid* $ax^2+by^2+cz^2=1$ *through the point* (α, β, γ). *Show that the perpendiculars from the centre of the conicoid to these planes generate the cone* $(\alpha x+\beta y+\gamma z)^2=x^2/a+y^2/b+z^2/c$.

(Rohilkhand 1979; Kanpur 81; Madras 77)

Solution. The centre of the conicoid $ax^2+by^2+cz^2=1$ is the origin. Hence it is the same problem as Ex. 5(a) above.

Ex. 6. *Find the locus of the foot of the central perpendicular on varying tangent planes to the ellipsoid*

$x^2/a^2+y^2/b^2+z^2/c^2=1$. **(Rewa 1970; Rajasthan 75; Kanpur 81)**

Solution. The equation of the given ellipsoid is

$$x^2/a^2+y^2/b^2+z^2/c^2=1. \qquad ...(1)$$

The equation of any tangent plane to the ellipsoid (1) is

$$lx+my+nz=\sqrt{(a^2l^2+b^2m^2+c^2n^2)}. \qquad ...(2)$$

The centre of the ellipsoid (1) is the origin and hence the equations of the normal to the plane (2) from the centre (0, 0, 0) of (1) are
$$x/l=y/m=z/n. \qquad ...(3)$$

The foot of the perpendicular from the centre on the tangent plane (2) is the point where the line (3) meets the plane (2) and hence its locus is obtained by eliminating l, m, n between (2) and (3) and, therefore, is given by

$$x.x+y.y+z.z=\sqrt{(a^2x^2+b^2y^2+c^2z^2)}.$$

Squaring, the required locus is.

$$(x^2+y^2+z^2)^2=a^2x^2+b^2y^2+c^2z^2.$$

Ex. 7. *Find the locus of the perpendiculars from the origin to the tangent planes to the surface* $x^2/a^2+y^2/b^2+z^2/c^2=1$ *which cut off from its axes intercepts, the sum of whose reciprocals is equal to a constant k.*

Solution. The equation of the given ellipsoid is

$$x^2/a^2+y^2/b^2+z^2/c^2=1. \qquad ...(1)$$

The equation of any tangent plane to the ellipsoid (1) is

$$lx+my+nz=\sqrt{(a^2l^2+b^2m^2+c^2n^2)}. \qquad ...(2)$$

The intercepts made by the plane (2) on the co-ordinate axes are $\sqrt{(a^2l^2+b^2n^2+c^2n^2)}/l$, $\sqrt{(a^2l^2+b^2m^2+c^2n^2)}/m$ and $\sqrt{(a^2l^2+b^2m^2+c^2n^2)}/n$ respectively.

The sum of the reciprocals of these intercepts is given to be k.

$$\therefore \quad \frac{l+m+n}{\sqrt{(a^2l^2+b^2m^2+c^2n^2)}}=k$$

or $\quad (l+m+n)^2=k^2\,(a^2l^2+b^2m^2+c^2n^2)$. ...(3)

Now the equations of the perpendicular from the origin to the tangent plane (2) are

$$x/l=y/m=z/n. \quad ..(4)$$

Eliminating l, m, n between (3) and (4), the locus of the perpendicular (4) is given by

$$(x+y+z)^2=k^2\,(a^2x^2+b^2y^2+c^2z^2). \quad \textbf{Ans.}$$

Ex. 8. *Prove that the equation to the two tangent planes to the central conicoid $ax^2+by^2+cz^2=1$ which pass through the line $u_1\equiv l_1x+m_1y+n_1z-p_1=0$, $u_2\equiv l_2x+m_2y+n_2z-p_2=0$ is*

$$u_1^2\left(\frac{l_2^2}{a}+\frac{m_2^2}{b}+\frac{n_2^2}{c}-p_2^2\right)-2u_1u_2\left(\frac{l_1l_2}{a}+\frac{m_1m_2}{b}+\frac{n_1n_2}{c}-p_1p_2\right)$$
$$+u_2^2\left(\frac{l_1^2}{a}+\frac{m_1^2}{b}+\frac{n_1^2}{c}-p^2\right)=0.$$

Solution. The equation of the given conicoid is

$$ax^2+by^2+cz^2=1. \quad ...(1)$$

The equation of any plane through the given line $u_1=0=u_2$ is

$$u_1+\lambda u_2=0 \quad ...(2)$$

or $\quad (l_1x+m_1y+n_1z-p_1)+\lambda\,(l_2x+m_2y+n_2z-p_2)=0$

or $\quad (l_1+\lambda l_2)\,x+(m_1+\lambda m_2)\,y+(n_1+\lambda n_2)\,z=(p_1+\lambda p_2)$. ...(3)

If the plane (3) touches the conicoid (1) then applying the condition "$l^2/a+m^2/b+n^2/c=p^2$", we have

$$(l_1+\lambda l_2)^2/a+(m_1+\lambda m_2)^2/b+(n_1+\lambda n_2)^2/c=(p_1+\lambda p_2)^2 \quad ...(4)$$

Now from (2), we have $\lambda=-u_1/u_2$. Putting this value of λ in (4), the required equation of the two tangent planes is given by

$$(l_1-u_1l_2/u_2)^2/a+(m_1-u_1m_2/u_2)^2/b+(n_1-u_1n_2/u_2)^2/c=(p_1-u_1p_2/u_2)^2$$

or $\quad (l_1u_2-u_1l_2)^2/a+(m_1u_2-u_1m_2)^2/b+(n_1u_2-u_1n_2)^2/c=(p_1u_2-u_1p_2)^2$

or $\quad u_1^2\left(\frac{l_2^2}{a}+\frac{m_2^2}{b}+\frac{n_2^2}{c}-p_2^2\right)-2u_1u_2\left(\frac{l_1l_2}{a}+\frac{m_1m_2}{b}+\frac{n_1n_2}{c}-p_1p_2\right)$

$$+u_2^2\left(\frac{l_1^2}{a}+\frac{m_1^2}{b}+\frac{n_1^2}{c}-p_1^2\right)=0.$$

Proved.

Ex. 9. *If 2r is the distance between two parallel tangent planes to the ellipsoid* $x^2/a^2+y^2/b^2+z^2/c^2=1$, *prove that a line through the origin perpendicular to the planes lies on the cone*

$$x^2(a^2-r^2)+y^2(b^2-r^2)+z^2(c^2-r^2)=0. \quad \textbf{(Kanpur 1977)}$$

Solution. The equation of the given ellipsoid is

$$x^2/a^2+y^2/b^2+z^2/c^2=1. \quad ...(1)$$

The equations of the two parallel tangent planes to the ellipsoid (1) are

$$lx+my+nz=\pm\sqrt{(a^2l^2+b^2m^2+c^2n^2)}. \quad ...(2)$$

The distance between the two parallel tangent planes given by (2)

= The difference of the perpendicular distances from the origin to the planes given by (2)

i.e. $$2r=\frac{2\sqrt{(a^2l^2+b^2m^2+c^2n^2)}}{\sqrt{(l^2+m^2+n^2)}}$$

or $$a^2l^2+b^2m^2+c^2n^2=r^2(l^2+m^2+n^2) \text{ [on squaring]}$$

or $$l^2(a^2-r^2)+m^2(b^2-r^2)+n^2(c^2-r^2)=0. \quad ...(3)$$

Now the equations of the line through the origin and perpendicular to the planes (2) are

$$x/l=y/m=z/n. \quad ...(4)$$

Eliminating *l, m, n* between (3) and (4), the required locus of the perpendicular (4) is given by

$$x^2(a^2-r^2)+y^2(b^2-r^2)+z^2(c^2-r^2)=0. \quad \textbf{Proved.}$$

Ex. 10. *Show that the tangent planes at the extremities of any diameter of an ellipsoid are parallel.* **(Rajasthan 1978)**

Solution. Let the equation of an ellipsoid be

$$x^2/a^2+y^2/b^2+z^2/c^2=1. \quad ...(1)$$

We know that the centre of the ellipsoid (1) is the origin. Hence every line passing through (0, 0, 0) and intersecting the ellipsoid (1) is a diameter of (1). Thus let the equations of a diameter of (1) be

$$x/l=y/m=z/n. \quad ...(2)$$

Any point on (2) is (lr, mr, nr). If it lies on (1), then

$$r^2(l^2/a^2+m^2/b^2+n^2/c^2)=1$$

or $$r=\pm 1/\sqrt{(l^2/a^2+m^2/b^2+n^2/c^2)}=\pm\lambda \text{ (say)}.$$

Now the extremities of a diameter are

$$(l\lambda, m\lambda, n\lambda) \text{ and } (-l\lambda, -m\lambda, -n\lambda).$$

The equations of the tangent planes to (1) at these points are

$$\frac{l\lambda x}{a^2}+\frac{m\lambda y}{b^2}+\frac{n\lambda z}{c^2}=1 \quad i.e., \quad \frac{lx}{a^2}+\frac{my}{b^2}+\frac{nz}{c^2}=\frac{1}{\lambda} \qquad ...(3)$$

and
$$\frac{-l\lambda x}{a^2}-\frac{m\lambda y}{b^2}-\frac{n\lambda z}{c^2}=1 \quad i.e., \quad \frac{lx}{a^2}+\frac{my}{b^2}+\frac{nz}{c^2}=-\frac{1}{\lambda}. \qquad ...(4)$$

The equations (3) and (4) are the equations of two parallel planes.

Ex. 11. *If P be the point of contact of a tangent plane to the ellipsoid which meets the co-ordinate axes in A, B and C and PL, PM, PN are the perpendiculars from P on the axes, prove that*

$$OL.OA=a^2, \; OM.OB=b^2, \; ON.OC=c^2.$$

Solution. Let the equation of the ellipsoid be

$$x^2/a^2+y^2/b^2+z^2/c^2=1. \qquad ...(1)$$

Let the co-ordinates of P be (α, β, γ), so that the equation of the tangent plane to the ellipsoid (1) at $P(\alpha, \beta, \gamma)$ is

$$\alpha x/a^2+\beta y/b^2+\gamma z/c^2=1. \qquad ...(2)$$

The plane (2) meets the co-ordinate axes in A, B and C and so OA, OB and OC are the intercepts made by (2) on the co-ordinate axes and hence we have

$$OA=a^2/\alpha, \; OB=b^2/\beta; \; OC=c^2/\gamma.$$

Again it is given that PL is the perpendicular from the point $P(\alpha, \beta, \gamma)$ on the x-axis so that $OL=\alpha$.

Similarly $\quad OM=\beta$ and $ON=\gamma$.

Thus $\quad OL.OA=\alpha.(a^2/\alpha)=a^2$; $OM.OB=\beta.(b^2/\beta)=b^2$

and $\quad ON.OC=\gamma\,(c^2/\gamma)=c^2.$

Ex. 12. *If the line of intersection of perpendicular tangent planes to the ellipsoid whose equation referred to rectangular axes is* $x^2/a^2+y^2/b^2+z^2/c^2=1$ *passes through the fixed point* $(0, 0, k)$, *show that it lies on the cone*

$$x^2(b^2+c^2-k^2)+y^2\,(c^2+a^2-k^2)+(z-k)^2\,(a^2+b^2)=0.$$

(Kurukshetra 1971)

Solution. The equation of the given ellipsoid is

$$x^2/a^2+y^2/b^2+z^2/c^2=1. \qquad ...(1)$$

The equation of any plane through the point $(0, 0, k)$ is

$$l(x-0)+m(y-0)+n(z-k)=0 \quad \text{or} \quad lx+my+nz=nk. \qquad ...(2)$$

If the plane (2) touches the ellipsoid (1), then we have

$$a^2l^2+b^2m^2+c^2n^2=n^2k^2 \quad \text{[See § 6(B)]}$$

or
$$a^2l^2+b^2m^2+(c^2-k^2)\,n^2=0. \qquad ...(3)$$

Now the equations of any line through the point (0, 0, k) are

$$\frac{x-0}{\lambda}=\frac{y-0}{\mu}=\frac{z-k}{\nu} \quad \text{or} \quad \frac{x}{\lambda}=\frac{y}{\mu}=\frac{z-k}{\nu}. \qquad \ldots(4)$$

If the line (4) lies in the plane (2), we have

$$l\lambda+m\mu+n\nu=0. \qquad \ldots(5)$$

The direction cosines l, m, n of the normal to the tangent plane (2) are related by the relations (3) and (5) and since (3) is a quadratic relation in l, m, n, it shows that there are two sets of values of l, m, n and hence for every line (4) through the fixed point (0, 0, k) there are two tangent planes to the ellipsoid (1) which intersect in the line (4).

Eliminating n between (3) and (5), we have

$$a^2l^2+b^2m^2+(c^2-k^2)\left(\frac{l\lambda+m\mu}{-\nu}\right)^2=0$$

or $$(a^2\nu^2+\lambda^2c^2-\lambda^2k^2)\, l^2+2lm\, \lambda\mu\, (c^2-k^2)+(b^2\nu^2+\mu^2c^2-\mu^2k^2)\, m^2=0$$

or $$(a^2\nu^2+\lambda^2c^2-\lambda^2k^2)\,(l/m)^2+2\lambda\mu\,(c^2-k^2)\,(l/m)+(b^2\nu^2+\mu^2c^2-\mu^2k^2)=0.$$

Let its roots be l_1/m_1, l_2/m_2.

Then the product of the roots $=\dfrac{l_1}{m_1}\cdot\dfrac{l_2}{m_2}=\dfrac{b^2\nu^2+\mu^2c^2-\mu^2k^2}{a^2\nu^2+\lambda^2c^2-\lambda^2k^2}$.

$$\therefore \quad \frac{l_1l_2}{b^2\nu^2+(c^2-k^2)\,\mu^2}=\frac{m_1m_2}{(c^2-k^2)\,\lambda^2+a^2\nu^2}=\frac{n_1n_2}{a^2\mu^2+b^2\lambda^2}$$

[by symmetry].

Since the tangent planes are to be perpendicular, we have

$$l_1l_2+m_1m_2+n_1n_2=0$$

or $$\{b^2\nu^2+(c^2-k^2)\,\mu^2\}+\{(c^2-k^2)\,\lambda^2+a^2\nu^2\}+\{a^2\mu^2+b^2\lambda^2\}=0$$

or $$(b^2+c^2-k^2)\,\lambda^2+(a^2+c^2-k^2)\,\mu^2+(a^2+b^2)\,\nu^2=0 \qquad \ldots(6)$$

Eliminating λ, μ, ν between (4) and (6), the equation of the required cone generated by (4) is given by

$$(b^2+c^2-k^2)\,x^2+(a^2+c^2-k^2)\,y^2+(a^2+b^2)\,(z-k)^2=0.$$

Ex. 13. *Through a fixed point* (k, 0, 0) *pairs of perpendicular tangent lines are drawn to the conicoid* $ax^2+by^2+cz^2=1$. *Show that the plane through any pair touches the cone*

$$\frac{(x-k)^2}{(b+c)\,(ak^2-1)}+\frac{y^2}{c\,(ak^2-1)-a}+\frac{z^2}{b^2\,(ak^2-1)-a}=0.$$

(Allahabad 1979)

Solution. The equation of the given conicoid is

$$ax^2+by^2+cz^2=1. \quad ...(1)$$

The equations of any line through the given point $(k, 0, 0)$ are

$$\frac{x-k}{l}=\frac{y}{m}=\frac{z}{n}=r \text{ (say)}. \quad ...(2)$$

The co-ordinates of any point on the line (2) are $(lr+k, mr, nr)$. If the line (2) meets the conicoid (1), then this point will lie on (1) and so we have

$$a(lr+k)^2+b(mr)^2+c(nr)^2=1$$

or $$r^2(al^2+bm^2+cn^2)+2kalr+(ak^2-1)=0. \quad ...(3)$$

If the line (2) touches the conicoid (1), then the two roots of (8) must be equal and hence applying the condition '$B^2-4AC=0$', we have

$$(2kal)^2-4(al^2+bm^2+cn^2)(ak^2-1)=0$$

or $$(al^2+bm^2+cn^2)(ak^2-1)=k^2a^2l^2. \quad ...(4)$$

Thus for any tangent line (2) to (1) through the point $(k, 0, 0)$, the values of l, m, n should satisfy the relation (4).

For any two perpendicular tangent lines to (1) through the point $(k, 0, 0)$, let the two sets of values of l, m, n be l_1, m_1, n_1 and l_2, m_2, n_2 so that the equations of these perpendicular tangent lines through $(k, 0, 0)$ are given by

$$\frac{x-k}{l_1}=\frac{y}{m_1}=\frac{z}{n_1} \text{ and } \frac{x-k}{l_2}=\frac{y}{m_2}=\frac{z}{n_2}. \quad ...(5)$$

Therefore, in view of (4), we have the following two relations

$$(al_1^2+bm_1^2+cn_1^2)(ak^2-1)=k^2a^2l_1^2$$

and $$(al_2^2+bm_2^2+cn_2^2)(ak^2-1)=k^2a^2l_2^2.$$

Adding, we get

$$\{a(l_1^2+l_2^2)+b(m_1^2+m_2^2)+c(n_1^2+n_2^2)\}(ak^2-1)=k^2a^2(l_1^2+l_2^2). \quad ...(6)$$

Let the line $(x-k)/l_3=y/m_3=z/n_3$ through the point $(k, 0, 0)$ be the normal to the plane containing the two tangent lines given by (5).

Thus we have three mutually perpendicular lines. Hence we have the relations

$$l_3^2+m_3^2+n_3^2=1=l_1^2+l_2^2+l_3^2 \text{ or } l_1^2+l_2^2=m_3^2+n_3^2.$$

Similarly $m_1^2+m_2^2=n_3^2+l_3^2$, and $n_1^2+n_2^2=l_3^2+m_3^2$.

Using these relations, (6) becomes

$$\{a\,(m_3^2+n_3^2)+b\,(n_3^2+l_3^2)+c\,(l_3^2+m_3^2)\}\,(ak^2-1)$$
$$=k^2a^2(m_3^2+n_3^2)$$

or $l_3^2\,(b+c)\,(ak^2-1)+m_3^2\,\{c(ak^2-1)-a\}+n_3^2\,\{b(ak^2-1)-a\}=0.$ ...(7)

The equation of the cone generated by the normal to the plane containing the perpendicular tangent lines given by (5) is obtained by eliminating l_3, m_3, n_3 between the equations (7) and $(x-k)/l_3=y/m_3=z/n_3$ and is therefore given by

$$(x-k)^2\,(b+c)\,(ak^2-1)+y^2\,\{c\,(ak^2-1)-a\}$$
$$+z^2\,\{b\,(ak^2-1)-a\}=0. \quad ...(8)$$

The cone reciprocal to the cone (8) is clearly given by

$$\frac{(x-k)^2}{(b+c)\,(ak^2-1)}+\frac{y^2}{c\,(ak^2-1)-a}+\frac{z^2}{b\,(ak^2-1)-a}=0$$

which is the required equation of the cone which is touched by the plane through the lines given by (5).

Ex. 14. *Prove that the locus of points from which three mutually perpendicular planes can be drawn to touch the ellipse*

$$x^2/a^2+y^2/b^2=1,\ z=0$$

is the sphere $x^2+y^2+z^2=a^2+b^2$. **(Punjab 1973)**

Solution. The equations of the given ellipse are

$$x^2/a^2+y^2/b^2=1,\ z=0. \quad ...(1)$$

Let the equation of one of the three mutually perpendicular planes be

$$l_1x+m_1y+n_1z=p_1. \quad ...(2)$$

The plane (2) meets the plane $z=0$ in the line given by

$$l_1x+m_1y=p_1,\ z=0. \quad ...(3)$$

Now if the plane (2) touches the ellipse (1) then the line (3) will touch the ellipse (1) in the xy-plane and the condition for the same is

$$a^2l_1^2+b^2m_1^2=p_1^2 \quad \text{or} \quad p_1=\sqrt{(a^2l_1^2+b^2m_1^2)}.$$

Putting this value of p_1 in (2), the equation (2) becomes

$$l_1x+m_1\,y+n_1z=\sqrt{(a^2l_1^2+b^2m_1^2)} \quad ...(4)$$

Similarly the equations of the other two tangent planes to the ellipse (1) are

$$l_2x+m_2y+n_2z=\sqrt{(a^2l_2^2+b^2m_2^2)} \quad ...(5)$$

and $$l_3x+m_3y+n_3z=\sqrt{(a^2l_3^2+b^2m_3^2)}. \quad ...(6)$$

Squaring (4), (5) and (6) and adding, we get

$$x^2\Sigma l_1^2+y^2\,\Sigma m_1^2+z^2\,\Sigma n_1^2+2yz\,\Sigma m_1n_1+2zx\,\Sigma n_1l_1$$
$$+2xy\,\Sigma l_1m_1=a^2\,\Sigma l_1^2+b^2\,\Sigma m_1^2$$

or $x^2.1+y^2.1+z^2.1+2yz.0+2zx.0+2xy.0=a^2.1+b^2.1$

or $x^2+y^2+z^2=a^2+b^2$ [$\because$ $\Sigma l_1^2=1$, $\Sigma l_1 m_1=0$ etc.]

which is the required locus.

§ 8. The Polar Plane. (Kanpur 1982)

Definition. *Let* $ax^2+by^2+cz^2=1$ ...(1)
be the equation of a conicoid and $A(\alpha, \beta, \gamma)$ be any point. Draw lines APQ to meet the conicoid (1) in the points P and Q. The locus of the point R such that AR is the harmonic mean of AP and AQ (i.e. AP, AR and AQ are in harmonic progression) is called the polar plane of the point A with respect to the given conicoid.

(A) The equation of the polar plane.

The equations of any line through the point $A(\alpha, \beta, \gamma)$ are

$$\frac{x-\alpha}{l}=\frac{y-\beta}{m}=\frac{z-\gamma}{n}=r \text{ (say)}, \quad ...(2)$$

where l, m, n are the actual d.c.'s of the line.

The co-ordinates of any point on (2) distant r from $A(\alpha, \beta, \gamma)$ are $(lr+\alpha, mr+\beta, nr+\gamma)$. Therefore, the distances of the points P and Q where the line (2) meets the given conicoid (1) are given by the quadratic in r^2

$$a(lr+\alpha)^2+b(mr+\beta)^2+c(nr+\gamma)^2=1$$

or $$r^2(al^2+bm^2+cn^2)+2r(al\alpha+bm\beta+cn\gamma)$$
$$+(a\alpha^2+b\beta^2+c\gamma^2-1)=0. \quad ...(3)$$

Let the two values of r be r_1 and r_2 and let $r_1=AP$ and $r_2=AQ$. Now AP, AR, AQ are in harmonic progression

$$\therefore \quad \frac{2}{AR}=\frac{1}{AP}+\frac{1}{AQ}=\frac{1}{r_1}+\frac{1}{r_2}=\frac{r_1+r_2}{r_1 r_2}$$

or $$\frac{2}{AR}=\frac{-2(al\alpha+bm\beta+cn\gamma)}{a\alpha^2+b\beta^2+c\gamma^2-1}$$

or $$a\alpha^2+b\beta^2+c\gamma^2-1=-\{a\alpha(l.AR)+b\beta(m.AR)+c\gamma(n.AR)\}. \quad ...(4)$$

Now let (x, y, z) be the co-ordinates of the point R on the line (1) whose distance from the point $A(\alpha, \beta, \gamma)$ is AR and so we have

$$\frac{x-\alpha}{l}=\frac{y-\beta}{m}=\frac{z-\gamma}{n}=AR.$$

$$\therefore \quad l.AR=x-\alpha,\ m.AR=y-\beta,\ n.AR=z-\gamma. \quad ...(5)$$

Now in order to find the locus of R, we are to eliminate l, m, n between (4) and (5) and so it is given by

$$a\alpha^2+b\beta^2+c\gamma^2-1=-\{a\alpha(x-\alpha)+b\beta(y-\beta)+c\gamma(z-\gamma)\}$$

or $$a\alpha x+b\beta y+c\gamma z=1. \qquad ...(6)$$

This is the required equation of the polar plane of the point $A(\alpha, \beta, \gamma)$ with respect to the conicoid (1).

Note. The equation (6) of the polar plane of the point $A(\alpha, \beta, \gamma)$ w.r.t. the conicoid (1) is of the same form as that of the tangent plane of the conicoid (1) at the point $A(\alpha, \beta, \gamma)$ on the conicoid.

(B) The pole of a given plane. **(Kanpur 1980)**

To find the pole of the plane $lx+my+nz=p$ w.r.t. the conicoid $ax^2+by^2+cz^2=1$.

The equation of the given conicoid is

$$ax^2+by^2+cz^2=1. \qquad ...(1)$$

Let the pole of the plane

$$lx+my+nz=p \qquad ...(2)$$

w.r.t. the conicoid (1) be the point $P(\alpha, \beta, \gamma)$. But the polar plane of $P(\alpha, \beta, \gamma)$ w.r.t. to (1) is

$$a\alpha x+b\beta y+c\gamma z=1. \qquad ...(3)$$

Therefore the equations (2) and (3) represent the same plane and so comparing their coefficients, we get

$$\frac{a\alpha}{l}=\frac{b\beta}{m}=\frac{c\gamma}{n}=\frac{1}{p} \text{ i.e. } \alpha=\frac{l}{ap}, \beta=\frac{m}{bp}, \gamma=\frac{n}{cp}.$$

$\therefore$ The required pole is $(l/(ap), m/(bp), n/(cp))$.

§ 9. Properties of the polar planes and the polar lines.

(A) Let $P(\alpha_1, \beta_1, \gamma_1)$ and $Q(\alpha_2, \beta_2, \gamma_2)$ be any two points. It clearly follows that if the polar plane of the point P with respect to a given conicoid passes through the point Q then the polar plane of Q w.r.t. the same conicoid will pass through P. The points P and Q satisfying this property are called the **Conjugate points.**

(B) Let $$u_1 \equiv l_1x+m_1y+n_1z-p_1=0$$
and $$u_2 \equiv l_2x+m_2y+n_2z-p_2=0$$
be the equations of the two planes. It clearly follows that if the pole of the plane $u_1=0$ lies on the plane $u_2=0$ then the pole of the plane $u_2=0$ will lie on the plane $u_1=0$. The two such planes $u_1=0$ and $u_2=0$ are called the **conjugate planes.**

(C) The polar lines. *The polar line or simply polar of a given line AB is another line PQ such that the polar planes of all points on AB pass through PQ.*

Let the equation of the conicoid be

$$ax^2+by^2+cz^2=1. \qquad ...(1)$$

Let the equations of the line AB be

$$\frac{x-\alpha}{l}=\frac{y-\beta}{m}=\frac{z-\gamma}{n}=r \text{ (say)}. \qquad ...(2)$$

Any point on (2) is $R\ (lr+\alpha, mr+\beta, nr+\gamma)$. The equation of the polar plane of the point R with respect to the conicoid (1) is

$$ax\ (lr+\alpha)+by\ (mr+\beta)+cz\ (nr+\gamma)=1$$

or
$$(a\alpha x+b\beta y+c\gamma z-1)+r\ (alx+bmy+cnz)=0.$$

This plane for all values of r clearly passes through the line of intersection of the fixed planes

$$a\alpha x+b\beta y+c\gamma z-1=0,\ alx+bmy+cnz=0.$$

Let this line be the line PQ.

Thus we observe that the polar plane of any point R on AB passes through every point of the line PQ and hence the polar plane of any point on the line PQ must pass through R. But R is an arbitrary point on AB and so the polar plane of every point on PQ will pass through every point of the line AB.

Thus we conclude that the lines AB and PQ are such that the polar plane of every point on AB passes through PQ and vice versa and the two such lines are called the *polar lines*.

(D) *To find the condition that the two given lines be the polar lines.*

Let the equation of the conicoid be

$$ax^2+by^2+cz^2=1. \qquad ...(1)$$

Let the two given lines be denoted by AB and PQ and let their equations be given by

$$\frac{x-\alpha}{l}=\frac{y-\beta}{m}=\frac{z-\gamma}{n} \text{ and } \frac{x-\alpha'}{l'}=\frac{y-\beta'}{m'}=\frac{z-\gamma'}{n'}$$

respectively.

Proceeding as in § 9 (C) above the polar line of AB with respect to the conicoid (1) is the line of intersection of the two planes given by

$$a\alpha x+b\beta y+c\gamma z-1=0 \qquad ...(2)$$

and
$$alx+bmy+cnz=0. \qquad ...(3)$$

Now if the polar line of AB be the given line PQ then PQ will lie on the planes (2) and (3) both. The conditions for which are

$$\left.\begin{aligned} a\alpha\alpha'+b\beta\beta'+c\gamma\gamma'-1=0 \\ a\alpha l'+b\beta m'+c\gamma n'=0 \end{aligned}\right\} \qquad ...(4)$$

and $$\left.\begin{aligned} al\alpha'+bm\beta'+cn\gamma'=0 \\ all'+bmm'+cnn'=0 \end{aligned}\right\} \quad \ldots(5)$$

Hence the required conditions are given by (4) and (5).

(E) Conjugate lines. *Two lines AB and PQ are called the conjugate lines if when the line PQ intersects the polar line of the line AB then the line AB also intersects the polar line of the line PQ.*

To find the condition for the two given lines to be conjugate lines.

First rewrite the steps upto equation (3) of § 9 (D) above.

Any point on the line PQ is $(l'r+\alpha', m'r+\beta', n'r+\gamma')$. If the line PQ intersects the polar line of AB [given by (2) and (3)] then for some value of r this point will satisfy both the equations of the planes (2) and (3) and so we get

$$a\alpha\,(l'r+\alpha')+b\beta\,(m'r+\beta')+c\gamma\,(n'r+\gamma')-1=0$$

and $$al\,(l'r+\alpha')+bm\,(m'r+\beta')+cn\,(n'r+\gamma')=0$$

or $$(a\alpha\alpha'+b\beta\beta'+c\gamma\gamma'-1)=-r\,(a\alpha l'+b\beta m'+c\gamma n') \quad \ldots(4)$$

and $$(a\alpha' l+b\beta' m+c\gamma' n)=-r\,(all'+bmm'+cnn'). \quad \ldots(5)$$

Eliminating r between (4) and (5), we get

$$(a\alpha\alpha'+b\beta\beta'+c\gamma\gamma'-1)\,(all'+bmm'+cnn')$$
$$=(a\alpha l'+b\beta m'+c\gamma n')\,(al\alpha'+bm\beta'+cn\gamma'). \quad \ldots(6)$$

This is the condition that the line PQ intersects the polar line of AB. The symmetry of the result (6) shows that the line AB will also intersect the polar line of PQ. Hence (6) is the required condition.

SOLVED EXAMPLES (B)

Ex. 1. *Prove that the locus of the poles of the tangent planes of* $ax^2+by^2+cz^2=1$ *with respect to* $a'x^2+b'y^2+c'z^2=1$ *is the conicoid* $(a'x)^2/a+(b'y)^2/b+(c'z)^2/c=1$. **(Allahabad 1982)**

Solution. The equations of the given conicoids are

$$ax^2+by^2+cz^2=1, \quad \ldots(1) \qquad a'x^2+b'y^2+c'z^2=1. \quad \ldots(2)$$

Let the equation of a tangent plane of the conicoid (1) be

$$lx+my+nz=p. \quad \ldots(3)$$

Then $$(l^2/a)+(m^2/b)+(n^2/c)=p^2. \quad \ldots(4)$$

Now let the pole of the plane (3) w.r.t. the conicoid (2) be (x_1, y_1, z_1) so that (3) is the same plane as

$$a'xx_1+b'yy_1+c'zz_1=1. \quad \ldots(5)$$

$\therefore$ Comparing the coefficients of the equations (3) and (5), we get

$$\frac{l}{a'x_1}=\frac{m}{b'y_1}=\frac{n}{c'z_1}=\frac{p}{1}$$

or $$l=a'x_1p,\ m=b'y_1p,\ n=c'z_1p.$$

Putting these values of l, m, n in (4), we have

$$(a'x_1p)^2/a+(b'y_1p)^2/b+(c'z_1p)^2/c=p^2$$

or $$(a'x_1)^2/a+(b'y_1)^2/b+(c'z_1)^2/c=1.$$

$\therefore$ The locus of the pole (x_1, y_1, z_1) of the plane (3) w.r.t. (2) is given by

$$(a'x)^2/a+(b'y)^2/b+(c'z)^2/c=1.$$ **Proved.**

Ex. 2. *Prove that the locus of the poles of the tangent planes of $a^2x^2+b^2y^2-c^2z^2=1$ with respect to $\alpha^2x^2+\beta^2y^2+\gamma^2z^2=1$ is the hyperboloid of one sheet.* **(Kurukshetra 1974)**

Solution. Proceeding exactly as in Ex. 1 above and replacing a by a^2, b by b^2, c by $-c^2$, a' by α^2, b' by β^2, c' by γ^2, the required locus is given by

$$\frac{\alpha^4x^2}{a^2}+\frac{\beta^4y^2}{b^2}-\frac{\gamma^4z^2}{c^2}=1$$

which is the equation of the hyperboloid of one sheet.

Ex. 3. *Show that the locus of the pole of the plane $lx+my+nz=p$ with respect to the system of conicoids $\Sigma\,[x^2/(a^2+k)]=1$, is a straight line perpendicular to the given plane where k is a parameter.* **[Kanpur 1976 ; Bundelkhand 72]**

Solution. The equation of given system of conicoids is

$$\frac{x^2}{a^2+k}+\frac{y^2}{b^2+k}+\frac{z^2}{c^2+k}=1 \quad ...(1)$$

The equation of the given plane is

$$lx+my+nz=p. \quad ...(2)$$

Let (α, β, γ) be the pole of (2) w. r. t. the conicoid (1). The polar plane of (α, β, γ) w.r.t. the conicoid (1) is

$$\frac{\alpha x}{a^2+k}+\frac{\beta y}{b^2+k}+\frac{\gamma z}{c^2+k}=1. \quad ...(3)$$

The equations (2) and (3) should represent the same plane and hence comparing their coefficients, we have

$$\frac{\alpha/(a^2+k)}{l}=\frac{\beta/(b^2+k)}{m}=\frac{\gamma/(c^2+k)}{n}=\frac{1}{p}.$$

$$\therefore\ \alpha=l\,(a^2+k)/p,\ \beta=m\,(b^2+k)/p,\ \gamma=n\,(c^2+k)/p$$

or $$\alpha-\frac{a^2l}{p}=\frac{lk}{p},\ \beta-\frac{mb^2}{p}=\frac{mk}{p},\ \gamma-\frac{nc^2}{p}=\frac{nk}{p}.$$

Therefore, clearly we have

$$\frac{\alpha-a^2l/p}{l}=\frac{\beta-mb^2/p}{m}=\frac{\gamma-nc^2/p}{n}=\frac{k}{p}.$$

$\therefore$ The locus of the pole (α, β, γ) is

$$\frac{x-a^2l/p}{l}=\frac{y-mb^2/p}{m}=\frac{z-nc^2/p}{n}.$$

This is a straight line with its direction cosines proportional to l, m, n which are also the direction ratios of the normal to the plane (2). Hence the locus is a straight line perpendicular to the given plane (2).

Ex. 4. *Find the locus of straight lines drawn through a fixed point (α, β, γ) at right angles to their polar with respect to the conicoid $ax^2+by^2+cz^2=1$.* **(Lucknow 1976, 80 ; Kanpur 82)**

Solution. The equation of the given conicoid is

$$ax^2+by^2+cz^2=1. \qquad ...(1)$$

The equations of any straight line through the point (α, β, γ) are

$$\frac{x-\alpha}{l}=\frac{y-\beta}{m}=\frac{z-\gamma}{n}=r \text{ (say)}. \qquad ...(2)$$

The coordinates of any point on (2) are $(lr+\alpha, mr+\beta, nr+\gamma)$. The equation of the polar plane of this point w.r.t. the conicoid (1) is

$$ax\,(lr+\alpha)+by\,(mr+\beta)+cz\,(nr+\gamma)=1$$

or
$$(a\alpha x+b\beta y+c\gamma z-1)+r\,(alx+bmy+cnz)=0.$$

This plane for all values of r will pass through the line

$$a\alpha x+b\beta y+c\gamma z-1=0,\ alx+bmy+cnz=0. \qquad ...(3)$$

This is the polar of the line (2) w.r.t. the conicoid (1).

Let λ, μ, ν be the direction ratios of the polar line (3) so that we have

$$a\alpha\lambda+b\beta\mu+c\gamma\nu=0,\ al\lambda+bm\mu+cn\nu=0.$$

Solving, $\dfrac{\lambda}{bc\,(n\beta-m\gamma)}=\dfrac{\mu}{ca\,(l\gamma-n\alpha)}=\dfrac{\nu}{ab\,(m\alpha-l\beta)}$. $\qquad ...(4)$

Since the lines (2) and (3) are given to be perpendicular, we have

$$l\lambda+m\mu+n\nu=0$$

or
$$lbc\,(n\beta-m\gamma)+mca\,(l\gamma-n\alpha)+nab\,(m\alpha-l\beta)=0.$$

Dividing by $abclmn$ throughout, we get

$$\frac{\beta}{am}-\frac{\gamma}{an}+\frac{\gamma}{bn}-\frac{\alpha}{bl}+\frac{\alpha}{cl}-\frac{\beta}{cm}=0$$

or
$$\frac{\alpha}{l}\left(\frac{1}{c}-\frac{1}{b}\right)+\frac{\beta}{m}\left(\frac{1}{a}-\frac{1}{c}\right)+\frac{\gamma}{n}\left(\frac{1}{b}-\frac{1}{a}\right)=0. \qquad ...(5)$$

The locus of the line (2) is obtained by eliminating l, m, n between (2) and (5) and hence is given by

$$\frac{\alpha}{x-\alpha}\left(\frac{1}{b}-\frac{1}{c}\right)+\frac{\beta}{y-\beta}\left(\frac{1}{c}-\frac{1}{a}\right)+\frac{\gamma}{z-\gamma}\left(\frac{1}{a}-\frac{1}{b}\right)=0.$$

Ex. 5. *If* $P(x_1, y_1, z_1)$ *and* $Q(x_2, y_2, z_2)$ *are any two points then find the equations of the polar of PQ with respect to the conicoid* $ax^2+by^2+cz^2=1$.

Solution. The equation of the given conicoid is

$$ax^2+by^2+cz^2=1. \quad ...(1)$$

Now the equations of the line joining $P(x_1, y_1, z_1)$ and $Q(x_2, y_2, z_2)$ are

$$\frac{x-x_1}{x_2-x_1}=\frac{y-y_1}{y_2-y_1}=\frac{z-z_1}{z_2-z_1}=r \text{ (say)}.$$

The co-ordinates of any point on this line PQ are

$$(x_1+r(x_2-x_1), y_1+r(y_2-y_1), z_1+r(z_2-z_1)).$$

The polar plane of this point w.r.t. the conicoid (1) is

$$ax\{x_1+r(x_2-x_1)\}+by\{y_1+r(y_2-y_1)\}+cz\{z_1+r(z_2-z_1)\}=1$$

or $$(axx_1+byy_1+czz_1-1)+r\{ax(x_2-x_1)+by(y_2-y_1)+cz(z_2-z_1)\}=0.$$

This plane for all values of r will pass through the line given by the planes

$$axx_1+byy_1+czz_1=1 \quad ...(2)$$

and $$ax(x_2-x_1)+by(y_2-y_1)+cz(z_2-z_1)=0$$

i.e. $$axx_2+byy_2+czz_2=axx_1+byy_1+czz_1$$

i.e. $$axx_2+byy_2+czz_2=1, \text{ [using (2)]}. \quad ...(3)$$

The equations (2) and (3) are the required equations of the polar of the line PQ.

Ex. 6. *If* $P(x_1, y_1, z_1)$ *and* $Q(x_2, y_2, z_2)$ *be any two points on a conicoid* $ax^2+by^2+cz^2=1$, *show that the polar of the line PQ is the line of intersection of the tangent planes at P and Q.* **(Alld. 1978)**

Solution. Proceeding as in Ex. 5 above the polar of the line PQ is the line of intersection of the planes given by the equations (2) and (3). But (2) and (3) are the equations of the tangent planes to the conicoid (1) at the points $P(x_1, y_1, z_1)$ and $Q(x_2, y_2, z_2)$. Hence the polar of the line PQ is the line of intersection of the tangent planes at P and Q.

Ex. 7. *Find the locus of straight lines through a fixed point* (α, β, γ) *whose polar lines with respect to the conicoids* $ax^2+by^2+cz^2=1$ *and* $a'x^2+b'y^2+c'z^2=1$ *are coplanar.*

Solution. The equations of the two conicoids are

$$ax^2+by^2+cz^2=1 \quad ...(1), \qquad a'x^2+b'y^2+c'z^2=1. \quad ...(2)$$

The equations of any line through the point (α, β, γ) are

$$\frac{x-\alpha}{l}=\frac{y-\beta}{m}=\frac{z-\gamma}{n}=r \text{ (say)}. \quad ...(3)$$

The equations of the polar line of the line (3) w.r.t. the conicoid (1) [See § 9 (C)] are

$$a\alpha x+b\beta y+c\gamma z=1,\ alx+bmy+cnz=0. \quad ...(4)$$

Also the equations of the polar line of the line (3) w.r.t. the conicoid (2) are

$$a'\alpha x+b'\beta y+c'\gamma z=1,\ a'lx+b'my+c'nz=0. \quad ...(5)$$

The two polar lines given by (4) and (5) are given to be coplanar and hence we have

$$\begin{vmatrix} a\alpha & b\beta & c\gamma & 1 \\ al & bm & cn & 0 \\ a'\alpha & b'\beta & c'\gamma & 1 \\ a'l & b'm & c'n & 0 \end{vmatrix}=0 \text{ or } \begin{vmatrix} (a-a')\alpha & (b-b')\beta & (c-c')\gamma & 0 \\ al & bm & cn & 0 \\ a'\alpha & b'\beta & c'\gamma & 1 \\ a'l & b'm & c'n & 0 \end{vmatrix}=0$$

or $\begin{vmatrix} (a-a')\,\alpha & (b-b')\,\beta & (c-c')\,\gamma \\ al & bm & cn \\ a'l & b'm & c'n \end{vmatrix}=0$, expanding the determinant along the fourth column

or $(a-a')\,\alpha\,(bc'-b'c)\,mn+(b-b')\,\beta\,(ca'-c'a)\,nl$

$$+(c-c')\,\gamma\,(ab'-a'b)\,lm=0.$$

Dividing by lmn throughout, we get

$$(a-a')\,(bc'-b'c)\,(\alpha/l)+(b-b')\,(ca'-ca')\,(\beta/m)$$
$$+(c-c')\,(ab'-a'b)\,(\gamma/n)=0 \quad ...(6)$$

The locus of the straight line (3) is obtained by eliminating l, m, n between (3) and (6), and therefore, it is given by

$$(a-a')\,(bc'-b'c)\left(\frac{\alpha}{x-\alpha}\right)+(b-b')\,(ca'-c'a)\left(\frac{\beta}{y-\beta}\right)$$
$$+(c-c')\,(ab'-a'b)\left(\frac{\gamma}{z-\gamma}\right)=0.$$

Ex. 8. *Prove that the lines through (α, β, γ) at right angles to their polars with respect to* $\dfrac{x^2}{a+b}+\dfrac{y^2}{2a}+\dfrac{z^2}{2b}=1$ *generate the cone*

$$(y-\beta)\,(\alpha z-\gamma x)+(z-\gamma)\,(\alpha y-\beta x)=0.$$

Solution. The equation of the given conicoid is

$$x^2/(a+b)+y^2/(2a)+z^2/(2b)=1.$$

For convenience let us put $a'=1/(a+b)$, $b'=1/(2a)$, $c'=1/(2b)$. Using these values the given equation of the conicoid becomes

$$a'x^2+b'y^2+c'z^2=1. \qquad ...(1)$$

Now proceeding exactly as in Ex. 4 above the equation of the required locus is

$$\frac{\alpha}{x-\alpha}\left(\frac{1}{b'}-\frac{1}{c'}\right)+\frac{\beta}{y-\beta}\left(\frac{1}{c'}-\frac{1}{a'}\right)+\frac{\gamma}{z-\gamma}\left(\frac{1}{a'}-\frac{1}{b'}\right)=0$$

or $$\frac{\alpha}{x-\alpha}(2a-2b)+\frac{\beta}{y-\beta}(2b-a-b)+\frac{\gamma}{z-\gamma}(a+b-2a)=0$$

[Putting the values of a', b', c']

or $$\frac{2\alpha(a-b)}{x-\alpha}-\frac{\beta(a-b)}{y-\beta}-\frac{\gamma(a-b)}{z-\gamma}=0, \text{ or } \frac{2\alpha}{x-\alpha}-\frac{\beta}{y-\beta}-\frac{\gamma}{z-\gamma}=0$$

or $$\left(\frac{\alpha}{x-\alpha}-\frac{\beta}{y-\beta}\right)+\left(\frac{\alpha}{x-\alpha}-\frac{\gamma}{z-\gamma}\right)=0$$

or $$\frac{(\alpha y-\beta x)}{(x-\alpha)(y-\beta)}+\frac{\alpha z-\gamma x}{(x-\alpha)(z-\gamma)}=0,$$

or $$(y-\beta)(\alpha z-\gamma x)+(z-\gamma)(\alpha y-\beta x)=0.$$ **Proved.**

§ 10. Locus of chords bisected at a given point. (Punjab 1976)

Let the equation of the conicoid be

$$ax^2+by^2+cz^2=1. \qquad ...(1)$$

Let (α, β, γ) be the middle point of a chord of (1) so that its equations may be given by

$$\frac{x-\alpha}{l}=\frac{y-\beta}{m}=\frac{z-\gamma}{n}=r \text{ (say)}, \qquad ...(2)$$

where l, m, n are the actual d.c.'s of the line.

Now the co-ordinates of any point on (2) at a distance r from (α, β, γ) are $(lr+\alpha, mr+\beta, nr+\gamma)$. Let this point lie on (1) so that the distances of the points of intersection of the chord (2) with the conicoid (1) from the point (α, β, γ) are given by the quadratic in r^2

$$a(lr+\alpha)^2+b(mr+\beta)^2+c(nr+\gamma)^2=1$$

or $$r^2(al^2+bm^2+cn^2)+2r(al\alpha+bm\beta+cn\gamma)$$
$$+(a\alpha^2+b\beta^2+c\gamma^2-1)=0. \qquad ...(3)$$

But (α, β, γ) being the middle point of the chord (2), the distances of the points of intersection from (α, β, γ) should be equal in magnitude but opposite in sign *i.e.* the sum of the two values of r should be zero and so we should have

$$r_1+r_2=\frac{-2(al\alpha+bm\beta+cn\gamma)}{al^2+bm^2+cn^2}=0$$

or $$al\alpha+bm\beta+cn\gamma=0. \quad ...(4)$$

Therefore, the locus of the chord (2) for varying values of l, m, n is obtained by eliminating l, m, n between (2) and (4) and is thus given by

$$a\alpha(x-\alpha)+b\beta(y-\beta)+c\gamma(z-\gamma)=0$$

or $$a\alpha x+b\beta y+c\gamma z=a\alpha^2+b\beta^2+c\gamma^2$$

or $$a\alpha x+b\beta y+c\gamma z-1=a\alpha^2+b\beta^2+c\gamma^2-1$$

or $$T=S_1 \quad ...(5)$$

where T and S_1 have their usual meanings.

Property. *The section of the conicoid by the plane* (5) *is a conic with its centre at* (α, β, γ).

We know that the section of a conicoid by a plane is a conic. Here the given plane (5) is the locus of the chords of the conicoid with their middle point as (α, β, γ). Therefore, all the chords of the conic section of the conicoid by the plane (5) and passing through the point (α, β, γ) are bisected at the point (α, β, γ) and hence by definition of centre the centre of the conic is (α, β, γ).

SOLVED EXAMPLES (C)

Ex. 1. *Find the equation to the plane which cuts* $3x^2+2y^2-15z^2=4$ *in a conic whose centre is at the point* $(-2, 3, -1)$.

Solution. The equation of the conicoid is

$$S\equiv\frac{3x^2}{4}+\frac{y^2}{2}-\frac{15z^2}{4}-1=0$$

and the centre of conic is $(-2, 3, -1)$.

We have

$$S_1=\frac{3(-2)^2}{4}+\frac{(3)^2}{3}-\frac{15(-1)^2}{4}-1=3+\frac{9}{4}-\frac{15}{4}-1=\frac{1}{2},$$

and $$T=\frac{3}{4}x(-2)+\frac{y}{2}(3)-\frac{15z}{4}(-1)-1=-\frac{3}{2}x+\frac{3}{2}y+\frac{15}{4}z-1.$$

$\therefore$ The required equation of the plane is $T=S_1$

or $$-\frac{3}{2}x+\frac{3}{2}y+\frac{15}{4}z-1=\tfrac{1}{2} \quad \text{or} \quad 2x-2y-5z+2=0.$$

Ans.

Ex. 2. *Find the centre of the conic*

$$x^2/9+y^2/16+z^2/4=1,\ 2x+2y-z=3.$$

Solution. The given conic is the section of the conicoid

$$x^2/9+y^2/16+z^2/4=1 \quad ...(1)$$

by the plane $$2x+2y-z=3. \quad ...(2)$$

Let (α, β, γ) be the centre of the given conic. Then the given conic is the section of the conicoid by the plane '$T=S_1$'

i.e. $$\frac{\alpha x}{9}+\frac{\beta y}{16}+\frac{\gamma z}{4}-1=\frac{\alpha^2}{9}+\frac{\beta^2}{16}+\frac{\gamma^2}{4}-1$$

or $$\frac{\alpha x}{9}+\frac{\beta y}{16}+\frac{\gamma z}{4}=\frac{\alpha^2}{9}+\frac{\beta^2}{16}+\frac{\gamma^2}{4} \quad ...(3)$$

The equations (2) and (3) must represent the same plane and hence comparing their coefficients, we have

$$\frac{(\alpha/9)}{2}=\frac{(\beta/16)}{2}=\frac{(\gamma/4)}{-1}=\frac{(\alpha^2/9)+(\beta^2/16)+(\gamma^2/4)}{3}=k \text{ (say).}$$

$$\therefore \quad \alpha=18k, \beta=32k, \gamma=-4k \quad ...(4)$$

and $$\frac{\alpha^2}{9}+\frac{\beta^2}{16}+\frac{\gamma^2}{4}=3k \quad ...(5)$$

Putting for α, β, γ from (4) in (5), we get

$$36k^2+64k^2+4k^2=3k \text{ or } k=3/104 \text{ (since } k\neq 0).$$

Putting for k in (4), we get

$$\alpha=\frac{27}{52}, \ \beta=\frac{12}{13}, \ \gamma=\frac{-3}{26}.$$

$\therefore$ The required centre is $\left(\frac{27}{52}, \frac{12}{13}, \frac{-3}{26}\right)$. **Ans.**

Ex. 3. *Prove that the centre of the conic $lx+my+nz=p$, $ax^2+by^2+cz^2=1$ is the point*

$$\left(\frac{lp}{ap_0^2}, \frac{mp}{bp_0^2}, \frac{np}{cp_0^2}\right),$$

where $l^2+m^2+n^2=1$ *and* $(l^2/a)+(m^2/b)+(n^2/c)=p_0^2$.

Solution. The given conic is the section of the conicoid

$$ax^2+by^2+cz^2=1 \quad ...(1)$$

by the plane $$lx+my+nz=p. \quad ...(2)$$

Let (α, β, γ) be the centre of the given conic. Then the given conic is the section of the conicoid by the plane '$T=S_1$'

i.e. $$a\alpha x+b\beta y+c\gamma z=a\alpha^2+b\beta^2+c\gamma^2. \quad ...(3)$$

The equations (2) and (3) should represent the same planes and hence comparing their coefficients, we have

$$\frac{a\alpha}{l}=\frac{b\beta}{m}=\frac{c\gamma}{n}=\frac{a\alpha^2+b\beta^2+c\gamma^2}{p}=k \text{ (say).}$$

$$\therefore \quad \alpha=kl/a,\ \beta=km/b,\ \gamma=kn/c \qquad \text{...(4)}$$

and $$a\alpha^2+b\beta^2+c\gamma^2=pk$$

or $a\left[\dfrac{k^2l^2}{a^2}\right]+b.\left[\dfrac{k^2m^2}{b^2}\right]+c.\left[\dfrac{k^2n^2}{c^2}\right]=pk$, using the relations (4)

or $l^2/a+m^2/b+n^2/c=pk$ or $p_0^2=pk$ or $k=p/p_0^2$.

Putting for k in (4), we get $\alpha=lp/p_0^2$, $\beta=mp/p_0^2$, $\gamma=np/p_0^2$.

$\therefore$ The required centre is $\left(\dfrac{lp}{p_0^2}, \dfrac{mp}{p_0^2}, \dfrac{np}{p_0^2}\right)$.

Ex. 4. *Prove that the centre of the section of the ellipsoid* $x^2/a^2+y^2/b^2+z^2/c^2=1$ *by the plane ABC whose equation is* $x/a+y/b+z/c=1$ *is the centroid of the triangle ABC.*

Solution. Let (α, β, γ) be the centre of the section of the ellipsoid

$$x^2/a^2+y^2/b^2+z^2/c^2=1 \qquad \text{...(1)}$$

by the plane $$x/a+y/b+z/c=1 \qquad \text{...(2)}$$

Now the conic section of the ellipsoid (1) having its centre as the point (α, β, γ) is given by the plane '$T=S_1$'

i.e. $$\frac{\alpha x}{a^2}+\frac{\beta y}{b^2}+\frac{\gamma z}{c^2}=\frac{\alpha^2}{a^2}+\frac{\beta^2}{b^2}+\frac{\gamma^2}{c^2} \qquad \text{...(3)}$$

The equations (2) and (3) represent the same plane and hence comparing their coefficients, we have

$$\frac{(\alpha/a^2)}{(1/a)}=\frac{(\beta/b^2)}{(1/b)}=\frac{(\gamma/c^2)}{(1/c)}=\frac{(\alpha^2/a^2)+(\beta^2/b^2)+(\gamma^2/c^2)}{1}=k \text{ (say).}$$

$$\therefore \quad \alpha=ak,\ \beta=bk,\ \gamma=ck \qquad \text{...(4)}$$

and $$\frac{\alpha^2}{a^2}+\frac{\beta^2}{b^2}+\frac{\gamma^2}{c^2}=k$$

or $\dfrac{a^2k^2}{a^2}+\dfrac{b^2k^2}{b^2}+\dfrac{c^2k^2}{c^2}=k$, using the relations (4)

or $3k^2=k$ or $k=\frac{1}{3}$ $\quad [\because k\neq 0]$.

Putting this value of k in (4), we get $\alpha=\frac{1}{3}a$, $\beta=\frac{1}{3}b$, $\gamma=\frac{1}{3}c$.

$\therefore$ The centre of the section is $(\frac{1}{3}a, \frac{1}{3}b, \frac{1}{3}c)$. ...(5)

Again the equation of the plane ABC is given by (2) and so the vertices of the triangle ABC are $A\,(a, 0, 0)$, $B\,(0, b, 0)$ and $C\,(0, 0, c)$. Hence the co-ordinates of the centroid of the triangle ABC are $(\frac{1}{3}a, \frac{1}{3}b, \frac{1}{3}c)$ which are the same as the co-ordinates of the centre given by (5). **Proved.**

Ex. 5. *Prove that the centres of the sections of* $ax^2+by^2+cz^2=1$ *by the planes which are at a constant distance p from the origin lie on the surface*

$$(ax^2+by^2+cz^2)^2=p^2\ (a^2x^2+b^2y^2+c^2z^2).$$

Solution. The equation of the given conicoid is

$$ax^2+by^2+cz^2=1. \qquad ...(1)$$

Let (α, β, γ) be the centre of a plane section of the conicoid (1). Then the equation of the plane giving this section of the conicoid is '$T=S_1$'

i.e.,
$$a\alpha x+b\beta y+c\gamma z=a\alpha^2+b\beta^2+c\gamma^2. \qquad ...(2)$$

If the plane (2) is at a constant distance p from the origin, then

$$p=\frac{a\alpha^2+b\beta^2+c\gamma^2}{\sqrt{(a^2\alpha^2+b^2\beta^2+c^2\gamma^2)}}.$$

$$\therefore\quad (a\alpha^2+b\beta^2+c\gamma^2)^2=p^2\ (a^2\alpha^2+b^2\beta^2+c^2\gamma^2).$$

Hence the locus of (α, β, γ) is the surface

$$(ax^2+by^2+cz^2)^2=p^2\ (a^2x^2+b^2y^2+c^2z^2).$$

Ex. 6 (a). *Show that the locus of the middle points of the chords of the conicoid* $ax^2+by^2+cz^2=1$ *which pass through a fixed point* (x', y', z') *is* $ax\ (x-x')+by\ (y-y')+cz\ (z-z')=0.$

(Lucknow 1979, 82; Kanpur 79; Allahabad 81)

Solution. The equation of the given conicoid is

$$ax^2+by^2+cz^2=1. \qquad ...(1)$$

Let (α, β, γ) be the middle point of a chord of the conicoid (1). Then this chord lies in the plane '$T=S_1$' *i.e.,*

$$a\alpha x+b\beta y+c\gamma z-1=a\alpha^2+b\beta^2+c\gamma^2-1$$

or
$$a\alpha x+b\beta y+c\gamma z=a\alpha^2+b\beta^2+c\gamma^2. \qquad ...(2)$$

Now the chords of the conicoid (1) having (α, β, γ) as their middle point pass through the fixed point (x', y', z'), then the point (x', y', z') should lie on the plane (2). Therefore, we have

$$a\alpha x'+b\beta y'+c\gamma z'=a\alpha^2+b\beta^2+c\gamma^2$$

or
$$a\alpha\ (\alpha-x')+b\beta\ (\beta-y')+c\gamma\ (\gamma-z')=0.$$

Hence the equation of the required locus of the middle point (α, β, γ) of the chords of the conicoid (1) which pass through the fixed point (x', y', z') is

$$ax\ (x-x')+by\ (y-y')+cz\ (z-z')=0.$$

Ex. 6 (b). *Show that the locus of the centres of all sections of the conicoid* $ax^2+by^2+cz^2=1$ *by planes which pass through a fixed point* (x', y', z') *is* $ax\ (x-x')+by\ (y-y')+cz\ (z-z')=0.$

Solution. It is the same problem as Ex. (6) a above.

Ex. 7. *Prove that the section of the ellipsoid*

$$x^2/a^2+y^2/b^2+z^2/c^2=1$$

whose centre is at the point $(\frac{1}{3}a, \frac{1}{3}b, \frac{1}{3}c)$ *passes through the extremities of the axes.* **(Rohilkhand 1981)**

Solution. The equation of the given ellipsoid is

$$S\equiv x^2/a^2+y^2/b^2+z^2/c^2-1=0.$$

The centre of the section is $(\frac{1}{3}a, \frac{1}{3}b, \frac{1}{3}c)$ and hence the equation of the plane giving this section is '$T=S_1$'

i.e.
$$\frac{x.\frac{1}{3}a}{a^2}+\frac{y.\frac{1}{3}b}{b^2}+\frac{z.\frac{1}{3}c}{c^2}-1=\frac{(\frac{1}{3}a)^2}{a^2}+\frac{(\frac{1}{3}b)^2}{b^2}+\frac{(\frac{1}{3}c)^2}{c^2}-1$$

or
$$x/a+y/b+z/c=1. \quad ...(1)$$

The extremities of the axes of the given ellipsoid are $(a, 0, 0)$ $(0, b, 0)$ and $(0, 0, c)$ and the plane (1) clearly passes through these three points. Hence the section whose centre is at the point $(\frac{1}{3}a, \frac{1}{3}b, \frac{1}{3}c)$ passes through the extremities of the axes.

Ex. 8. *Prove that a line joining a point P to the centre of a conicoid passes through the centre of the section of the conicoid by the polar plane of P.*

Solution. Let the equation of the conicoid be

$$ax^2+by^2+cz^2=1 \quad ...(1)$$

Let the co-ordinates of the point P be (x', y', z') so that the polar plane of $P(x', y', z')$ w.r.t. the conicoid (1) is

$$axx'+byy'+czz'=1 \quad ...(2)$$

Let (α, β, γ) be the centre of the section of the conicoid (1) by the plane (2) so that the equation of the plane giving this section is

'$T=S_1$'

i.e.,
$$ax\alpha+by\beta+cz\gamma-1=a\alpha^2+b\beta^2+c\gamma^2-1$$

or
$$a\alpha x+b\beta y+c\gamma z=a\alpha^2+b\beta^2+c\gamma^2. \quad ...(3)$$

The equations (2) and (3) represent the same planes and hence comparing their coefficients, we have

$$\frac{a\alpha}{ax'}=\frac{b\beta}{by'}=\frac{c\gamma}{cz'} \text{ or } \frac{\alpha}{x'}=\frac{\beta}{y'}=\frac{\gamma}{z'} \quad ..(4)$$

Again the centre of the conicoid (1) is $(0, 0, 0)$ so that the equations of the line joining $P(x', y', z')$ and $(0, 0, 0)$ are

$$\frac{x-0}{x'-0}=\frac{y-0}{y'-0}=\frac{z-0}{z'-0} \text{ or } \frac{x}{x'}=\frac{y}{y'}=\frac{z}{z'}. \quad ...(5)$$

If the line (5) is to pass through the point (α, β, γ) then the co-ordinates of the point (α, β, γ) should satisfy (5) and so we should have $\frac{\alpha}{x'}=\frac{\beta}{y'}=\frac{\gamma}{z'}$, which is true by virtue of (4). Hence proved.

Ex. 9. *Triads of tangent planes at right angles are drawn to the ellipsoid $x^2/a^2+y^2/b^2+z^2/c^2=1$. Show that the locus of the centre of section of the surface by the plane through the points of contact is*

$$(x^2+y^2+z^2)=(a^2+b^2+c^2)\left(\frac{x^2}{a^2}+\frac{y^2}{b^2}+\frac{z^2}{c^2}\right)^2.$$

Solution. The equation of the given ellipsoid is

$$x^2/a^2+y^2/b^2+z^2/c^2=1. \qquad \text{...(1)}$$

Let (x', y', z') be the co-ordinates of the point from which three tangent planes at right angles are drawn to the given ellipsoid (1). Then by definition of the director sphere the point (x', y', z') will lie on the director sphere of the ellipsoid (1) *i.e.* on

$$x^2+y^2+z^2=a^2+b^2+c^2. \quad \text{[See § 7]}$$

$$\therefore \quad x'^2+y'^2+z'^2=a^2+b^2+c^2. \qquad \text{...(2)}$$

Now the plane through the points of contact is the plane of contact of the point (x', y', z') with respect to the ellipsoid (1) and its equation is given by

$$x'x/a^2+y'y/b^2+z'z/c^2=1. \qquad \text{...(3)}$$

Again let (α, β, γ) be the centre of the section of the ellipsoid (1) by the plane (3), so that the equation of the plane giving this section is '$T=S_1$'

i.e. $\quad \alpha x/a^2+\beta y/b^2+\gamma z/c^2-1=\alpha^2/a^2+\beta^2/b^2+\gamma^2/c^2-1$

or $\quad \alpha x/a^2+\beta y/b^2+\gamma z/c^2=\alpha^2/a^2+\beta^2/b^2+\gamma^2/c^2. \qquad \text{...(4)}$

The equations (3) and (4) represent the same plane and hence comparing their coefficients, we have

$$\frac{x'}{\alpha}=\frac{y'}{\beta}=\frac{z'}{\gamma}=\frac{1}{(\alpha^2/a^2)+(\beta^2/b^2)+(\gamma^2/c^2)}. \qquad \text{...(5)}$$

Putting the values of x', y', z' from (5) in (2), we get

$$\frac{\alpha^2+\beta^2+\gamma^2}{[(\alpha^2/a^2)+(\beta^2/b^2)+(\gamma^2/c^2)]^2}=a^2+b^2+c^2.$$

$\therefore$ The locus of the centre (α, β, γ) is given by

$(x^2+y^2+z^2)=(a^2+b^2+c^2)\,[(x^2/a^2)+(y^2/b^2)+(z^2/c^2)]^2.$

Ex. 10 (a). *Show that the centres of the sections of a central conicoid that are (i) parallel to a given line lie on a fixed plane and (ii) that pass through a given line lie on a conic.*

Solution. Let the equation of the central conicoid be

$$ax^2+by^2+cz^2=1. \qquad \text{...(1)}$$

Let (α, β, γ) be the centre of a section of the given central conicoid (1). Then the equation of the plane giving this section is '$T=S_1$'

i.e., $$a\alpha x+b\beta y+c\gamma z-1=a\alpha^2+b\beta^2+c\gamma^2-1$$

or $$a\alpha x+b\beta y+c\gamma z=a\alpha^2+b\beta^2+c\gamma^2. \quad \ldots(2)$$

Again let the equations of a given line be

$$\frac{x-x_1}{l}=\frac{y-y_1}{m}=\frac{z-z_1}{n}. \quad \ldots(3)$$

(i) If the plane (2) is parallel to the line (3) then we have

$$(a\alpha).l+(b\beta).m+(c\gamma).n=0.$$

∴ The locus of the centre (α, β, γ) is

$$alx+bmy+cnz=0$$

which is the equation of a fixed plane since a, b, c, l, m, n are all constants being given numbers.

(ii) If the plane (2) passes through the line (3), we have

$$a\alpha x_1+b\beta y_1+c\gamma z_1=a\alpha^2+b\beta^2+c\gamma^2,$$

and $$(a\alpha).l+(b\beta).m+(c\gamma).n=0.$$

∴ The locus of (α, β, γ) is the curve of intersection of the surfaces

$$\left.\begin{aligned} ax^2+by^2+cz^2-ax_1x-by_1y+cz_1z&=0 \\ \text{and} \quad alx+bmy+cnz&=0. \end{aligned}\right\} \quad \ldots(4)$$

The two equations given by (4) together represent a conic. Hence the locus of the centre is a conic.

Ex. 10(b). *Show that the centres of the section of the ellipsoid* $x^2/a^2+y^2/b^2+z^2/c^2=1$ *that are (i) parallel to a given line lie on a fixed plane and (ii) that pass through a given line lie on a conic.*

Solution. Proceed exactly as in Ex. 10(a) above.

Ex. 11. *Find the locus of the centre of the section of the conicoid* $ax^2+by^2+cz^2=1$ *which touches* $Ax^2+By^2+Cz^2=1$.

(Madras 1978; Allahabad 76)

Solution. Let (α, β, γ) be the co-ordinates of the centre of a plane section of the conicoid $ax^2+by^2+cz^2=1$.

Then the equation of the piane giving this section is '$T=S_1$'

i.e., $$a\alpha x+b\beta y+c\gamma z-1=a\alpha^2+b\beta^2+c\gamma^2-1$$

or $$a\alpha x+b\beta y+c\gamma z=a\alpha^2+b\beta^2+c\gamma^2. \quad \ldots(1)$$

Now if the plane (1) touches the conicoid $Ax^2+By^2+Cz^2=1$, then we have

$$\frac{(a\alpha)^2}{A}+\frac{(b\beta)^2}{B}+\frac{(c\gamma)^2}{C}=(a\alpha^2+b\beta^2+c\gamma^2)^2. \quad \text{[using § 6(A)]}$$

$\therefore$ The locus of (α, β, γ) is

$$a^2x^2/A+b^2y^2/B+c^2z^2/C=(ax^2+by^2+cz^2)^2.$$

Ex. 12. *Prove that the middle points of the chords of*

$$ax^2+by^2+cz^2=1$$

which are parallel to $x=0$ *and touch* $x^2+y^2+z^2=r^2$ *lie on the surface*

$$by^2(bx^2+by^2+cz^2-br^2)+cz^2(cx^2+by^2+cz^2-cr^2)=0.$$

(Kanpur 1982)

Solution. The equation of the conicoid is

$$ax^2+by^2+cz^2=1, \quad \ldots(1)$$

Let (α, β, γ) be the middle point of a chord. The equations of any straight line passing through the point (α, β, γ) and parallel to the plane $x=0$ (*i.e.* YOZ plane) are given by

$$\frac{x-\alpha}{0}=\frac{y-\beta}{m}=\frac{z-\gamma}{n}=\lambda \text{ (say)}, \quad \ldots(2)$$

where $0, m, n$ are the actual d.c.'s of the line.

Any point on the line (2) at a distance λ from (α, β, γ) is $(\alpha, m\lambda+\beta, n\lambda+\gamma)$. If it lies on the conicoid (1) then distances λ of the points of intersection of (1) and (2) from (α, β, γ) are given by

$$a\alpha^2+b(m\lambda+\beta)^2+c(n\lambda+\gamma)^2=1$$

or $$\lambda^2(bm^2+cn^2)+2\lambda(bm\beta+cn\gamma)+(a\alpha^2+b\beta^2+c\gamma^2-1)=0.$$

Since (α, β, γ) is the middle point of the chord intercepted by (2) on (1), therefore the sum of the roots (*i.e.* $\lambda_1+\lambda_2$) of the above equation should be zero and for it we have

$$bm\beta+cn\gamma=0 \quad \text{or} \quad (m/n)=-(c\gamma/b\beta). \quad \ldots(3)$$

Now according to the given question if the chord (2) touches the sphere $x^2+y^2+z^2=r^2$, then we have

the length of the perpendicular from the centre $(0, 0, 0)$ of the sphere to the line (2) = the radius r of the sphere

i.e. $$\begin{vmatrix} 0-\beta & 0-\gamma \\ m & n \end{vmatrix}^2+\begin{vmatrix} 0-\gamma & 0-\alpha \\ n & 0 \end{vmatrix}^2+\begin{vmatrix} 0-\alpha & 0-\beta \\ 0 & m \end{vmatrix}^2=r^2$$

or $$(m\gamma-\beta n)^2+n^2\alpha^2+m^2\alpha^2=r^2(m^2+n^2)$$

$$[\because 0^2+m^2+n^2=1]$$

or $$(m\gamma-\beta n)^2+(m^2+n^2)\alpha^2=r^2(m^2+n^2)$$

or $$(-r^2+\alpha^2)(m^2+n^2)+(n\gamma-\beta n)^2=0$$

or $$(-r^2+\alpha^2)\left\{1+\left(\frac{m}{n}\right)^2\right\}+\left\{\beta-\frac{m\gamma}{n}\right\}^2=0$$

or $$(-r^2+\alpha^2)\left\{1+\frac{c^2\gamma^2}{b^2\beta^2}\right\}+\left\{\beta+\frac{c\gamma}{b\beta}\cdot\gamma\right\}^2=0, \text{ using (3)}$$

or $$(-r^2+\alpha^2)\,(b^2\beta^2+c^2\gamma^2)+(b\beta^2+c\gamma^2)^2=0.$$

$\therefore$ The locus of (α, β, γ) is

$$(-r^2+x^2)\,(b^2y^2+c^2z^2)+(by^2+cz^2)^2=0$$

or $$-r^2b^2y^2-r^2c^2z^2+b^2x^2y^2+c^2x^2z^2+b^2y^4+c^2z^4+2bcy^2z^2=0$$

or $$by^2\,(bx^2+by^2+cz^2-br^2)+cz^2\,(cx^2+by^2+cz^2-cr^2)=0$$

Proved.

§ 11. Normal to a Conicoid.

(A) *To find the equation of the normal to a central conicoid at the point* (α, β, γ). **(Agra 1982; Rohilkhand 80; Utkal 70)**

Let the equation of the central conicoid be

$$ax^2+by^2+cz^2=1. \quad \ldots(1)$$

The equation of the tangent plane at (α, β, γ) to the conicoid (1) is

$$a\alpha x+b\beta y+c\gamma z=1. \quad \ldots(2)$$

The normal to the conicoid (1) at (α, β, γ) is the straight line perpendicular to the tangent plane (2) and passing through (α, β, γ) and hence the required equations of the normal are

$$\frac{x-\alpha}{a\alpha}=\frac{y-\beta}{b\beta}=\frac{z-\gamma}{c\gamma} \quad \ldots(3)$$

where $a\alpha$, $b\beta$, $c\gamma$ are the direction ratios of the normal (3).

Now let p be the length of the perpendicular from the origin to the tangent plane (2) so that

$$p=\frac{1}{\sqrt{(a^2\alpha^2+b^2\beta^2+c^2\gamma^2)}} \text{ or } (a\alpha p)^2+(b\beta p)^2+(c\gamma p)^2=1. \quad \ldots(4)$$

In view of (4) the actual direction cosines of the normal (3) are $a\alpha p$, $b\beta p$, $c\gamma p$ and hence the equations (3) of the normal to the conicoid (1) at (α, β, γ) in terms of actual direction cosines are given by

$$\frac{x-\alpha}{a\alpha p}=\frac{y-\beta}{b\beta p}=\frac{z-\gamma}{c\gamma p}. \quad \ldots(5)$$

(B) *To find the equations of the normal to the ellipsoid*

$$x^2/a^2+y^2/b^2+z^2/c^2=1$$

at the point (α, β, γ). **(Kanpur 1980; Lucknow 81; Kurushetra 73)**

Proceeding exactly as in § 11 (A), the equations of the normal to the given ellipsoid at (α, β, γ) are

$$\frac{x-\alpha}{\alpha p/a^2}=\frac{y-\beta}{\beta p/b^2}=\frac{z-\gamma}{\gamma p/c^2}, \quad ...(1)$$

where $\frac{1}{p^2}=\frac{\alpha^2}{a^4}+\frac{\beta^2}{b^4}+\frac{\gamma^2}{c^4}$ and

where $\alpha p/a^2$, $\beta p/b^2$, $\gamma p/c^2$ are direction cosines

or $$\frac{x-\alpha}{\alpha/a^2}=\frac{y-\beta}{\beta/b^2}=\frac{z-\gamma}{\gamma/c^2},$$

where α/a^2, β/b^2, γ/c^2 are direction ratios.

SOLVED EXAMPLES (D)

Ex. 1. *The normal at $P(\alpha, \beta, \gamma)$ of a central conicoid meets the three principal planes at G_1, G_2, G_3; show that PG_1, PG_2, PG_3 are in a constant ratio.* **(Agra 1980; Kanpur 78)**

Again if $PG_1^2+PG_2^2+PG_3^2=k^2$, then find the locus of P. **(Rohilkhand 1981)**

Solution. Let the equation of the central conicoid be

$$ax^2+by^2+cz^2=1. \quad ...(1)$$

The equations of the normal to the conicoid (1) at the point (α, β, γ) are

$$\frac{x-\alpha}{a\alpha p}=\frac{y-\beta}{b\beta p}=\frac{z-\gamma}{c\gamma p}=r \quad ...(2)$$

where $p=1/\sqrt{(a^2\alpha^2+b^2\beta^2+c^2\gamma^2)}$ and where r denotes the actual distance of any point on the normal (2) from $P(\alpha, \beta, \gamma)$.

We know that the principal planes of the central conicoid (1) are the co-ordinate planes. The normal (2) meets the plane $x=0$ in G_1. So we have $r=PG_1$.

$\therefore$ from (2), $\frac{0-\alpha}{a\alpha p}=PG_1$ or $PG_1=-1/(ap)$.

Similarly if the normal (2) meets the planes $y=0$ and $z=0$ in the points G_2 and G_3 respectively, we have

$$PG_2=-1/(bp) \text{ and } PG_3=-1/(cp).$$

$$\therefore \quad PG_1 : PG_2 : PG_3=-1/(ap) : -1/(bp) : -1/(cp)$$
$$=(1/a) : (1/b) : (1/c)$$

which are in a constant ratio since a, b, c are fixed for the given conicoid.

Second Part.

Now it is given that

$$PG_1^2+PG_2^2+PG_3^2=k^2$$

or $$\left(-\frac{1}{ap}\right)^2+\left(-\frac{1}{bp}\right)^2+\left(+\frac{1}{cp}\right)^2=k^2$$

or
$$\frac{1}{p^2}\left(\frac{1}{a^2}+\frac{1}{b^2}+\frac{1}{c^2}\right)=k^2$$
or
$$(a^2\alpha^2+b^2\beta^2+c^2\gamma^2)\,(1/a^2+1/b^2+1/c^2)=k^2$$
$$[\because\ 1/p^2=a^2\alpha^2+b^2\beta^2+c^2\gamma^2]$$

$\therefore$ the point $P(\alpha, \beta, \gamma)$ also lies on the surface
$$(a^2x^2+b^2y^2+c^2z^2)\,(1/a^2+1/b^2+1/c^2)=k^2. \quad \ldots(3)$$

But the point $P(\alpha, \beta, \gamma)$ lies on the given central conicoid (1) and, therefore, the locus of P is the curve of intersection of the conicoid (1) and the surface (3).

Ex. 2. *Find the distances of the points of intersection of the normal at $P(\alpha, \beta, \gamma)$ to a central conicoid with the co-ordinate planes.*

Solution. It is the same as the first part of Ex. 1 above.

Particular case when the given conicoid is an ellipsoid. Let the central conicoid be the ellipsoid
$$x^2/a^2+y^2/b^2+z^2/c^2=1. \quad \ldots(1)$$

The equations of the normal to (1) at $P(\alpha, \beta, \gamma)$ are
$$\frac{x-\alpha}{\alpha p/a^2}=\frac{y-\beta}{\beta p/b^2}=\frac{z-\gamma}{\gamma p/c^2}=r \text{ (say)} \quad \ldots(2)$$
where $1/p^2=\alpha^2/a^4+\beta^2/b^4+\gamma^2/c^4$ and where r denotes the actual distance of any point on the normal (2) from $P(\alpha, \beta, \gamma)$. If the normal (2) meets the plane $x=0$ in G_1 then putting $r=PG_1$ in (2), we get
$$\frac{0-\alpha}{\alpha p/a^2}=PG_1 \text{ or } PG_1=-a^2/p.$$

Similarly if the normal (2) meets the co-ordinate planes $y=0$ and $z=0$ in G_2 and G_3 respectively then
$$PG_2=-b^2/p \text{ and } PG_3=-c^2/p.$$

Ex. 3. *If Q is any point on the normal at P to the ellipsoid $x^2/a^2+y^2/b^2+z^2/c^2=1$ such that $3PQ=PG_1+PG_2+PG_3$ where G_1, G_2, G_3, are the points where the normal at P meets the co-ordinate planes respectively, then the locus of the point Q is*
$$\frac{a^2x^2}{(2a^2-b^2-c^2)^2}+\frac{b^2y^2}{(2b^2-c^2-a^2)^2}+\frac{c^2z^2}{(2c^2-a^2-b^2)^2}=\frac{1}{9}.$$

(Kanpur 1977; Bundelkhand 79)

Solution. The equation of the ellipsoid is
$$x^2/a^2+y^2/b^2+z^2/c^2=1. \quad \ldots(1)$$

Let the co-ordinates of a point P on (1) be (α, β, γ) so that the equations of the normal at $P\,(\alpha, \beta, \gamma)$ are

$$\frac{x-\alpha}{p\alpha/a^2}=\frac{y-\beta}{p\beta/b^2}=\frac{z-\gamma}{p\gamma/c^2}=r \text{ (say)} \qquad ...(2)$$

where $$\frac{1}{p^2}=\frac{\alpha^2}{a^4}+\frac{\beta^2}{b^4}+\frac{\gamma^2}{c^4}. \qquad ...(3)$$

Let Q be the point (x_1, y_1, z_1). Since Q lies on (2), we have

$$\frac{x_1-\alpha}{p\alpha/a^2}=\frac{y_1-\beta}{p\beta/b^2}=\frac{z_1-\gamma}{p\gamma/c^2}=r.$$

$\therefore$ $x_1=\alpha+(p\alpha r/a^2)$, $y_1=\beta+(p\beta r/b^2)$, $z_1=\gamma+(p\gamma r/c^2)$. ...(4)

Now $P(\alpha, \beta, \gamma)$ lies on the ellipsoid (1) so that

$$\alpha^2/a^2+\beta^2/b^2+\gamma^2/c^2=1. \qquad ...(5)$$

Again it is given that $3PQ=PG_1+PG_2+PG_3$.

$\therefore$ $3r=-\dfrac{a^2}{p}-\dfrac{b^2}{p}-\dfrac{c^2}{p}$ [$\because$ $PQ=r$ and putting the values of PG_1 etc. as found in Ex. 2 above]

or $r=-(a^2+b^2+c^2)/(3p)$.

Putting this value of r in (4), we get

$$x_1=\alpha-\frac{\alpha\,(a^2+b^2+c^2)}{3a^2}=\alpha\left(\frac{2a^2-b^2-c^2}{3a^2}\right),$$

so that $$\frac{\alpha}{a}=\frac{3ax_1}{2a^2-b^2-c^2}.$$

Similarly $$\frac{\beta}{b}=\frac{3by_1}{2b^2-c^2-a^2},\ \frac{\gamma}{c}=\frac{3cz_1}{2c^2-a^2-b^2}.$$

Putting these values in (5), we get

$$\frac{9a^2x_1^2}{(2a^2-b^2-c^2)^2}+\frac{9b^2y_1^2}{(2b^2-c^2-a^2)^2}+\frac{2c^2z_1^2}{(2c^2-a^2-b^2)^2}=1.$$

$\therefore$ the locus of $Q(x_1, y_1, z_1)$ is

$$\frac{a^2x^2}{(2a^2-b^2-c^2)^2}+\frac{b^2y^2}{(2b^2-c^2-a^2)^2}+\frac{c^2z^2}{(2c^2-a^2-b^2)^2}=\frac{1}{9}.$$ **Proved.**

Ex. 4. *Find the length of the normal chord through P of the ellipsoid $x^2/a^2+y^2/b^2+z^2/c^2=1$ and prove that if it is equal to $4PG_3$, where G_3 is the point where the normal chord through P meets the plane $z=0$, then P lies on the cone*

$$x^2\,(2c^2-a^2)/a^6+y^2\,(2c^2-b^2)/b^6+z^2/c^4=0.$$

Solution. The equation of the ellipsoid is

$$x^2/a^2+y^2/b^2+z^2/c^2=1. \qquad ...(1)$$

Let the co-ordinates of a point P on (1) be (α, β, γ), so that

$$\alpha^2/a^2+\beta^2/b^2+\gamma^2/c^2=1. \qquad ...(2)$$

The equations of the normal to the ellipsoid (1) at $P(\alpha, \beta, \gamma)$ are

$$\frac{x-\alpha}{p\alpha/a^2}=\frac{y-\beta}{p\beta/b^2}=\frac{z-\gamma}{p\gamma/c^2}=r \text{ (say)} \quad \text{...(3)}$$

where $$\frac{1}{p^2}=\frac{\alpha^2}{a^4}+\frac{\beta^2}{b^4}+\frac{\gamma^2}{c^4}. \quad \text{...(4)}$$

The co-ordinates of any point Q (say) on the normal (3) are
$\alpha+(p\alpha r/a^2)$, $\beta+(p\beta r/b^2)$, $\gamma+(p\gamma r/c^2)$ where $r=PQ$.

If PQ is the normal chord of the ellipsoid (1) then Q will lie on (1) and so we get

$$\frac{1}{a^2}\left(\alpha+\frac{p\alpha r}{a^2}\right)^2+\frac{1}{b^2}\left(\beta+\frac{p\beta r}{b^2}\right)^2+\frac{1}{c^2}\left(\gamma+\frac{p\gamma r}{c^2}\right)^2=1$$

or $$p^2r^2\left(\frac{\alpha^2}{a^6}+\frac{\beta^2}{b^6}+\frac{\gamma^2}{c^6}\right)+2pr\left(\frac{\alpha^2}{a^4}+\frac{\beta^2}{b^4}+\frac{\gamma^2}{c^4}\right)+\left(\frac{\alpha^2}{a^2}+\frac{\beta^2}{b^2}+\frac{\gamma^2}{c^2}-1\right)=0$$

or $$p^2r^2\left(\frac{\alpha^2}{a^6}+\frac{\beta^2}{b^6}+\frac{\gamma^2}{c^6}\right)+\frac{2pr}{p^2}=0, \text{ using (2) and (4)}$$

or $$r=\frac{-2}{p^3\left[(\alpha^2/a^6)+(\beta^2/b^6)+(\gamma^2/c^6)\right]}$$

$=PQ$, the length of the normal chord. ...(5)

Now if $PQ=4PG_3$ (as given) then $PQ=-4c^2/p$

[See Ex. 2 above for the value of PG_3]

or $$\frac{-2}{p^3[(\alpha^2/a^6)+(\beta^2/b^6)+(\gamma^2/c^6)]}=-\frac{4c^2}{p}$$

[Putting the value of PQ from (5)]

or $$2c^2\left[\frac{\alpha^2}{a^6}+\frac{\beta^2}{b^6}+\frac{\gamma^2}{c^6}\right]=\frac{1}{p^2}=\frac{\alpha^2}{a^4}+\frac{\beta^2}{b^4}+\frac{\gamma^2}{c^4}, \text{ using (4)}$$

or $$\alpha^2\left(\frac{2c^2}{a^6}-\frac{1}{a^4}\right)+\beta^2\left(\frac{2c^2}{b^6}-\frac{1}{b^4}\right)+\gamma^2\left(\frac{2c^2}{c^6}-\frac{1}{c^4}\right)=0.$$

$\therefore$ The locus of $P(\alpha, \beta, \gamma)$ is

$x^2(2c^2-a^2)/a^6+y^2(2c^2-b^2)/b^6+z^2/c^4=0$, which is a cone.

Ex. 5. *If a length PQ be taken on the normal at any point P of the ellipsoid $x^2/a^2+y^2/b^2+z^2/c^2=1$ such that $PQ=\lambda^2/p$ where λ is constant and p is the length of the perpendicular from the origin to the tangent plane at P, the locus of Q is*

$$\frac{a^2x^2}{(a^2+\lambda^2)^2}+\frac{b^2y^2}{(b^2+\lambda^2)^2}+\frac{c^2z^2}{(c^2+\lambda^2)^2}=1.$$

Solution. The equation of the given ellipsoid is

$$x^2/a^2+y^2/b^2+z^2/c^2=1. \quad \text{...(1)}$$

Let the co-ordinates of a point P on (1) be (α, β, γ), so that

$$\alpha^2/a^2+\beta^2/b^2+\gamma^2/c^2=1. \qquad \text{...(1)}$$

The equations of the normal to the ellipsoid (1) at $P(\alpha, \beta, \gamma)$ are

$$\frac{x-\alpha}{p\alpha/a^2}=\frac{y-\beta}{p\beta/b^2}=\frac{z-\gamma}{p\gamma/c^2}=r \text{ (say)}, \qquad \text{...(3)}$$

where $p\alpha/a^2$, $p\beta/b^2$, $p\gamma/c^2$ are the actual d.c.'s of the normal.

Let (x_1, y_1, z_1) be the co-ordinates of a point Q on the normal (3) such that $PQ=\lambda^2/p$ (as given).

Then putting $x=x_1$, $y=y_1$, $z=z_1$ and $r=\lambda^2/p$ in (3), we get

$$x_1=\alpha+\frac{\alpha\lambda^2}{a^2},\ y_1=\beta+\frac{\beta\lambda^2}{b^2},\ z_1=\gamma+\frac{\gamma\lambda^2}{c^2}.$$

$$\therefore \quad \alpha=\frac{a^2x_1}{a^2+\lambda^2},\ \beta=\frac{b^2y_1}{b^2+\lambda^2},\ \gamma=\frac{c^2z_1}{c^2+\lambda^2}.$$

Putting these values of α, β, γ in (2), we get

$$\frac{a^2x_1^2}{(a^2+\lambda^2)^2}+\frac{b^2y_1^2}{(b^2+\lambda^2)^2}+\frac{c^2z_1^2}{(c^2+\lambda^2)^2}=1.$$

$\therefore$ The locus of the point Q (x_1, y_1, z_1) is given by

$$\frac{a^2x^2}{(a^2+\lambda^2)^2}+\frac{b^2y^2}{(b^2+\lambda^2)^2}+\frac{c^2z^2}{(c^2+\lambda^2)^2}=1.$$

Proved.

Ex. 6. *The normal at a variable point P of the ellipsoid $x^2/a^2+y^2/b^2+z^2/c^2=1$ meets the plane $z=0$ (i.e. the xy plane) in G_3 and G_3Q is drawn parallel to z-axis and equal to G_3P. Show that the locus of Q is given by*

$$x^2/(a^2-c^2)+y^2/(b^2-c^2)+z^2/c^2=1.$$

Also find the locus of R if OR is drawn from the centre equal and parallel to G_3P.

Solution. The equation of the ellipsoid is

$$x^2/a^2+y^2/b^2+z^2/c^2=1. \qquad \text{...(1)}$$

Let (α, β, γ) be the co-ordinates of a point P on the ellipsoid (1), so that

$$-\alpha^2/a^2+\beta^2/b^2+\gamma^2/c^2=1. \qquad \text{...(2)}$$

The equations of the normal to the ellipsoid (1) at P (α, β, γ) are

$$\frac{x-\alpha}{p\alpha/a^2}=\frac{y-\beta}{p\beta/b^2}=\frac{z-\gamma}{p\gamma/e^2}=r \text{ (say)}, \qquad \text{...(3)}$$

where $p\alpha/a^2$, $p\beta/b^2$, $p\gamma/c^2$ are the actual d.c.'s of the normal so that r denotes the actual distance of any point on the normal (3) from the point $P(\alpha, \beta, \gamma)$. If the normal (3) meets the plane $z=0$ in G_3 then putting $z=0$ and $r=PG_3$ in (3), we get

$$\frac{0-\gamma}{p\gamma/c^2}=PG_3, \text{ so that } PG_3=-\frac{c^2}{p}.$$

Putting $r=PG_3=-c^2/p$ in (3), the co-ordinates of G_3 are

$$\left(\alpha-\frac{c^2\alpha}{a^2}, \beta-\frac{c^2\beta}{b^2}, 0\right).$$

Now G_3 is a point in the xy-plane and G_3Q is a line drawn parallel to z axis such that $G_3Q=G_3P=-c^2/p$. If (x_1, y_1, z_1) are the co-ordinates of Q, then

$$x_1=x\text{-co-ordinate of } G_3=\alpha-(c^2\alpha/a^2),$$

$$y_1=y\text{-co-ordinate of } G_3=\beta-(c^2\beta/b^2),$$

and $$z_1=G_3Q=-c^2/p.$$

$$\therefore \quad \alpha=\frac{a^2x_1}{a^2-c^2}, \quad \beta=\frac{b^2y_1}{b^2-c^2}, \quad \frac{z_1}{c}=-\frac{c}{p}. \quad \ldots(4)$$

From $\frac{z_1}{c}=-\frac{c}{p}$, we have

$$\frac{z_1^2}{c^2}=\frac{c^2}{p^2} \text{ or } \frac{z_1^2}{c^2}=c^2\left[\frac{\alpha^2}{a^4}+\frac{\beta^2}{b^4}+\frac{\gamma^2}{c^4}\right]$$

[Putting for $1/p^2$ from § 11 (B)]

or $$\frac{\gamma^2}{c^2}=\frac{z_1^2}{c^2}-c^2\left(\frac{\alpha^2}{a^4}+\frac{\beta^2}{b^4}\right) \quad \ldots(5)$$

Putting the values of α, β and γ from (4) and (5) in (2), we get

$$\frac{a^2x_1^2}{(a^2-c^2)^2}+\frac{b^2y_1^2}{(b^2-c^2)^2}+\left\{\frac{z_1^2}{c^2}-c^2\left(\frac{\alpha^2}{a^4}+\frac{\beta^2}{b^4}\right)\right\}=1$$

or $$\frac{a^2x_1^2}{(a^2-c^2)^2}+\frac{b^2y_1^2}{(b^2-c^2)^2}+\frac{z_1^2}{c^2}-\frac{c^2x_1^2}{(a^2-c^2)^2}-\frac{c^2y_1^2}{(b^2-c^2)^2}=1$$

[Again using (4) for α and β]

or $$\frac{x_1^2(a^2-c^2)}{(a^2-c^2)^2}+\frac{y_1^2(b^2-c^2)}{(b^2-c^2)^2}+\frac{z_1^2}{c^2}=1$$

or $$\frac{x_1^2}{a^2-c^2}+\frac{y_1^2}{b^2-c^2}+\frac{z_1^2}{c^2}=1.$$

$\therefore$ The locus of $Q(x_1, y_1, z_1)$ is

$$\frac{x^2}{(a^2-c^2)}+\frac{y^2}{(b^2-c^2)}+\frac{z^2}{c^2}=1.$$ **Proved.**

Second part. The equations of the line OR passing through $O(0, 0, 0)$ and drawn parallel to the normal at P are

$$\frac{x}{(p\alpha/a^2)}=\frac{y}{(p\beta/b^2)}=\frac{z}{(p\gamma/c^2)}=k \text{ (say)}.$$

Taking $k=OR=G_3P=-c^2/p$, the co-ordinates of R are

$$\left(-\frac{\alpha c^2}{a^2}, -\frac{\beta c^2}{b^2}, -\gamma\right).$$

Also let the co-ordinates of R be (x_2, y_2, z_2), so that we have

$$x_2=-\alpha c^2/a^2,\ y_2=-\beta c^2/b^2,\ z^2=-\gamma$$

or $$\alpha=-a^2x_2/c^2,\ \beta=-b^2y_2/c^2,\ \gamma=-z_2.$$

Putting these values of α, β, γ in (5), we get

$$a^2x_2^2/c^4+b^2y_2^2/c^4+z_2^2/c^2=1.$$

$\therefore$ The locus of $R\ (x_2, y_2, z_2)$ is $a^2x^2+b^2y^2+c^2z^2=c^4$. **Ans.**

Ex. 7. *The normals at P and P', points of the ellipsoid $x^2/a^2+y^2/b^2+z^2/c^2=1$, meet the plane $z=0$ in G_3 and G_3' and make angles θ, θ' with PP'. Show that*

$$PG_3 \cos\theta+P'G_3' \cos\theta'=0. \qquad \textbf{(Agra 1976)}$$

Solution. Let (α, β, γ) and $(\alpha', \beta', \gamma')$ be the co-ordinates of the points P and P' respectively. Now proceeding exactly as in Ex. 2 above, we have

$$PG_3=-c^2/p,\ P'G'_3=-c^2/p',$$

where p and p' have their meanings as given in § 11.

The d.c.'s of the normal at P are $p\alpha/a^2, p\beta/b^2, p\gamma/c^2$ and the d.c.'s of the normal at P' are $p'\alpha'/a^2, p'\beta'/b^2, p'\gamma'/c^2$. The direction ratios of PP' are $\alpha'-\alpha, \beta'-\beta, \gamma'-\gamma$ and so the d.c.'s of PP' are $(\alpha'-\alpha)/PP', (\beta'-\beta)/PP', (\gamma'-\gamma)/PP'$.

Since θ is the angle between the normal at P and the line PP', we have

$$\cos\theta=\frac{p\alpha}{a^2}\cdot\frac{\alpha'-\alpha}{PP'}+\frac{p\beta}{b^2}\cdot\frac{\beta'-\beta}{PP'}+\frac{p\gamma}{c^2}\cdot\frac{\gamma'-\gamma}{PP'}.$$

$$\therefore\ PG_3\cos\theta=-\frac{c^2}{p}\cdot\frac{p}{PP'}\left[\frac{\alpha(\alpha'-\alpha)}{a^2}+\frac{\beta(\beta'-\beta)}{b^2}+\frac{\gamma(\gamma'-\gamma)}{c^2}\right]$$

$$=-\frac{c^2}{PP'}\left[\frac{\alpha\alpha'}{a^2}+\frac{\beta\beta'}{b^2}+\frac{\gamma\gamma'}{c^2}-\left(\frac{\alpha^2}{a^2}+\frac{\beta^2}{b^2}+\frac{\gamma^2}{c^2}\right)\right]$$

$$=-\frac{c^2}{PP'}\left[\frac{\alpha\alpha'}{a^2}+\frac{\beta\beta'}{b^2}+\frac{\gamma\gamma'}{c^2}-1\right],$$

since $P\ (\alpha, \beta, \gamma)$ lies on the given ellipsoid.

Similarly $$P'G_3'\cos\theta'=-\frac{c^2}{PP'}\left[1-\left(\frac{\alpha\alpha'}{a^2}+\frac{\beta\beta'}{b^2}+\frac{\gamma\gamma'}{c^2}\right)\right].$$

$$\therefore\ P'G'_3\cos\theta'=\frac{c^2}{PP'}\left[\left(\frac{\alpha\alpha'}{a^2}+\frac{\beta\beta'}{b^2}+\frac{\gamma\gamma'}{c^2}\right)-1\right]$$

$$=-PG_3 \cos \theta$$

or $$PG_3 \cos \theta + P'G_3' \cos \theta' = 0.$$ **Proved.**

Ex. 8. *If the normals at P and Q, points on the ellipsoid $x^2/a^2+y^2/b^2+z^2/c^2=1$, intersect then prove that PQ is at right angles to its polar with respect to the ellipsoid.*

Solution. The equation of the given ellipsoid is

$$x^2/a^2+y^2/b^2+z^2/c^2=1. \quad \text{...(1)}$$

Let the co-ordinates of the points P and Q on (1) be $(\alpha_1, \beta_1, \gamma_1)$ and $(\alpha_2, \beta_2, \gamma_2)$ respectively.

The equations of the normals to the ellipsoid (1) at the points P and Q are respectively given by

$$\frac{x-\alpha_1}{\alpha_1/a^2}=\frac{y-\beta_1}{\beta_1/b^2}=\frac{z-\gamma_1}{\gamma_1/c^2} \quad \text{...(2)}$$

and $$\frac{x-\alpha_2}{\alpha_2/a^2}=\frac{y-\beta_2}{\beta_2/b^2}=\frac{z-\gamma_2}{\gamma_2/c^2}. \quad \text{...(3)}$$

If the normals (2) and (3) intersect, then we have

$$\begin{vmatrix} \alpha_1-\alpha_2 & \beta_1-\beta_2 & \gamma_1-\gamma_2 \\ \alpha_1/a^2 & \beta_1/b^2 & \gamma_1/c^2 \\ \alpha_2/a^2 & \beta_2/b^2 & \gamma_2/c^2 \end{vmatrix}=0$$

or $$(\alpha_1-\alpha_2)\left(\frac{\beta_1\gamma_2-\beta_2\gamma_1}{b^2c^2}\right)+(\beta_1-\beta_2)\left(\frac{\gamma_1\alpha_2-\gamma_2\alpha_1}{c^2a^2}\right)$$
$$+(\gamma_1-\gamma_2)\left(\frac{\alpha_1\beta_2-\alpha_2\beta_1}{a^2b^2}\right)=0. \quad \text{...(4)}$$

Now the equations of the line PQ are

$$\frac{x-\alpha_1}{\alpha_1-\alpha_2}=\frac{y-\beta_1}{\beta_1-\beta_2}=\frac{z-\gamma_1}{\gamma_1-\gamma_2}. \quad \text{...(5)}$$

The polar of PQ *i.e.* the polar of the line (5) [See § 9 (C)] with respect to the ellipsoid (1) is given by

$$\frac{\alpha_1 x}{a^2}+\frac{\beta_1 y}{b^2}+\frac{\gamma_1 z}{c^2}-1=0 \quad \text{...(6)}$$

and $$(\alpha_1-\alpha_2)\frac{x}{a^2}+(\beta_1-\beta_2)\frac{y}{b^2}+(\gamma_1-\gamma_2)\frac{z}{c^2}=0. \quad \text{...(7)}$$

Subtracting (7) from (6), we get

$$\frac{\alpha_2 x}{a^2}+\frac{\beta_2 y}{b^2}+\frac{\gamma_2 z}{c^2}=1. \quad \text{...(8)}$$

Let l_1, m_1, n_1 be the d.c.'s of the polar line of PQ *i.e.* of the line of intersection of the planes (6) and (8). Then we have

$$\frac{l_1}{\dfrac{\beta_1\gamma_2-\beta_2\gamma_1}{b^2c^2}}=\frac{m_1}{\dfrac{\gamma_1\alpha_2-\gamma_2\alpha_1}{c^2a^2}}=\frac{n_1}{\dfrac{\alpha_1\beta_2-\alpha_2\beta_1}{a^2b^2}}. \quad ...(9)$$

Therefore, if the line PQ [given by (5)] and its polar [whose d.c.'s are given by (9)] are to be perpendicular then applying the condition for perpendicularity, we have

$$(\alpha_1-\alpha_2)\left(\frac{\beta_1\gamma_2-\beta_2\gamma_1}{b^2c^2}\right)+(\beta_1-\beta_2)\left(\frac{\gamma_1\alpha_2-\gamma_2\alpha_1}{c^2a^2}\right)$$
$$+(\gamma_1-\gamma_2)\left(\frac{\alpha_1\beta_2-\alpha_2\beta_1}{a^2b^2}\right)=0$$

which is true by virtue of (4). Hence the result.

§ 12. Number of normals.

To prove that six normals can be drawn to an ellipsoid from a given point (x_1, y_1, z_1).

(Allahabad 1975, 78 ; Lucknow 71, 74, 77 ; Madras 76 ; Meerut 70 ; Rohilkhand 78 ; Punjabi 72)

Let the equation of the ellipsoid be

$$x^2/a^2+y^2/b^2+z^2/c^2=1. \quad ...(1)$$

The equations of the normal to the ellipsoid (1) at $P(\alpha, \beta, \gamma)$ are

$$\frac{x-\alpha}{\alpha/a^2}=\frac{y-\beta}{\beta/b^2}=\frac{z-\gamma}{\gamma/c^2}=\lambda \text{ (say)}. \quad ...(2)$$

If the normal (2) passes through the given point (x_1, y_1, z_1), then this point will satisfy (2) and hence we have

$$\frac{x_1-\alpha}{\alpha/a^2}=\frac{y_1-\beta}{\beta/b^2}=\frac{z_1-\gamma}{\gamma/c^2}=\lambda.$$

$$\therefore \quad x_1=\alpha+\frac{\alpha\lambda}{a^2},\ y_1=\beta+\frac{\beta\lambda}{b^2},\ z_1=\gamma+\frac{\gamma\lambda}{c^2}$$

or
$$\frac{\alpha}{a}=\frac{ax_1}{a^2+\lambda},\ \frac{\beta}{b}=\frac{by_1}{b^2+\lambda},\ \frac{\gamma}{c}=\frac{cz_1}{c^2+\lambda}. \quad ...(3)$$

But the point $P(\alpha, \beta, \gamma)$ lies on the ellipsoid (1).

$$\therefore \quad \alpha^2/a^2+\beta^2/b^2+\gamma^2/c^2=1$$

or
$$\frac{a^2x_1^2}{(a^2+\lambda)^2}+\frac{b^2y_1^2}{(b^2+\lambda)^2}+\frac{c^2z_1^2}{(c^2+\lambda)^2}=1. \quad ...(4)$$

[Putting the values from (3)]

This equation is of sixth degree in λ and hence gives six values of λ. Putting these six values of λ one by one in (3), we get six values of α, β, γ *i.e.* we get six points on the ellipsoid (1) the normals at which pass through a given point (x_1, y_1, z_1). *Hence from a given point six normals can be drawn to an ellipsoid.*

Corollary. Proceeding exactly as above, we can prove that from a given point (x_1, y_1, z_1) six normals can be drawn to any central conicoid $ax^2+by^2+cz^2=1$.

§ 13. Cubic curve through the feet of the normals.

To prove that the six feet of normals (drawn from a given point to an ellipsoid) are the intersection of a cubic curve with the given ellipsoid.

Let the equation of the ellipsoid be

$$x^2/a^2+y^2/b^2+z^2/c^2=1. \quad \ldots(1)$$

Let (x_1, y_1, z_1) be the given point. Now if the normal at $P(\alpha, \beta, \gamma)$ to the ellipsoid (1) passes through (x_1, y_1, z_1) then proceeding as in § 12, we get

$$\alpha=\frac{a^2x_1}{a^2+\lambda},\ \beta=\frac{b^2y_1}{b^2+\lambda},\ \gamma=\frac{c^2z_1}{c^2+\lambda} \quad \ldots(2)$$

Now consider the curve whose parametric equations are

$$x=\frac{a^2x_1}{b^2+\lambda},\ y=\frac{b^2y_1}{b^2+\lambda},\ z=\frac{c^2z_1}{c^2+\lambda} \quad \ldots(3)$$

where λ is a parameter. We have proved in § 12 that λ has six values [given by equation (4) of § 12] and hence corresponding to each of these six values of λ, we shall get a point on the curve (3).

Again consider a plane $Ax+By+Cz+D=0$. (4)

The points of intersection of the curve (3) with the plane (4) are given by

$$A\left(\frac{a^2x_1}{a^2+\lambda}\right)+B\left(\frac{b^2y_1}{b^2+\lambda}\right)+C\left(\frac{c^2z_1}{c^2+\lambda}\right)+D=0. \quad \ldots(3)$$

This equation being a cubic in λ gives three values of λ and shows that the curve (3) meets the plane (4) in three points and hence the curve (3) is a cubic curve.

Hence we conclude that the six feet of the normals that are drawn from a given point (x_1, y_1, z_1) to the ellipsoid (1) are the intersection of the ellipsoid (1) with the cubic curve (3).

§ 14. *To find the equation of the cone through six concurrent normals (the six normals drawn from a point to an ellipsoid).*

(Lucknow 1971, 81 ; Rohilkhand 79)

Let the equation of the ellipsoid be

$$x^2/a^2+y^2/b^2+z^2/c^2=1. \quad \ldots(1)$$

Let (x_1, y_1, z_1) be any point (not on the ellipsoid). We know that from (x_1, y_1, z_1) six normals can be drawn to the ellipsoid (1) [See § 12].

Now the equations of any line through the point (x_1, y_1, z_1) are

$$\frac{x-x_1}{l}=\frac{y-y_1}{m}=\frac{z-z_1}{n} \quad ...(2)$$

If the line (2) is the normal to the ellipsoid (1) at the point (α, β, γ), then we have

$$l=p\alpha/a^2,\ m=p\beta/b^2,\ n=p\gamma/c^2 \quad ...(3)$$

Now if the normal at $P(\alpha, \beta, \gamma)$ to the ellipsoid (1) passes through (x_1, y_1, z_1) then proceeding as in § 12, we get

$$\alpha=\frac{a^2x_1}{a^2+\lambda},\ \beta=\frac{b^2y_1}{b^2+\lambda},\ \gamma=\frac{c^2z_1}{c^2+\lambda} \quad ...(4)$$

Putting the values of α, β, γ from (4) in (3), we get

$$l=\frac{p}{a^2}\cdot\frac{a^2x_1}{a^2+\lambda},\ m=\frac{p}{b^2}\cdot\frac{b^2y_1}{b^2+\lambda},\ n=\frac{p}{c^2}\cdot\frac{c^2z_1}{c^2+\lambda}$$

or $$\frac{px_1}{l}=a^2+\lambda,\ \frac{py_1}{m}=b^2+\lambda,\ \frac{pz_1}{n}=c^2+\lambda.$$

From the above relations, we see that

$$\frac{px_1}{l}(b^2-c^2)+\frac{py_1}{m}(c^2-a^2)+\frac{pz_1}{n}(a^2-b^2)$$

$$=(a^2+\lambda)(b^2-c^2)+(b^2+\lambda)(c^2-a^2)+(c^2+\lambda)(a^2-b^2)$$

$$=0. \quad ...(5)$$

Eliminating l, m, n between (2) and (5), the equation of the cone on which the normal (2) lies is given by

$$\frac{px_1(b^2-c^2)}{x-x_1}+\frac{py_1(c^2-a^2)}{y-y_1}+\frac{pz_1(a^2-b^2)}{z-z_1}=0$$

or $$\frac{x_1(b^2-c^2)}{x-x_1}+\frac{y_1(c^2-a^2)}{y-y_1}+\frac{z_1(a^2-b^2)}{z-z_1}=0. \quad ...(6)$$

This is the required equation of the cone on which lie all the six normals drawn from (x_1, y_1, z_1) to the ellipsoid (1).

Corollary. *To prove that the curve through the six feet of the normals drawn from a point (x_1, y_1, z_1) to an ellipsoid lies on the cone through the six concurrent normals.*

The parametric equations of the cubic curve through the feet of six normals are given by [See § 13]

$$x=\frac{a^2x_1}{a^2+\lambda},\ y=\frac{b^2y_1}{b^2+\lambda},\ z=\frac{c^2z_1}{c^2+\lambda} \quad ...(7)$$

where λ is a parameter.

If this curve is to lie on the cone (6) then the values of x, y, z from (7) should satisfy the equation (6). Putting the values of x, y, z from (7) in (6), we get

$$\sum \left\{ \frac{x_1 (b^2-c^2)}{\frac{a^2x_1}{a^2+\lambda}-x_1} \right\}=0 \quad \text{or} \quad (a^2+\lambda)(b^2-c^2)=0$$

or $(a^2+\lambda)(b^2-c^2)+(b^2+\lambda)(c^2-a^2)+(c^2+\lambda)(a^2-b^2)=0$

or $0=0$, which is true. Hence the required result is proved.

SOLVED EXAMPLES (E)

Ex. 1 (a). *Prove that the feet of the six normals drawn to the ellipsoid $x^2/a^2+y^2/b^2+z^2/c^2=1$ from any point (x_1, y_1, z_1) lie on the curve of intersection of the ellipsoid and the cone*

$$\frac{a^2(b^2-c^2)x_1}{x}+\frac{b^2(c^2-a^2)y_1}{y}+\frac{c^2(a^2-b^2)z_1}{z}=1.$$

(Rohilkhand 1980; Madras 77; Gurunanakdev 75; Lucknow 74)

Solution. The equation of the ellipsoid is

$$x^2/a^2+y^2/b^2+z^2/c^2=1 \quad ...(1)$$

Proceeding as in § 12, the co-ordinates (α, β, γ) of the six feet of six normals drawn to the ellipsoid (1) from the given point (x_1, y_1, z_1) are given by

$\alpha=\frac{a^2x_1}{a^2+\lambda},\ \beta=\frac{b^2y_1}{b^2+\lambda},\ \gamma=\frac{c^2z_1}{c^2+\lambda}$ where λ is a parameter and is given by an equation of sixth degree.

Solving each of the above relations for λ, we get

$$\lambda=\frac{a^2x_1}{\alpha}-a^2,\ \lambda=\frac{b^2y_1}{\beta}-b^2,\ \lambda=\frac{c^2z_1}{\gamma}-c^2.$$

Now we clearly have

$$\left(\frac{a^2x_1}{\alpha}-a^2\right)(b^2-c^2)+\left(\frac{b^2y_1}{\beta}-b^2\right)(c^2-a^2)+\left(\frac{c^2z_1}{\gamma}-c^2\right)(a^2-b^2)$$

$$=\lambda(b^2-c^2)+\lambda(c^2-a^2)+\lambda(a^2-b^2)=0$$

or $$\frac{a^2x_1(b^2-c^2)}{\alpha}+\frac{b^2y_1(c^2-a^2)}{\beta}+\frac{c^2z_1(a^2-b^2)}{\gamma}$$

$$=a^2(b^2-c^2)+b^2(c^2-a^2)+c^2(a^2-b^2)$$

$$=0.$$

$\therefore$ The six feet (α, β, γ) of the normals to (1) drawn from (x_1, y_1, z_1) lie on the surface

$$\frac{a^2x_1(b^2-c^2)}{x}+\frac{b^2y_1(c^2-a^2)}{y}+\frac{c^2z_1(a^2-b^2)}{z}=0. \quad ...(2)$$

The equation (2) is a homogeneous equation of second degree and hence it represents a cone. But since the six feet (α, β, γ) of these normals lie on the given ellipsoid (1), therefore they lie on the curve of intersection of the ellipsoid (1) and the cone (2).

Ex. 1 (b). *Prove that the feet of the six normals drawn to the central conicoid $ax^2+by^2+cz^2=1$ from any point (x_1, y_1, z_1) lie on the curve of intersection of the given ellipsoid and the cone*

$$\frac{a(b-c)x_1}{x}+\frac{b(c-a)y_1}{y}+\frac{c(a-b)z_1}{z}=0.$$

(Rohilkhand 1977)

Solution. Replacing a^2 by $1/a$, b^2 by $1/b$ and c^2 by $1/c$ in Ex. 1 (a) above and proceeding exactly in the same way we get the required result.

Ex. 2. *If A, B, C; A'. B', C' are the feet of the six normals from a given point to the ellipsoid $x^2/a^2+y^2/b^2+z^2/c^2=1$ and the plane ABC is given by $lx+my+nz=p$, prove that the plane A' B' C' is given by $(x/a^2l)+(y/b^2m)+(z/c^2n)+(1/p)=0$.* **(Punjab 1977)**

Solution. The equation of the given ellipsoid is

$$x^2/a^2+y^2/b^2+z^2/c^2=1. \quad ...(1)$$

Let the co-ordinates of the given point be (x_1, y_1, z_1). Now the co-ordinates (α, β, γ) of the feet of six normals from (x_1, y_1, z_1) to (1) are given by

$$\alpha=a^2x_1/(a^2+\lambda),\ \beta=b^2y_1/(b^2+\lambda),\ \gamma=c^2z_1/(c^2+\lambda) \quad ..(2)$$

where λ is a parameter and its six values are given by the equation

$$\frac{a^2x_1^2}{(a^2+\lambda)^2}+\frac{b^2y_1^2}{(b^2+\lambda)^2}+\frac{c^2z_1^2}{(c^2+\lambda)^2}=1. \quad (3)$$

Now the equation of the plane ABC is given to be

$$lx+my+nz=p$$

and three of the six feet of normals given by (2) lie on this plane, so that we have

$$\frac{la^2x_1}{a^2+\lambda}+\frac{mb^2y_1}{b^2+\lambda}+\frac{nc^2z_1}{c^2+\lambda}-p=0 \quad ...(4)$$

This being a cubic equation in λ gives us three values of λ. Again let the equation of the plane $A'\ B'\ C'$ be

$$l'x+m'y+n'z-p'=0.$$

According to the question the remaining three of the six feet of normals given by (2) lie on this plane and so we have

$$\frac{l'a^2x_1}{(a^2+\lambda)}+\frac{m'b^2y_1}{(b^2+\lambda)}+\frac{n'c^2z_1}{(c^2+\lambda)}-p'=0. \quad ...(5)$$

This equation is of third degree in λ and hence gives us the remaining three values of λ.

Clearly the product of the equations (4) and (5) must give the same equation as is equation (3). Hence comparing the like terms, we get

$$\frac{ll'\ a^4x_1^2}{(a^2+\lambda)^2}=\frac{a^2x_1^2}{(a^2+\lambda)^2} \quad \text{or} \quad l'=\frac{1}{a^2l}$$

Similarly, we have

$$m'=\frac{1}{b^2m},\ n'=\frac{1}{c^2n},\ p'=-\frac{1}{p}.$$

Putting these values in $l'x+m'y+n'z-p'=0$, the required equation of the plane $A'\ B'\ C'$ is given by

$$\frac{x}{a^2l}+\frac{y}{b^2m}+\frac{z}{c^2n}+\frac{1}{p}=0.$$

Proved.

Ex. 3. *If the feet of the three normals from P to the ellipsoid $x^2/a^2+y^2/b^2+z^2/c^2=1$ lie in the plane $x/a+y/b+z/c=1$, prove that the feet of the other three lie in the plane $x/a+y/b+z/c\ \ 1=0$ and P lies on the line*

$$a\ (b^2-c^2)\ x=b\ (c^2-a^2)\ y=c\ (a^2-b^2)\ z.$$

(Allahabad 1979)

Solution. The equation of the ellipsoid is

$$x^2/a^2+y^2/b^2+z^2/c^2=1. \quad (1)$$

The first part is exactly similar to Ex. 2 above.

Now clearly the six feet of the normals lie on

$$(x/a+y/b+z/c-1)\ (x/a+y/b+z/c+1)=0$$

or

$$(x/a+y/b+z/c)^2-1=0$$

or $(x^2/a^2+y^2/b^2+z^2/c^2-1)+2\ \{(yz/bc)+(zx/ca)+(xy/ab)\}=0$. (2)

Since these six feet lie on the ellipsoid (1), therefore, using (1) the equation (2) becomes

$$\frac{yz}{bc}+\frac{zx}{ca}+\frac{xy}{ab}=0 \quad \text{or} \quad ayz+bzx+cxy=0, \quad (3)$$

Now if the normals be drawn from $P(x_1, y_1, z_1)$ to the ellipsoid (1) then these six feet of the normals lie on the cone.

[See Ex. 1 (a) above]

$$\frac{a^2x_1(b^2-c^2)}{x}+\frac{b^2y_1(b^2-c^2)}{y}+\frac{c^2z_1(a^2-b^2)}{z}=0$$

or $\quad a^2x_1(b^2-c^2)\,yz+b^2y_1(b^2-c^2)\,zx+c^2z_1(a^2-b^2)\,xy=0 \quad \text{.. (4)}$

Comparing (3) and (4), we get

$$a^2x_1(b^2-c^2)/a=b^2y_1(b^2-c^2)/b=c^2z_1(a^2-b^2)/c$$

or $$a(b^2-c^2)\,x_1=b(b^2-c^2)\,y_1=c(a^2-b^2)\,z_1.$$

∴ The locus of $P(x_1, y_1, z_1)$ is the line given by

$$a(b^2-c^2)\,x=b(b^2-c^2)\,y=c(a^2-b^2)\,z.$$

Ex. 4. *Prove that the lines drawn from the origin parallel to the normals to $ax^2+by^2+cz^2=1$ at its points of intersection with the plane $lx+my+nz=p$ generate the cone*

$$p^2\left(\frac{x^2}{a}+\frac{y^2}{b}+\frac{z^2}{c}\right)=\left(\frac{lx}{a}+\frac{my}{b}+\frac{nz}{c}\right)^2.$$ **(Kanpur 1977)**

Solution. The equation of the given conicoid is

$$ax^2+by^2+cz^2=1. \quad \text{...(1)}$$

The equation of the given plane is

$$lx+my+nz=p. \quad \text{...(2)}$$

Let (α, β, γ) be a point of intersection of the conicoid (1) with the plane (2), so that we have

$$a\alpha^2+b\beta^2+c\gamma^2=1 \text{ and } l\alpha+m\beta+n\gamma=p. \quad \text{.. (3)}$$

Now the equations of the normal to the conicoid (1) at (α, β, γ) are $\dfrac{x-\alpha}{a\alpha}=\dfrac{y-\beta}{b\beta}=\dfrac{z-\gamma}{c\gamma}$. $\quad$ (4)

The d.r.'s of this normal are $a\alpha, b\beta, c\gamma$.

The equations of the line from the origin parallel to the normal (4) are $\dfrac{x}{a\alpha}=\dfrac{y}{b\beta}=\dfrac{z}{c\gamma}$. $\quad$ ...(5)

From the relations (3), we have

$$a\alpha^2+b\beta^2+c\gamma^2=\left(\frac{l\alpha+m\beta+n\gamma}{p}\right)^2$$

or $$p^2\{a\alpha^2+b\beta^2+c\gamma^2\}=(l\alpha+m\beta+n\gamma)^2$$

or $$p^2\left\{\frac{(a\alpha)^2}{a}+\frac{(b\beta)^2}{b}+\frac{(c\gamma)^2}{c}\right\}=\left\{\frac{l(a\alpha)}{a}+\frac{m(b\beta)}{b}+\frac{n(c\gamma)}{c}\right\}^2. \quad \text{.. (6)}$$

Eliminating $a\alpha, b\beta, c\gamma$ between (5) and (6), we see that the line (5) generates the cone

$$p^2\left\{\frac{x^2}{a}+\frac{y^2}{b}+\frac{z^2}{c}\right\}=\left(\frac{lx}{a}+\frac{my}{b}+\frac{nz}{c}\right)^2$$ **Proved.**

Ex. 5. *Prove that the points on the ellipsoid the normals at which intersect a given straight line lie on the curve of intersection of the ellipsoid and a conicoid.*

Solution. Let the equation of the ellipsoid be

$$x^2/a^2+y^2/b^2+z^2/c^2=1. \quad ...(1)$$

Let (α, β, γ) be a point on the ellipsoid (1). The equations of the normal at (α, β, γ) to the ellipsoid (1) are

$$\frac{x-\alpha}{\alpha/a^2}=\frac{y-\beta}{\beta/b^2}=\frac{z-\gamma}{\gamma/c^2}. \quad ..(2)$$

Let the equations of the given line be

$$\frac{x-x_1}{l}=\frac{y-y_1}{m}=\frac{z-z_1}{n}. \quad (3)$$

If the normal (2) intersects the given line (3), then the lines (2) and (3) are coplanar so that we have

$$\begin{vmatrix} x_1-\alpha & y_1-\beta & z_1-\gamma \\ \alpha/a^2 & \beta/b^2 & \gamma/c^2 \\ l & m & n \end{vmatrix}=0$$

or $(x_1-\alpha)\left(\frac{n\beta}{b^2}-\frac{m\gamma}{c^2}\right)+(y_1-\beta)\left(\frac{l\gamma}{c^2}-\frac{n\alpha}{a^2}\right)+(z_1-\gamma)\left(\frac{m\alpha}{a^2}-\frac{l\beta}{b^2}\right)=0.$

$\therefore$ the locus of (α, β, γ) is

$$(x_1-x)\left(\frac{ny}{b^2}-\frac{mz}{c^2}\right)+(y_1-y)\left(\frac{lz}{c^2}-\frac{nx}{a^2}\right)+(z_1-z)\left(\frac{mx}{a^2}-\frac{ly}{b^2}\right)=0 \quad ...(4)$$

This is the equation of a conicoid. But the point (α, β, γ) lies on the ellipsoid (1) as well. Hence the locus of (α, β, γ) is the curve of intersection of the ellipsoid (1) and the conicoid (4).

Ex. 6 *Two planes are drawn through the six feet of the normals drawn to the ellipsoid $x^2/a^2+y^2/b^2+z^2/c^2=1$ from a given point, each plane containing three. Prove that if A_1 and A_2 be the poles of these planes with respect to the ellipsoid then*

$$A_1A_2^2-OA_1^2-OA_2^2=2(a^2+b^2+c^2).$$

Solution. The equation of the ellipsoid is

$$x^2/a^2+y^2/b^2+z^2/c^2=1. \quad ...(1)$$

Let $P(x_1, y_1, z_1)$ be the given point. Proceeding as in § 12, the values of λ giving the feet of six normals drawn from $P(x_1, y_1, z_1)$ to the ellipsoid (1) are given by

$$\frac{a^2x_1^2}{(a^2+\lambda)^2}+\frac{b^2y_1^2}{(b^2+\lambda)^2}+\frac{c^2z_1^2}{(c^2+\lambda)^2}-1=0. \quad ...(2)$$

Let the co-ordinates of the poles A_1 and A_2 of the two planes be (x_2, y_2, z_2) and (x_3, y_3, z_3) respectively, so that the equations of the polar planes of A_1 and A_2 are respectively given by

$$\frac{xx_2}{a^2}+\frac{yy_2}{b^2}+\frac{zz_2}{c^2}-1=0 \text{ and } \frac{xx_3}{a^2}+\frac{yy_3}{b^2}+\frac{zz_3}{c^2}-1=0. \quad ...(3)$$

The feet of the six normals, namely

$$\left(\frac{a^2x_1}{a^2+\lambda}, \frac{b^2y_1}{b^2+\lambda}, \frac{c^2z_1}{c^2+\lambda}\right),$$

where λ has six values, lie on the two planes given by (3) and so we have

$$\Sigma\left(\frac{a^2x_1}{a^2+\lambda}\cdot\frac{x_2}{a^2}\right)-1=0 \text{ and } \Sigma\left(\frac{a^2x_1}{a^2+\lambda}\cdot\frac{x_3}{a^2}\right)-1=0$$

or
$$\frac{x_1x_2}{a^2+\lambda}+\frac{y_1y_2}{b^2+\lambda}+\frac{z_1z_2}{c^2+\lambda}-1=0 \quad (4)$$

and
$$\frac{x_1x_3}{a^2+\lambda}+\frac{y_1y_3}{b^2+\lambda}+\frac{z_1z_3}{c^2+\lambda}-1=0. \quad ...(5)$$

Obviously (2) is the same as the product of (4) and (5), so comparing them, we have

$$\frac{x_2x_3}{a^2}=\frac{y_2y_3}{b^2}=\frac{z_2z_3}{c^2}=\frac{1}{-1}.$$

$$\therefore \quad x_2x_3=-a^2,\ y_2y_3=-b^2,\ z_2z_3=-c^2. \quad ..(6)$$

Now $A_1A_2^2-OA_1^2-OA_2^2=\{(x_2-x_3)^2+(y_2-y_3)^2+(z_2-z_3)^2\}$
$-(x_2^2+y_2^2+z_2^2)-(x_3^2+y_3^2+z_3^2)$

$=-2\,(x_2x_3+y_2y_3+z_2z_3)$

$=-2\,(-a^2-b^2-c^2)$, using (6)

$=2\,(a^2+b^2+c^2)$. **Proved.**

Ex. 7. *A is a fixed point and P a variable point such that its polar plane is at right angles to AP. Show that the locus of P is a cubic curve through the feet of the normals from A to an ellipsoid.*

Solution. Let the equation of the ellipsoid be

$$x^2/a^2+y^2/b^2+z^2/c^2=1. \quad ...(1)$$

Let the co-ordinates of the points A and P be (x_1, y_1, z_1) and (α, β, γ) respectively.

The equation of the polar plane of $P(\alpha, \beta, \gamma)$ w.r.t. the ellipsoid (1) is

$$\frac{\alpha x}{a^2}+\frac{\beta y}{b^2}+\frac{\gamma z}{c^2}=1. \quad ...(2)$$

Now the d.r.'s of the line AP are $x_1-\alpha$, $y_1-\beta$, $z_1-\gamma$.

If the polar plane (2) of P is at right angles to AP then the normal to the plane (2) is parallel to the line AP and so we have

$$\frac{x_1-\alpha}{\alpha/a^2}=\frac{y_1-\beta}{\beta/b^2}=\frac{z_1-\gamma}{\gamma/c^2}=\lambda \text{ (say)}.$$

$$\therefore \quad x_1-\alpha=\frac{\alpha\lambda}{a^2} \text{ or } \alpha=\frac{a^2x_1}{a^2+\lambda}.$$

Similarly $\beta=\dfrac{b^2y_1}{b^2+\lambda}$ and $\gamma=\dfrac{c^2z_1}{c^2+\lambda}$.

$\therefore$ The locus of $P(\alpha, \beta, \gamma)$ is

$$x=\frac{a^2x_1}{a^2+\lambda},\ y=\frac{b^2y_1}{b^2+\lambda},\ z=\frac{c^2z_1}{c^2+\lambda}$$

which are the parametric equations of the cubic curve through the feet of the six normals drawn from $A(x_1, y_1, z_1)$ to the ellipsoid (1). [See § 13].

§ 15. Diamertal plane.

Definition. *For a central conicoid, a diametral plane is the locus of the middle points of a system of parallel chords.*

(A) To find the equation of a diametral plane.

Let the equation of a central conicoid be

$$ax^2+by^2+cz^2=1. \qquad ...(1)$$

Let the equations of a system of parallel chords be

$$\frac{x-\alpha}{l}=\frac{y-\beta}{m}=\frac{z-\gamma}{n}=r \text{ (say)}, \qquad ...(2)$$

where l, m, n are the direction cosines of each chord and so are fixed, and r is the actual distance of any point $(\alpha+lr, \beta+mr, \gamma+nr)$ on (2) from (α, β, γ). If (2) meets (1), then the distances of the points of intersection of (1) and (2) from (α, β, γ) are the roots of the quadratic in r given by

$$a(\alpha+lr)^2+b(\beta+mr)^2+c(\gamma+nr)^2=1$$

or $$r^2(al^2+bm^2+cn^2)+2r(al\alpha+bm\beta+cn\gamma)$$
$$+(a\alpha^2+b\beta^2+c\gamma^2-1)=0. \qquad ..(3)$$

If (α, β, γ) be the middle point of the chord, then its distances from the two points of intersection should be equal in magnitude and opposite in sign and hence the sum of the two values of r should be zero, so that we have $al\alpha+bm\beta+cn\gamma=0$.

$\therefore$ The locus of the middle point (α, β, γ) of the system of parallel chords with d.c.'s l, m, n *i.e.* the equation of a diametral plane for the conicoid (1) is :

$$alx+bmy+cnz=0. \qquad ..(4)$$

Clearly the diametral plane (4) passes through the centre (0, 0, 0) of the conicoid (1).

If l, m, n are the d.r.'s of a direction, even then the equation of the corresponding diametral plane is given by (4).

Corollary. In case of the ellipsoid $x^2/a^2+y^2/b^2+z^2/c^2=1$, proceeding as above, the equation of a diametral plane is

$$\frac{lx}{a^2}+\frac{my}{b^2}+\frac{nz}{c^2}=0. \qquad ...(5)$$

This plane bisects a system of parallel chords of the ellipsoid with direction cosines l, m, n.

(B) *To prove that every plane through the centre is a diametral plane of the central conicoid corresponding to same direction.*

Let the equation of the central conicoid be

$$ax^2+by^2+cz^2=1. \qquad ...(1)$$

Consider a plane $\qquad Ax+By+Cz=0 \qquad ...(2)$

through the centre (0, 0, 0) of the conicoid (1).

We are to prove that the plane (2) is a diametral plane of (1) corresponding to some direction l, m, n (say).

Now the equation of the diametral plane of (1) corresponding to the direction l, m, n is

$$alx+bmy+cnz=0. \qquad ...(3)$$

The planes (2) and (3) should be the same and hence comparing them, we get

$$\frac{al}{A}=\frac{bm}{B}=\frac{cn}{C} \quad \text{or} \quad \frac{l}{A/a}=\frac{m}{B/b}=\frac{n}{C/c}. \qquad ..(4)$$

Hence the plane (2) is a diametral plane of the conicoid (1) corresponding to the direction l, m, n given by (4).

§ 16. Conjugate diameters and conjugate diametral planes.

Let the equation of the ellipsoid be

$$x^2/a^2+y^2/b^2+z^2/c^2=1 \qquad ...(1)$$

with its centre at $O(0, 0, 0)$.

Let $P(x_1, y_1, z_1)$ be any point on the ellipsoid (1) so that d.r.'s of the line OP are x_1, y_1, z_1. The equation of the diametral plane [See § 15 (A)] of the line OP is

$$xx_1/a^2+yy_1/b^2+zz_1/c^2=0. \qquad (2)$$

Now take a point $Q(x_2, y_2, z_2)$ on the section of the ellipsoid (1) by the plane (2). This point Q will satisfy both the equations of the ellipsoid (1) and the plane (2).

$$\therefore \quad x_2x_1/a^2+y_2y_1/b^2+z_2z_1/c^2=0. \qquad ...(3)$$

Thus the relation (3) is the condition that the diametral plane of the line OP passes through another point Q on the ellipsoid (1). But the result (3) is symmetrical in x_1, y_1, z_1 and x_2, y_2, z_2 and hence it shows that the diametral plane of the line OQ will also pass through the point P.

Thus we conclude that if the diametral plane of a line OP passes through the point Q then the diametral plane of the line OQ will also pass through the point P.

Now let the line of intersection of the diametral planes of OP and OQ cut the surface of the given ellipsoid in the point $R(x_3, y_3, z_3)$, so that R lies on both the diametral planes of OP and OQ and consequently the points P and Q lie on the diametral plane of the line OR *i.e.* on the plane

$$xx_3/a^2+yy_3/b^2+zz_3/c^2=0. \qquad ...(4)$$

Hence it shows that the diametral plane of OR is the plane POQ. In a similar way the diametral planes of OP and OQ are the planes QOR and ROP respectively.

Now we shall define *conjugate semi-diameters* and *conjugate planes or conjugate diametral planes.*

Conjugate semi-diameters. *The three semi-diameters OP, OQ and OR of an ellipsoid which are such that the plane containing any two is the diametral plane of the third, are called the conjugate semi-diameters.*

Conjugate planes. *The three planes POQ, QOR and ROP which are such that each is the diametral plane of the line of intersection of the other two, are called the conjugate planes or conjugate diametral planes.*

§ 17. The relationship between the co-ordinates of the points P, Q, R where OP, OQ and OR are the conjugate semi-diameters of an ellipsoid.

Let the equation of the ellipsoid be

$$x^2/a^2+y^2/b^2+z^2/c^2=1. \qquad ...(1)$$

Let the co-ordinates of the points P, Q, R be (x_1, y_1, z_1), (x_2, y_2, z_2), (x_3, y_3, z_3) respectively and OP, OQ, OR be the conjugate semi-diameters of the ellipsoid (1) with $O(0, 0, 0)$ as centre. Since the points P, Q, R lie on the ellipsoid (1), we have

$$\left.\begin{aligned} x_1^2/a^2+y_1^2/b^2+z_1^2/c^2=1 \\ x_2^2/a^2+y_2^2/b^2+z_2^2/c^2=1 \\ x_3^2/a^2+y_3^2/b^2+z_3^2/c^2=1 \end{aligned}\right\}. \quad \ldots(2)$$

We know that the diametral plane of any one of OP, OQ and OR passes through the extremities of the other two and therefore, we have

$$\left.\begin{aligned} x_1x_2/a^2+y_1y_2/b^2+z_1z_2/c^2=0 \\ x_2x_3/a^2+y_2y_3/b^2+z_2z_3/c^2=0 \\ x_3x_1/a^2+y_3y_1/b^2+z_3z_1/c^2=0 \end{aligned}\right\}. \quad \ldots(3)$$

If l, m, n be the direction cosines of any line then we know that $l^2+m^2+n^2=1$. In view of this relation, the relations (2) imply that $x_1/a, y_1/b, z_1/c$; $x_2/a, y_2/b, z_2/c$ and $x_3/a, y_3/b, z_3/c$ are the direction cosines of some three lines.

Also if l_1, m_1, n_1 and l_2, m_2, n_2 be the direction cosines of two perpendicular lines then we know that $l_1l_2+m_1m_2+n_1n_2=0$. In view of this relation, the relations (3) imply that the above three lines are mutually perpendicular to each other.

Again if l_1, m_1, n_1; l_2, m_2, n_2; l_3, m_3, n_3 are direction cosines of three mutually perpendicular lines then we know that l_1, l_2, l_3; m_1, m_2, m_3; n_1, n_2, n_3 are also the direction cosines of three lines which are mutually perpendicular so that

$$l_1^2+l_2^2+l_3^2=1 \text{ etc.} \quad \text{and} \quad l_1m_1+l_2m_2+l_3m_3=0 \text{ etc.}$$

In view of these relations, we have

$$x_1^2/a^2+x_2^2/a^2+x_3^2/a^2=1$$

i.e. $x_1^2+x_2^2+x_3^2=a^2,$

Similarly $y_1^2+y_2^2+y_3^2=b^2,$

and $z_1^2+z_2^2+z_3^2=c^2.$ ...(4)

Also $\dfrac{x_1}{a}\cdot\dfrac{y_1}{b}+\dfrac{x_2}{a}\cdot\dfrac{y_2}{b}+\dfrac{x_3}{a}\cdot\dfrac{y_3}{b}=0$

i.e. $x_1y_1+x_2y_2+x_3y_3=0,$

Similarly $y_1z_1+y_2z_2+y_3z_3=0,$

and $z_1x_1+z_2x_2+z_3x_3=0.$ ...(5)

Solving the first and third equations of (3) for $x_1/a, y_1/b, z_1/c$, we get

$$\frac{x_1/a}{\dfrac{y_2z_3-y_3z_2}{bc}}=\frac{y_1/b}{\dfrac{z_2x_3-z_3x_2}{ca}}=\frac{z_1/c}{\dfrac{x_2y_3-x_3y_2}{ab}}$$

$$=\pm\frac{\sqrt{(x_1^2/a^2+y_1^2/b^2+z_1^2/c^2)}}{\sqrt{[\Sigma\{(y_2z_3-y_3z_2)/bc\}^2]}}=\pm\frac{1}{\sin 90^\circ}=\pm 1.$$

$$\therefore\quad \frac{x_1}{a}=\pm\frac{y_2z_3-y_3z_2}{bc},\ \frac{y_1}{b}=\pm\frac{z_2x_3-z_3x_2}{ca},\ \frac{z_1}{c}=\pm\frac{x_2y_3-x_3y_2}{ab}. \quad \ldots(6)$$

Note. The results (2), (3), (4), (5) and (6) given above should be committed to memory.

§ 18. Properties of conjugate semi-diameters of an ellipsoid.

Here we shall give some properties of conjugate semi-diameters of an ellipsoid. The meanings of OP, OQ and OR are the same as already defined in § 16 and § 17 above.

I. *The sum of the squares of any three conjugate semi diameters of any ellipsoid is constant.*

(Allahabad 1978, 80; Agra 82; Madras 76; Kurushetra 77)

We have $\quad OP^2+OQ^2+OR^2$

$$=(x_1^2+y_1^2+z_1^2)+(x_2^2+y_2^2+z_2^2)+(x_3^2+y_3^2+z_3^2)$$
$$=(x_1^2+x_2^2+x_3^2)+(y_1^2+y_2^2+y_3^2)+(z_1^2+z_2^2+z_3^2)$$
$$=a^2+b^2+c^2 \qquad \text{[using relations (4) of § 17]}$$

which is a constant. Hence proved.

II. *The volume of the parallelopiped having three conjugate semi-diameters of an ellipsoid as coterminous edges is constant.*

(Rohilkhand 1981)

Let OP, OQ, OR be the three conjugate semi-diameters of an ellipsoid. The volume V of the parallelopiped having OP, OQ and OR as three coterminous edges $=6\times$(the volume of the tetrahedron $OPQR$)

i.e., $$V=6\times\tfrac{1}{6}\begin{vmatrix} x_1 & y_1 & z_1 \\ x_2 & y_2 & z_2 \\ x_3 & y_3 & z_3 \end{vmatrix}.$$

$$\therefore\quad V^2=\begin{vmatrix} x_1 & y_1 & z_1 \\ x_2 & y_2 & z_2 \\ x_3 & y_3 & z_3 \end{vmatrix}\begin{vmatrix} x_1 & y_1 & z_1 \\ x_2 & y_2 & z_2 \\ x_3 & y_3 & z_3 \end{vmatrix}$$

$$= \begin{vmatrix} x_1 & x_2 & x_3 \\ y_1 & y_2 & y_3 \\ z_1 & z_2 & z_3 \end{vmatrix} \begin{vmatrix} x_1 & x_2 & x_3 \\ y_1 & y_2 & y_3 \\ z_1 & z_2 & z_3 \end{vmatrix}$$

$$= \begin{vmatrix} x_1^2+x_2^2+x_3^2 & x_1y_1+x_2y_2+x_3y_3 & x_1z_1+x_2z_2+x_3z_3 \\ x_1y_1+x_2y_2+x_3y_3 & y_1^2+y_2^2+y_3^2 & y_1z_1+y_2z_2+y_3z_3 \\ z_1x_1+z_2x_2+z_3x_3 & y_1z_1+y_2z_2+y_3z_3 & z_1^2+z_2^2+z_3^2 \end{vmatrix}$$

$$= \begin{vmatrix} a^2 & 0 & 0 \\ 0 & b^2 & 0 \\ 0 & 0 & c^2 \end{vmatrix} \quad \text{[using relations (4) and (5) of § 17]}$$

or $V^2 = a^2b^2c^2$ or $V = abc$ which is constant.

III. *The sum of the squares of the projections of three conjugate semi-diameters on a line is constant.*

Let the direction cosines of a given line be l, m, n. Let OP, OQ and OR be the conjugate semi-diameters of an ellipsoid.

The projection of OP on the line whose d.c.'s are l, m, n

$$=(x_1-0)\, l+(y_1-0)\, m+(z_1-0)\, n = lx_1+my_1+nz_1.$$

Similarly the projections of OQ and OR on the given line are $lx_2+my_2+nz_2$ and $lx_3+my_3+nz_3$ respectively.

$\therefore$ The sum of the squares of the projections of OP, OQ and OR on the given line

$$=(lx_1+my_1+nz_1)^2+(lx_2+my_2+nz_2)^2+(lx_3+my_3+nz_3)^2$$

$$=l^2(x_1^2+x_2^2+x_3^2)+m^2\,\Sigma y_1^2+n^2\,\Sigma z_1^2+2lm\,\Sigma x_1y_1 +2mn\,\Sigma y_1z_1+2nl\,\Sigma z_1x_1$$

$$=l^2a^2+m^2b^2+n^2c^2+0+0+0$$

[using the relations (4) and (5) of § 17 above]

$$=a^2l^2+b^2m^2+c^2n^2, \text{ which is a constant.}$$

IV. *The sum of the squares of projections of three conjugate semi-diameters (of an ellipsoid) on any plane is constant.*

Let the direction cosines of the normal to a given plane be l, m, n, so that the square of the projection of OP on the given plane is equal to

$$OP^2-(lx_1+my_1+nz_1)^2.$$

Similarly the squares of the projections of OQ and OR on the given plane are

$$OQ^2-(lx_2+my_2+nz_2)^2 \text{ and } OR^2-(lx_3+my_3+nz_3)^2$$

respectively.

$\therefore$ The sum of the squares of projections of OP OQ and OR on the given plane

$$=OP^2+OQ^2+OR^2-\{(lx_1+my_1+nz_1)^2+(lx_2+my_2+nz_2)^2 +(lx_3+my_3+nz_3)^2\}$$

$$=(a^2+b^2+c^2)-(a^2l^2+b^2m^2+c^2n^2)$$

[Putting the values from properties I and III above]

$$=a^2(1-l^2)+b^2(1-m^2)+c^2(1-n^2)$$

=constant, since l, m, n are constants for a given plane.

V. *If OP, OQ and OR are the conjugate semi-diameters of an ellipsoid, then the sum of the squares of the areas of the faces QOR, ROP and POQ of the parallelopiped having OP, OQ, OR as coterminous edges is constant.* **(Rohilkhand 1979)**

Let l_1, m_1, n_1; l_2, m_2, n_2 and l_3, m_3, n_3 be the direction cosines of the normals to the planes QOR, ROP and POQ respectively. Also let A_1, A_2 and A_3 be the areas of the faces QOR, ROP and POQ respectively.

Let (x_1, y_1, z_1), (x_2, y_2, z_2) and (x_3, y_3, z_3) be the co-ordinates of the points P, Q and R respectively. Now if we project the area QOR on the yz-plane *i.e.* on the plane $x=0$, then we get a triangle whose vertices are $(0, y_2, z_2)$, $(0, 0, 0)$ and $(0, y_3, z_3)$ and the area of this triangle

$$=\tfrac{1}{2}(y_2z_3-y_3z_2)=\pm\frac{bcx_1}{2a} \text{ [using relations (6) of § 17 above].}$$

But the projection of the area A_1 on the yz-plane$=A_1l_1$.

$$\therefore \quad A_1l_1=\pm(bcx_1)/(2a).$$

Similarly if we project the area QOR *i.e.* A_1 on the planes ZOX and XOY, we get

$$A_1m_1=\pm(cay_1)/(2b) \text{ and } A_1n_1=\pm(abz_1)/(2c).$$

Squaring and adding these three relations, we get

$$A_1^2(l_1^2+m_1^2+n_1^2)=[(bcx_1)^2/(2a)^2+(cay_1)^2/(2b)^2+(abz_1)^2/(2c)^2]$$

or
$$A_1^2=\frac{b^2c^2}{4a^2}x_1^2+\frac{c^2a^2}{4b^2}y_1^2+\frac{a^2b^2}{4c^2}z_1^2 \qquad \text{...(1)}$$

In a similar way, the areas A_2 and A_3 are given by

$$A_2^2=\frac{b^2c^2}{4a^2}x_2^2+\frac{c^2a^2}{4b^2}y_2^2+\frac{a^2b^2}{4c^2}z_2^2 \qquad \text{...(2)}$$

and $A_3^2 = \frac{b^2c^2}{4a^2} x_3^2 + \frac{c^2a^2}{4b^2} y_3^2 + \frac{a^2b^2}{4c^2} z_3^2$. ...(3)

Adding (1), (2) and (3), we get

$$A_1^2+A_2^2+A_3^2 = \frac{b^2c^2}{4a^2} \Sigma x_1^2 + \frac{c^2a^2}{4b^2} \Sigma y_1^2 + \frac{a^2b^2}{4c^2} \Sigma z_1^2$$

$$= \frac{b^2c^2}{4a^2} . a^2 + \frac{c^2a^2}{4b^2} . b^2 + \frac{a^2b^2}{4c^2} . c^2.$$

[See relations (4) of § 17 above]

$$= \tfrac{1}{4} (b^2c^2+c^2a^2+a^2b^2) \text{ which is constant.}$$

SOLVED EXAMPLES (F)

Note. In all the exercises given below we shall denote OP, OQ and OR as conjugate semi-diameters of the ellipsoid

$$x^2/a^2+y^2/b^2+z^2/c^2=1$$

and (x_1, y_1, z_1), (x_2, y_2, z_2) and (x_3, y_3, z_3) as co-ordinates of the points P, Q and R respectively unless otherwise stated.

Ex. 1. *Let OP, OQ, OR be the conjugate semi-diameters of $3x^2+\lambda y^2+z^2=1$. Find λ if $OP^2+OQ^2+OR^2=2$.*

(Allahabad 1979)

Solution. The equation of the given ellipsoid is

$$3x^2+\lambda y^2+z^2=1.$$

$$\therefore \quad a^2=\tfrac{1}{3},\ b^2=1/\lambda,\ c^2=1.$$

We know that $OP^2+OQ^2+OR^2=a^2+b^2+c^2$.

[See property 1, § 18 above]

$$\therefore \quad 2=\tfrac{1}{3}+1/\lambda+1 \text{ or } \lambda=3/2.$$

Ex. 2. *Show that the sum of the squares of the projections of three conjugate diameters of an ellipsoid on the x-axis is constant.*

(Allahabad 1979)

Solution. The direction cosines of x-axis are 1, 0, 0. From property III of § 18 above, putting $l=1$, $m=0$, $n=0$, we get that the required sum $=a^2.(1)^2+b^2.(0)^2+c^2.(0)^2=a^2$ which is constant.

Ex. 3. *Find the equation of the plane PQR.*

(Allahabad 1975, 81 ; Agra 75, 79, 81 ; Bundelkhand 78 ; Madras 76 ; Rohilkhand 77, 80 ; Ravishanker 70, 71)

Solution. Let the equation of the plane PQR be

$$lx+my+nz=p. \qquad ..(1)$$

Since the plane (1) passes through $P(x_1, y_1, z_1)$, $Q(x_2, y_2, z_2)$ and $R(x_3, y_3, z_3)$, we have

$$lx_1+my_1+nz_1=p, \qquad ...(2)$$

$$lx_2+my_2+nz_2=p, \qquad ...(3)$$

and $$lx_3+my_3+nz_3=p. \quad \ldots(4)$$

Multiplying the equations (2), (3) and (4) by x_1, x_2 and x_3 respectively and adding, we have

$$l(x_1^2+x_2^2+x_3^2)+m(x_1y_1+x_2y_2+x_3y_3)+n(x_1z_1+x_2z_2+x_3z_3)$$
$$=p(x_1+x_2+x_3),$$

or $$l.a^2+m.0+n.0=p(x_1+x_2+x_3),$$

using the relations (4) and (5) of § 17

or $$l=p(x_1+x_2+x_3)/a^2.$$

Similarly we have

$$m=p(y_1+y_2+y_3)/b^2,\ n=p(z_1+z_2+z_3)/c^2.$$

Putting the above values of l, m, n in (1), the required equation of the plane PQR is given by

$$\frac{x}{a^2}(x_1+x_2+x_3)+\frac{y}{b^2}(y_1+y_2+y_3)+\frac{z}{c^2}(z_1+z_2+z_3)=1.$$

Ex. 4. *Prove that if the plane* $lx+my+nz=p$ *passes through the extremities P, Q, R of the three conjugate semi-diameters, then*

$$a^2l^2+b^2m^2+c^2n^2=3p^2. \quad \textbf{(Kanpur 1980 ; Lucknow 75)}$$

Solution. Rewriting the steps of Ex. 3 above upto equation (4) and then squaring (2), (3) and (4) and adding, we get

$$(lx_1+my_1+nz_1)^2+(lx_2+my_2+nz_2)^2+(lx_3+my_3+nz_3)^2=3p^2$$

or $$l^2\,\Sigma\,x_1^2+m^2\,\Sigma\,y_1^2+n^2\,\Sigma\,z_1^2+2mn\,\Sigma\,y_1z_1+2nl\,\Sigma\,z_1x_1$$
$$+2lm\,\Sigma\,x_1y_1=3p^2$$

or $$l^2a^2+m^2b^2+n^2c^2=3p^2$$

[using relations (4) and (5) of § 17 above].

Ex 5. *Prove that the plane PQR touches the ellipsoid*

$$x^2/a^2+y^2/b^2+z^2/c^2=\tfrac{1}{3}$$

at the centroid of the triangle PQR. **(Kurukshetra 1977)**

Solution. Proceeding as in Ex. 3 above, the equation of the plane PQR is

$$\frac{x}{a^2}(x_1+x_2+x_3)+\frac{y}{b^2}(y_1+y_2+y_3)+\frac{z}{c^2}(z_1+z_2+z_3)=1. \quad \ldots(1)$$

Now clearly the co-ordinates of the centroid G of the triangle PQR are

$$\left(\frac{x_1+x_2+x_3}{3},\ \frac{y_1+y_2+y_3}{3},\ \frac{z_1+z_2+z_3}{3}\right)$$

It can be easily seen that this point lies on the ellipsoid

$$x^2/a^2+y^2/b^2+z^2/c^2=\tfrac{1}{3}.$$

The equation of the tangent plane to the ellipsoid

$$x^2/a^2+y^2/b^2+z^2/c^2=\tfrac{1}{3}$$

at the point G is

$$\frac{x.(x_1+x_2+x_3)}{3a^2}+\frac{y.(y_1+y_2+y_3)}{3b^2}+\frac{z.(z_1+z_2+z_3)}{3c^2}=1/3$$

or
$$\frac{x\,(x_1+x_2+x_3)}{a^2}+\frac{y\,(y_1+y_2+y_3)}{b^2}+\frac{z\,(z_1+z_2+z_3)}{c^2}=1. \quad ...(2)$$

The equation (2) comes out to be the same as the equation (1) and hence it shows that the plane PQR touches the ellipsoid $\Sigma\,(x^2/a^2)=1/3$ at the centroid of the $\triangle PQR$.

Ex. 6. *Prove that the pole of the plane PQR lies on the ellipsoid* $x^2/a^2+y^2/b^2+z^2/c^2=3$. **(Agra 1978 : Robilkhand 78)**

OR

Prove that the locus of the pole of the plane PQR is $x^2/a^2+y^2/b^2+z^2/c^2=3$.

Solution. Proceeding as in Ex. 3 above the equation of the plane PQR is

$$\frac{x}{a^2}(x_1+x_2+x_3)+\frac{y}{b^2}(y_1+y_2+y_3)+\frac{z}{c^2}(z_1+z_2+z_3)=1. \quad ...(1)$$

Let the pole of the plane (1) with respect to the given ellipsoid $x^2/a^2+y^2/b^2+z^2/c^2=1$ be (α, β, γ).

The equation of the polar plane of (α, β, γ) with respect to the ellipsoid $x^2/a^2+y^2/b^2+z^2/c^2=1$ is

$$\alpha x/a^2+\beta y/b^2+\gamma z/c^2=1 \quad ...(2)$$

Comparing (1) and (2), we get

$$\frac{\alpha}{x_1+x_2+x_3}=\frac{\beta}{y_1+y_2+y_3}=\frac{\gamma}{z_1+z_2+z_3}=\frac{1}{1}.$$

$\therefore \quad \alpha=x_1+x_2+x_3,\ \beta=y_1+y_2+y_3,\ \gamma=z_1+z_2+z_3.$

Now, we have

$$\frac{\alpha^2}{a^2}+\frac{\beta^2}{b^2}+\frac{\gamma^2}{c^2}=\frac{(x_1+x_2+x_3)^2}{a^2}+\frac{(y_1+y_2+y_3)^2}{b^2}+\frac{(z_1+z_2+z_3)^2}{c^2}$$

$$=\frac{\Sigma x_1^2}{a^2}+\frac{\Sigma y_1^2}{b^2}+\frac{\Sigma z_1^2}{c^2}+2\left\{\left(\frac{x_1x_2}{a^2}+\frac{y_1y_2}{b^2}+\frac{z_1z_2}{c^2}\right)+\left(\frac{x_2x_3}{a^2}+\frac{y_2y_3}{b^2}+\frac{z_2z_3}{c^2}\right)+\left(\frac{x_3x_1}{a^2}+\frac{y_3y_1}{b^2}+\frac{z_3z_1}{c^2}\right)\right\}$$

$=\dfrac{a^2}{a^2}+\dfrac{b^2}{b^2}+\dfrac{c^2}{c^2}$ [Using relations (4) and (3) of § 17 above]

$=3.$

$\therefore$ The locus of the pole (α, β, γ) is $\dfrac{x^2}{a^2}+\dfrac{y^2}{b^2}+\dfrac{z^2}{c^2}=3.$

Ex. 7. *Prove that the locus of the centre of the section of the ellipsoid* $x^2/a^2+y^2/b^2+z^2/c^2=1$ *by the plane PQR is the ellipsoid* $x^2/a^2+y^2/b^2+z^2/c^2=\frac{1}{3}$. *Prove further that this is also the locus of the centroid of the triangle PQR.*

Solution. The equation of the given ellipsoid is

$$S \equiv x^2/a^2+y^2/b^2+z^2/c^2-1=0 \qquad \text{...(1)}$$

Proceeding exactly as in Ex. 3 above the equation of the plane PQR is given by

$$\frac{x}{a^2}(x_1+x_2+x_3)+\frac{y}{b^2}(y_1+y_2+y_3)+\frac{z}{c^2}(z_1+z_2+z_3)=1 \qquad \text{...(2)}$$

Let (α, β, γ) be the co-ordinates of the centre of the section of the ellipsoid (1) by the plane PQR so that the equation of the plane PQR is given by '$T=S_1$,

i.e. $$\frac{\alpha x}{a^2}+\frac{\beta y}{b^2}+\frac{\gamma z}{c^2}=\frac{\alpha^2}{a^2}+\frac{\beta^2}{b^2}+\frac{\gamma^2}{c^2} \qquad \text{...(3)}$$

The equations (2) and (3) represent the same plane and hence comparing them, we get

$$\frac{\alpha}{x_1+x_2+x_3}=\frac{\beta}{y_1+y_2+y_3}=\frac{\gamma}{z_1+z_2+z_3}=\frac{\alpha^2/a^2+\beta^2/b^2+\gamma^2/c^2}{1}.$$

$$\therefore \quad \frac{\alpha}{a}=\left(\frac{x_1+x_2+x_3}{a}\right)\left(\frac{\alpha^2}{a^2}+\frac{\beta^2}{b^2}+\frac{\gamma^2}{c^2}\right), \frac{\beta}{b}=\left(\frac{y_1+y_2+y_3}{b}\right)\left(\frac{\alpha^2}{a^2}+\frac{\beta^2}{b^2}+\frac{\gamma^2}{c^2}\right)$$

and $$\frac{\gamma}{c}=\left(\frac{z_1+z_2+z_3}{c}\right)\left(\frac{\alpha^2}{a^2}+\frac{\beta^2}{b^2}+\frac{\gamma^2}{c^2}\right).$$

Squaring and adding the above three relations, we get

$$\frac{\alpha^2}{a^2}+\frac{\beta^2}{b^2}+\frac{\gamma^2}{c^2}=\left(\frac{\alpha^2}{a^2}+\frac{\beta^2}{b^2}+\frac{\gamma^2}{c^2}\right)^2\cdot\left\{\frac{(x_1+x_2+x_3)^2}{a^2}+\frac{(y_1+y_2+y_3)^2}{b^2}+\frac{(z_1+z_2+z_3)^2}{c^2}\right\}$$

or $$\left(\frac{\alpha^2}{a^2}+\frac{\beta^2}{b^2}+\frac{\gamma^2}{c^2}\right)=\left(\frac{\alpha^2}{a^2}+\frac{\beta^2}{b^2}+\frac{\gamma^2}{c^2}\right)^2.3 \text{ [Proceeding as in Ex. 6 above]}$$

or $$\frac{\alpha^2}{a^2}+\frac{\beta^2}{b^2}+\frac{\gamma^2}{c^2}=\frac{1}{3}.$$

$\therefore$ The locus of (α, β, γ) is $x^2/a^2+y^2/b^2+z^2/c^2=\frac{1}{3}$. ...(4)

Second part. Let the co-ordinates of the centroid of the triangle PQR be (α, β, γ), so that we have

$$\alpha=\tfrac{1}{3}(x_1+x_2+x_3),\ \beta=\tfrac{1}{3}(y_1+y_2+y_3),\ \gamma=\tfrac{1}{3}(z_1+z_2+z_3).$$

$$\therefore \quad \frac{\alpha^2}{a^2}+\frac{\beta^2}{b^2}+\frac{\gamma^2}{c^2}=\frac{1}{9}\left[\frac{(x_1+x_2+x_3)^2}{a^2}+\frac{(y_1+y_2+y_3)^2}{b^2}+\frac{(z_1+z_2+z_3)^2}{c^2}\right]$$

$=\frac{1}{9}.3$ [Proceeding as in Ex. 6 above]

$=\frac{1}{3}$.

$\therefore$ The locus of (α, β, γ) is $x^2/a^2+y^2/b^2+z^2/c^2=\frac{1}{3}$ which is the same as (4). **Proved.**

Ex. 8. *Find the equation of the plane through the points* (x_1, x_2, x_3), (y_1, y_2, y_3) *and* (z_1, z_2, z_3) *where* (x_r, y_r, z_r) $r=1, 2, 3$ *are the extremities of the three conjugate semi-diameters and show that it touches a fixed sphere.*

Solution. Let the equation of the required plane be

$$lx+my+nz=p. \quad \ldots(1)$$

The plane (1) passes through the points (x_1, x_2, x_3), (y_1, y_2, y_3) and (z_1, z_2, z_3), so we have

$$lx_1+mx_2+nx_3=p, \quad \ldots(2)$$

$$ly_1+my_2+ny_3=p, \quad \ldots(3)$$

and $$lz_1+mz_2+nz_3=p. \quad \ldots(4)$$

Now multiplying the equations (2), (3) and (4) by x_1/a^2, y_1/b^2 and z_1/c^2 respectively and adding, we get

$$l\left(\frac{x_1^2}{a^2}+\frac{y_1^2}{b^2}+\frac{z_1^2}{c^2}\right)+m\left(\frac{x_1x_2}{a^2}+\frac{y_1y_2}{b^2}+\frac{z_1z_2}{c^2}\right)+n\left(\frac{x_1x_3}{a^2}+\frac{y_1y_3}{b^2}+\frac{z_1z_3}{c^2}\right)$$

$$=p\left(\frac{x_1}{a^2}+\frac{y_1}{b^2}+\frac{z_1}{c^2}\right)$$

or $l=p\,(x_1/a^2+y_1/b^2+z_1/c^2)$. [using relations (2), (3) of § 17].

Similarly $m=p\,(x_2/a^2+y_2/b^2+z_2/c^2)$, $n=p\,(x_3/a^2+y_3/b^2+z_3/c^2)$.

Putting the values of l, m, n in (1), the equation of the required plane is

$$x\left(\frac{x_1}{a^2}+\frac{y_1}{b^2}+\frac{z_1}{c^2}\right)+y\left(\frac{x_2}{a^2}+\frac{y_2}{b^2}+\frac{z_2}{c^2}\right)+z\left(\frac{x_3}{a^2}+\frac{y_3}{b^2}+\frac{z_3}{c^2}\right)=1. \quad \ldots(5)$$

Again we are to show that the plane (5) touches a fixed sphere.

The length of the perpendicular from the origin to the plane (5)

$$=1\Big/\sqrt{\left[\left(\frac{x_1}{a^2}+\frac{y_1}{b^2}+\frac{z_1}{c^2}\right)^2+\left(\frac{x_2}{a^2}+\frac{y_2}{b^2}+\frac{z_2}{c^2}\right)^2+\left(\frac{x_3}{a^2}+\frac{y_3}{b^2}+\frac{z_3}{c^2}\right)^2\right]}$$

$$=1\Big/\sqrt{\left[\frac{\Sigma x_1^2}{a^4}+\frac{\Sigma y_1^2}{b^4}+\frac{\Sigma z_1^2}{c^4}+\frac{2\Sigma x_1y_1}{a^2b^2}+\frac{2\Sigma y_1z_1}{b^2c^2}+\frac{2\Sigma z_1x_1}{c^2a^2}\right]}$$

$$=1\Big/\sqrt{\left[\frac{a^2}{a^4}+\frac{b^2}{b^4}+\frac{c^2}{c^4}+0+0+0\right]}$$

[Using the relations (4) and (5) of § 17 above]

$$=1\Big/\sqrt{\left(\frac{1}{a^2}+\frac{1}{b^2}+\frac{1}{c^2}\right)}=\frac{abc}{\sqrt{(b^2c^2+c^2a^2+a^2b^2)}},$$ which is constant.

Hence the plane (5) touches the fixed sphere

$$x^2+y^2+z^2=\frac{a^2b^2c^2}{b^2c^2+c^2a^2+a^2b^2}.$$

Ex. 9. *Prove that the locus of the foot of the perpendicular from the centre of the ellipsoid $x^2/a^2+y^2/b^2+z^2/c^2=1$ on the plane PQR is*

$$a^2x^2+b^2y^2+c^2z^2=3\,(x^2+y^2+z^2)^2.$$ **(Allahabad 1976)**

Solution. The equation of the given ellipsoid is

$$x^2/a^2+y^2/b^2+z^2/c^2=1. \quad ...(1)$$

Proceeding exactly as in Ex. 3 above, the equation of the plane PQR is

$$\frac{x}{a^2}(x_1+x_2+x_3)+\frac{y}{b^2}(y_1+y_2+y_3)+\frac{z}{c^2}(z_1+z_2+z_3)=1. \quad ...(2)$$

Let N (α, β, γ) be the foot of the perpendicular from the centre O (0, 0, 0) of the ellipsoid (1) to the plane PQR.

Let p be the length of the perpendicular ON so that

$p=ON=$ the distance between O (0, 0, 0) and N (α, β, γ)

$$=\sqrt{(\alpha^2+\beta^2+\gamma^2)}. \quad ...(3)$$

The d.c.'s of ON, the normal to the plane PQR, are

$$\alpha/\sqrt{(\alpha^2+\beta^2+\gamma^2)},\ \beta/\sqrt{(\alpha^2+\beta^2+\gamma^2)},\ \gamma/\sqrt{(\alpha^2+\beta^2+\gamma^2)}$$

i.e., $\alpha/p,\ \beta/p,\ \gamma/p$, using (3).

Hence the equation of the plane PQR is also given by

$$(\alpha/p)\,x+(\beta/p)\,y+(\gamma/p)\,z=p \quad \text{or} \quad \alpha x+\beta y+\gamma z=p^2. \quad ...(4)$$

Comparing the equations (2) and (4), we get

$$\frac{x_1+x_2+x_3}{a^2\alpha}=\frac{y_1+y_2+y_3}{b^2\beta}=\frac{z_1+z_2+z_3}{c^2\gamma}=\frac{1}{p^2}.$$

$$\therefore \quad \frac{x_1+x_2+x_3}{a^2}=\frac{a\alpha}{p^2},\ \frac{y_1+y_2+y_3}{b^2}=\frac{b\beta}{p^2},\ \frac{z_1+z_2+z_3}{c^2}=\frac{c\gamma}{p^2}.$$

Squaring and adding, we get

$$\frac{(x_1+x_2+x_3)^2}{a^2}+\frac{(y_1+y_2+y_3)^2}{b^2}+\frac{(z_1+z_2+z_3)^2}{c^2}=\frac{a^2\alpha^2+b^2\beta^2+c^2\gamma^2}{p^4}$$

or $$\frac{\Sigma x_1^2}{a^2}+\frac{\Sigma y_1^2}{b^2}+\frac{\Sigma z_1^2}{c^2}+\left[2\Sigma\left(\frac{x_1x_2}{a^2}\right)+2\Sigma\left(\frac{x_3x_1}{a^2}\right)+2\Sigma\left(\frac{x_2x_3}{a^2}\right)\right]$$

$$=\frac{a^2\alpha^2+b^2\beta^2+c^2\gamma^2}{p^4}$$

or $(1+1+1+0+0+0).\ p^4=a^2\alpha^2+b^2\beta^2+c^2\gamma^2$

[using (4) and (3) of § 17]

or $3(\alpha^2+\beta^2+\gamma^2)^2=(a^2\alpha^2+b^2\beta^2+c^2\gamma^2)$, from (3).

$\therefore$ The locus of (α, β, γ) is

$$3(x^2+y^2+z^2)^2=a^2x^2+b^2y^2+c^2z^2.$$ **Proved**

Ex. 10. *If λ, μ, ν are the angles between a set of equal conjugate diameters of the ellipsoid $x^2/a^2+y^2/b^2+z^2/c^2=1$, then show that*

$$\cos^2\lambda+\cos^2\mu+\cos^2\nu=\frac{3\Sigma(b^2-c^2)^2}{2(a^2+b^2+c^2)^2}.$$

Solution. The equation of the given ellipsoid is

$$x^2/a^2+y^2/b^2+z^2/c^2=1. \quad ...(1)$$

Let OP, OQ, OR be a set of equal conjugate semi-diameters of the ellipsoid (1) so that

$$OP=OQ=OR=r \text{ (say)}.$$

We know that $OP^2+OQ^2+OR^2=a^2+b^2+c^2$.

$$\therefore \quad 3r^2=a^2+b^2+c^2. \quad ...(2)$$

If the co-ordinates of P, Q, R are (x_1, y_1, z_1), (x_2, y_2, z_2), (x_3, y_3, z_3) respectively, then the d.r.'s of OQ and OR are x_2, y_2, z_2 and x_3, y_3, z_3 respectively. If λ be the angle between OQ and OR, then

$$\cos\lambda=\frac{x_2x_3+y_2y_3+z_2z_3}{\sqrt{(x_2^2+y_2^2+z_2^2)}\sqrt{(x_3^2+y_3^2+z_3^2)}}=\frac{x_2x_3+y_2y_3+z_2z_3}{r^2}.$$

$$\therefore \quad \cos^2\lambda=(x_2x_3+y_2y_3+z_2z_3)^2/r^4. \quad ...(3)$$

From Lagrange's identity, we have

$$(x_2^2+y_2^2+z_2^2)(x_3^2+y_3^2+z_3^2)-(x_2x_3+y_2y_3+z_2z_3)^2=\Sigma(y_2z_3-y_3z_2)^2.$$

Putting from (3) on the L.H.S. and from the relations (6) of § 17 on the R.H.S. of this identity, we have

$$r^2.r^2-r^4\cos^2\lambda=\frac{b^2c^2x_1^2}{a^2}+\frac{c^2a^2y_1^2}{b^2}+\frac{a^2b^2z_1^2}{c^2}$$

Dividing by r^4 and transposing, we get

$$\cos^2\lambda=1-\frac{a^2b^2c^2}{r^4}\left(\frac{x_1^2}{a^4}+\frac{y_1^2}{b^4}+\frac{z_1^2}{c^4}\right). \quad ...(4)$$

Similarly $\cos^2\mu=1-\dfrac{a^2b^2c^2}{r^4}\left(\dfrac{x_2^2}{a^4}+\dfrac{y_2^2}{b^4}+\dfrac{z_2^2}{c^4}\right)$, ...(5)

and $\cos^2\nu=1-\dfrac{a^2b^2c^2}{r^4}\left(\dfrac{x_3^2}{a^4}+\dfrac{y_3^2}{b^4}+\dfrac{z_3^2}{c^4}\right).$ ...(6)

Adding (4), (5) and (6), we have

$$\cos^2\lambda+\cos^2\mu+\cos^2\nu$$

$$=3-\frac{a^2b^2c^2}{r^4}\left[\frac{\Sigma x_1^2}{a^4}+\frac{\Sigma y_1^2}{b^4}+\frac{\Sigma z_1^2}{c^4}\right]=3-\frac{a^2b^2c^2}{r^4}\left[\frac{a^2}{a^4}+\frac{b^2}{b^4}+\frac{c^2}{c^4}\right]$$

$$=3-\frac{1}{r^4}(b^2c^2+c^2a^2+a^2b^2)=3-\frac{9(b^2c^2+c^2a^2+a^2b^2)}{(a^2+b^2+c^2)^2} \quad \text{[See (2)]}$$

$$=\frac{3[(a^2+b^2+c^2)^2-3(b^2c^2+c^2a^2+a^2b^2)]}{(a^2+b^2+c^2)^2}$$

$$=3\,[a^4+b^4+c^4-b^2c^2-c^2a^2-a^2b^2]/(a^2+b^2+c^2)^2$$

$$=\frac{3\,[2a^4+2b^4+2c^4-2b^2c^2-2c^2a^2-2a^2b^2]}{2\,(a^2+b^2+c^2)^2}$$

$$=\frac{3\,[(b^4-2b^2c^2+c^4)+(c^4-2c^2a^2+a^4)+(a^4-2a^2b^2+b^4)]}{2\,(a^2+b^2+c^2)^2}$$

$$=\frac{3\,[(b^2-c^2)^2+(c^2-a^2)^2+(a^2-b^2)^2]}{2\,(a^2+b^2+c^2)^2}$$ **Proved.**

§ 19. The Cone.

The standard equation of the cone with the vertex at the origin is

$$ax^2+by^2+cz^2=0. \quad \text{...(1)}$$

Proceeding exactly as in § 1 (a) we see that all the chords passing through the origin are bisected at the origin. Therefore the cone (1) can be considered a central surface for which the vertex of the cone is the centre.

The co-ordinate axes are the conjugate diameters and the co-ordinate planes are the conjugate diametral planes.

The different results obtained above for the other central conicoids can also be obtained for the cone (1) also.

SOLVED EXAMPLES

Ex. 1. *Show that the equation to the normal plane of the cone $ax^2+by^2+cz^2=0$ which passes through the generator $x/l=y/m=z/n$ is*

$$mn\,(b-c)\,x+nl\,(c-a)\,y+lm\,(a-b)z=0.$$

Solution. The equation of the cone is

$$ax^2+by^2+cz^2=0. \quad \text{...(1)}$$

The equation of the generator is

$$\frac{x}{l}=\frac{y}{m}=\frac{z}{n}=r \text{ (say).} \quad \text{...(2)}$$

The co-ordinates of any point on the generator (2) are (lr, mr, nr). So the equation of the tangent plane to the cone at (lr, mr, nr) is

$$alx+bmy+cnz=0. \quad \text{...(3)}$$

The equation of any plane through the generator (2) is

$$Ax+By+Cz=0 \qquad \ldots(4)$$

where $$Al+Bm+Cn=0. \qquad \ldots(5)$$

Let (4) be the normal plane of the cone and hence it will be perpendicular to (3), so that, we have

$$A.al+B.bm+C.cn=0. \qquad \ldots(6)$$

Solving equations (5) and (6), for A, B, C, we get

$$\frac{A}{mn\,(c-b)}=\frac{B}{nl\,(a-c)}=\frac{C}{lm\,(b-a)}.$$

Putting these values of A, B, C in (4), the required equation of the normal plane is

$$mn\,(c-b)\,x+nl\,(a-c)\,y+lm\,(b-a)\,z=0$$

or $$mn\,(b-c)\,x+nl\,(c-a)\,y+lm\,(a-b)\,z=0.$$

Ex. 2. *Show that the lines drawn through the origin at right angles to the normal planes of the cone* $ax^2+by^2+cz^2=0$ *generates the cone*

$$a\,(b-c)^2/x^2+b\,(c-a)^2/y^2+c\,(a-b)^2/z^2=0.$$

Solution. The equation of the cone is

$$ax^2+by^2+cz^2=0. \qquad \ldots(1)$$

Let the generator of the cone be

$$\frac{x}{l}=\frac{y}{m}=\frac{z}{n} \qquad \ldots(2)$$

where $$al^2+bm^2+cn^2=0. \qquad \ldots(3)$$

Now the equation of the normal plane of the cone (1) which passes through the generator (2) is [See Ex. 1 above]

$$mn\,(b-c)\,x+nl\,(c-a)\,y+lm\,(a-b)\,z=0$$

or $$(b-c)\,x/l+(c-a)\,y/m+(a-b)\,z/n=0. \qquad \ldots(4)$$

Thus the equation of any line through the origin at right angles to the normal plane (4) of the cone (1) is

$$\frac{x}{(b-c)/l}=\frac{y}{(c-a)/m}=\frac{z}{(a-b)/n}. \qquad \ldots(5)$$

Eliminating l, m, n between (3) and (5), the required locus is given by

$$a\left(\frac{b-c}{x}\right)^2+b\left(\frac{c-a}{y}\right)^2+c\left(\frac{a-b}{z}\right)^2=0.$$

Proved.

Miscellaneous Examples

The normals to a central conicoid.

Ex. 1. *Show that the generators of the cone which contains the normals from a given point to an ellipsoid are at right angles to their polars with respect to the ellipsoid.*

Solution. Let the equation of the ellipsoid be

$$x^2/a^2+y^2/b^2+z^2/c^2=1. \qquad ...(1)$$

It is given that the generators of the cone are the normals to the ellipsoid (1) which pass through a given point. Let the equations of any one of them be

$$\frac{x-\alpha}{(\alpha/a^2)}=\frac{y-\beta}{(\beta/b^2)}=\frac{z-\gamma}{(\gamma/c^2)}. \qquad ...(2)$$

The equations of its polar with respect to the ellipsoid (1) are

$$\frac{\alpha x}{a^2}+\frac{\beta y}{b^2}+\frac{\gamma z}{c^2}-1=0 \text{ and } \frac{\alpha x}{a^4}+\frac{\beta y}{b^4}+\frac{\gamma z}{c^4}=0. \qquad ...(3)$$

Let l', m', n' be the direction cosines of the polar line given by the equations (3), so that we have

$$\frac{l'}{\frac{\beta\gamma}{b^2c^2}\left(\frac{1}{c^2}-\frac{1}{b^2}\right)}=\frac{m'}{\frac{\gamma\alpha}{c^2a^2}\left(\frac{1}{a^2}-\frac{1}{c^2}\right)}=\frac{n'}{\frac{\alpha\beta}{a^2b^2}\left(\frac{1}{b^2}-\frac{1}{a^2}\right)}. \qquad ...(4)$$

Now it is required to show that the generator [*i.e.* the normal (2)] is at right angles to its polar whose d.c.'s l', m', n' are given by (4). For this we must have '$ll'+mm'+nn'=0$'

i.e. $$\frac{\alpha}{a^2}\cdot\frac{\beta\gamma}{b^2c^2}\left(\frac{1}{c^2}-\frac{1}{b^2}\right)+\frac{\beta}{b^2}\cdot\frac{\gamma\alpha}{c^2a^2}\left(\frac{1}{a^2}-\frac{1}{c^2}\right)+\frac{\gamma}{c^2}\cdot\frac{\alpha\beta}{a^2b^2}\left(\frac{1}{b^2}-\frac{1}{a^2}\right)=0$$

or $$\frac{\alpha\beta\gamma}{a^2b^2c^2}\left(\frac{1}{c^2}-\frac{1}{b^2}+\frac{1}{a^2}-\frac{1}{c^2}+\frac{1}{b^2}-\frac{1}{a^2}\right)=0 \text{ or } 0=0$$

which is satisfied. Hence proved.

Ex. 2. *Prove that for all values of* λ, *the normals to the conicoid* $\frac{x^2}{a^2+\lambda}+\frac{y^2}{b^2+\lambda}+\frac{z^2}{c^2+\lambda}=1$ *which pass through a point* (α, β, γ) *meet the plane* $z=0$ *in points on the conic*

$$(c^2-a^2)(\alpha/x)+(b^2-c^2)(\beta/y)+a^2-b^2=0.$$

Solution. The equation of the given conicoid is

$$\frac{x^2}{a^2+\lambda}+\frac{y^2}{b^2+\lambda}+\frac{z^2}{c^2+\lambda}=1. \qquad ...(1)$$

The equation of the cone on which lie the six normals to the conicoid (1) which pass through (α, β, γ) is

$$\frac{\alpha \{(b^2+\lambda)-(c^2+\lambda)\}}{x-\alpha}+\frac{\beta \{(c^2+\lambda)-(a^2+\lambda)\}}{y-\beta}$$
$$+\frac{\gamma \{(a^2+\lambda)-(b^2+\lambda)\}}{z-\gamma}=0 \qquad \text{[See § 14]}$$

or $$\frac{\alpha (b^2-c^2)}{x-\alpha}+\frac{\beta (c^2-a^2)}{y-\beta}+\frac{\gamma (a^2-b^2)}{z-\gamma}=0. \qquad ...(2)$$

The equation (2) being free from λ, we get the same equation of the cone for all values of λ.

The equation (2) of the cone meets the plane $z=0$, where

$$\frac{\alpha (b^2-c^2)}{x-\alpha}+\frac{\beta (c^2-a^2)}{y-\beta}+\frac{\gamma (a^2-b^2)}{z-\gamma}=0$$

or $(\alpha y-\alpha\beta)(b^2-c^2)+(\beta x-\alpha\beta)(c^2-a^2)-(x-\alpha)(y-\beta)(a^2-b^2)=0$

or $\alpha y(b^2-c^2+a^2-b^2)+\beta x(c^2-a^2+a^2-b^2)$

$$-\alpha\beta(b^2-c^2+c^2-a^2+a^2-b^2)-xy(a^2-b^2)=0$$

or $$\alpha y(a^2-c^2)+\beta x(c^2-b^2)-xy(a^2-b^2)=0.$$

Dividing throughout by $(-xy)$, we get

$$(c^2-a^2)(\alpha/x)+(b^2-c^2)(\beta/y)+(a^2-b^2)=0.$$

This being a second degree equation in x and y represents a conic lying in the plane $z=0$.

Ex. 3. *If the feet of the six normals from (x', y', z') to the ellipsoid be $(\alpha_r, \beta_r, \gamma_r)$, $r=1, 2, \ldots, 6$; prove that*

$$a^2x' \Sigma\left(\frac{1}{\alpha_r}\right)+b^2y' \Sigma\left(\frac{1}{\beta_r}\right)+c^2z' \Sigma\left(\frac{1}{\gamma_r}\right)=0. \qquad \textbf{[Allahabad 1977]}$$

Solution. Let the equation of the ellipsoid be

$$x^2/a^2+y^2/b^2+z^2/c^2=1. \qquad ...(1)$$

The equations of the normal to the ellipsoid (1) at any point (α, β, γ) are

$$\frac{x-\alpha}{\alpha/a^2}=\frac{y-\beta}{\beta/b^2}=\frac{z-\gamma}{\gamma/c^2}=\lambda \text{ (say)}. \qquad ...(2)$$

If the normal (2) passes through the point (x', y', z'), then we have

$$\frac{x'-\alpha}{\alpha/a^2}=\frac{y'-\beta}{\beta/b^2}=\frac{z'-\gamma}{\gamma/c^2}=\lambda.$$

$$\therefore \quad x'-\alpha=\frac{\alpha\lambda}{a^2} \quad \text{or} \quad x'=\alpha\left(\frac{a^2+\lambda}{a^2}\right) \quad \text{or} \quad \alpha=\frac{a^2x'}{a^2+\lambda}.$$

Similarly we find the values of β and γ. Thus we have

$$\alpha=a^2x'/(a^2+\lambda),\ \beta=b^2y'/(b^2+\lambda),\ \gamma=c^2z'/(c^2+\lambda). \qquad ...(3)$$

Since (α, β, γ) is a point on the ellipsoid (1), so we have

$$\alpha^2/a^2+\beta^2/b^2+\gamma^2/c^2=1 \qquad ...(4)$$

Putting the values of α, β, γ from (3) in (4), we get

$$\frac{a^2x'^2}{(a^2+\lambda)^2}+\frac{b^2y'^2}{(b^2+\lambda)^2}+\frac{c^2z'^2}{(c^2+\lambda)^2}=1 \qquad ...(5)$$

or $$\Sigma \{a^2x'^2 (b^2+\lambda)^2 (c^2+\lambda)^2\}=(a^2+\lambda)^2 (b^2+\lambda)^2 (c^2+\lambda)^2$$

or $$\lambda^6+2 (a^2+b^2+c^2) \lambda^5+...=0. \qquad ...(6)$$

This equation is of degree six in λ and gives us six values of λ corresponding to each of which we get a point (α, β, γ) on the ellipsoid (1) the normal at which passes through the point (x', y', z'). Let the six values of λ be $\lambda_1, \lambda_2, ..., \lambda_6$. We have

$$\Sigma\lambda_1=\lambda_1+\lambda_2+...+\lambda_6=-2 (a^2+b^2+c^2). \qquad ...(7)$$

From the equations (3), the co-ordinates $(\alpha_1, \beta_1, \gamma_1)$ of the foot of the normal corresponding to the value λ_1 of λ are given by

$$\alpha_1=\frac{a^2x'}{a^2+\lambda_1} \quad \text{or} \quad \frac{1}{\alpha_1}=\frac{a^2+\lambda_1}{a^2x'}.$$

Similarly $$\frac{1}{\beta_1}=\frac{b^2+\lambda_1}{b^2y'}, \frac{1}{\gamma_1}=\frac{c^2+\lambda_1}{c^2z'}.$$

Similar expressions can be obtained for $1/\alpha_2$, $1/\beta_2$, $1/\gamma_2$ etc.

$$\therefore \quad a^2x' \, \Sigma \left(\frac{1}{\alpha_r}\right)=a^2x' \left\{\frac{a^2+\lambda_1}{a^2x'}+\frac{a^2+\lambda_2}{a^2x'}+...+\frac{a^2+\lambda_6}{a^2x'}\right\}$$

$$=6a^2+(\lambda_1+\lambda_2+...+\lambda_6)=6a^2+\Sigma\lambda_1. \qquad ...(8)$$

Similarly $$b^2y' \, \Sigma \left(\frac{1}{\beta_r}\right)=6b^2+\Sigma\lambda_1 \qquad ...(9)$$

and $$c^2z' \, \Sigma \left(\frac{1}{\gamma_r}\right)=6c^2+\Sigma\lambda_1. \qquad ...(10)$$

Adding (8), (9) and (10), we get

$$a^2x' \, \Sigma \left(\frac{1}{\alpha_r}\right)+b^2y' \, \Sigma \left(\frac{1}{\beta_r}\right)+c^2z' \, \Sigma \left(\frac{1}{\gamma_r}\right)=6 (a^2+b^2+c^2)+3\Sigma\lambda_1$$

$$=6 (a^2+b^2+c^2)-3 . 2 (a^2+b^2+c^2) \qquad \text{[using (7)]}$$

$=0.$ **Proved.**

Ex. 4. *Prove that the four normals to the ellipsoid*

$$x^2/a^2+y^2/b^2+z^2/c^2=1$$

pass through any point on the curve of intersection of the ellipsoid and the conicoid

$$(b^2+c^2) x^2+(c^2+a^2) y^2+(a^2+b^2) z^2=b^2c^2+c^2a^2+a^2b^2.$$

Solution. Let (x', y', z') be the point from which normals are drawn to the given ellipsoid and if this point lies on the curve of intersection of the given ellipsoid and the given conicoid, then we have

$$x'^2/a^2+y'^2/b^2+z'^2/c^2=1 \quad ...(1)$$

and $(b^2+c^2)\, x'^2+(c^2+a^2)\, y'^2+(a^2+b^2)\, z'^2=b^2c^2+c^2a^2+a^2b^2$. ...(2)

Now proceeding as in Ex. 3 above upto equation (6), we have

$$\lambda^6+2\,(a^2+b^2+c^2)\,\lambda^5+...+2a^2b^2c^2\,\{x'^2\,(b^2+c^2)+y'^2\,(c^2+a^2)$$
$$+z'^2\,(a^2+b^2)-(a^2b^2+b^2c^2+c^2a^2)\}\,\lambda$$
$$+(a^2b^4c^4x'^2+b^2c^4a^4y'^2+c^2a^4b^4z'^2-a^4b^4c^4)=0. \quad ...(3)$$

This equation is of degree six in λ and gives us six values of λ corresponding to each of which we get a normal passing through (x', y', z'). If only four normals can be drawn, then two roots of equation (3) should be zero and as such the constant term and the coefficient of λ should be zero.

The constant term in equation (3) is

$$a^2b^4c^4x'^2+b^2c^4a^4y'^2+c^2a^4b^4z'^2-a^4b^4c^4$$

i.e. $\quad a^4b^4c^4\,(x'^2/a^2+y'^2/b^2+z'^2/c^2-1)$

i.e. $\quad a^4b^4c^4\,(0)$ using (1), *i.e.* 0.

Again the coefficient of λ in equation (3) is

$$2a^2b^2c^2\,\{x'^2\,(b^2+c^2)+y'^2\,(c^2+a^2)+z'^2\,(a^2+b^2)$$
$$-(a^2b^2+b^2c^2+c^2a^2)\}$$

i.e. $\quad 2a^2b^2c^2\,(0)$, using (2) *i.e.* 0.

Hence equation (3) gives only four values of λ and so only four normals can be drawn.

Ex. 5. *Prove that the greatest value of shortest distance between the axis of x and a normal to the ellipsoid $x^2/a^2+y^2/b^2+z^2/c^2=1$ is $(b-c)$.*

Solution. The equations of the normal to the ellipsoid $x^2/a^2+y^2/b^2+z^2/c^2=1$ at (α, β, γ) are

$$\frac{x-\alpha}{\alpha/a^2}=\frac{y-\beta}{\beta/b^2}=\frac{z-\gamma}{\gamma/c^2}. \quad ...(1)$$

The equations of the x-axis are $\dfrac{x}{1}=\dfrac{y}{0}=\dfrac{z}{0}$ ...(2)

$\therefore$ The length of the shortest distance between the lines (1) and (2)

$$=\begin{vmatrix} \alpha-0 & \beta-0 & \gamma-0 \\ \alpha/a^2 & \beta/b^2 & \gamma/c^2 \\ 1 & 0 & 0 \end{vmatrix} \div \sqrt{\left(\frac{\gamma^2}{c^4}+\frac{\beta^2}{b^4}\right)}$$

$$=\left(\frac{\beta\gamma}{c^2}-\frac{\beta\gamma}{b^2}\right)\div\frac{\sqrt{(b^4\gamma^2+c^4\beta^2)}}{c^2b^2}=\frac{\beta\gamma\ (b^2-c^2)}{\sqrt{(b^4\gamma^2+c^4\gamma^2)}}$$

$$=(b^2-c^2)\div\sqrt{(b^4/\beta^2+c^4/\gamma^2)}. \quad ...(3)$$

The length of the shortest distance given by (3) will be maximum when its denominator is minimum because the numerator is a constant. Thus we are to find the minimum value of

$$\frac{b^4}{\beta^2}+\frac{c^4}{\gamma^2}=\lambda \text{ (say)} \quad ..(4)$$

Since (α, β, γ) lies on the given ellipsoid, therefore

$$\alpha^2/a^2+\beta^2/b^2+\gamma^2/c^2=1. \quad ...(5)$$

Now we are to find the minimum value of λ given by (4) subject to the condition (5). This will be done by using Lagrange's method of undetermined multipliers for finding the maximum and minimum values of a function of several variables.

Differentiating (4) and (5), we have

$$(b^4/\beta^3)\ d\beta+(c^4/\gamma^3)\ d\gamma=0 \quad ...(6)$$

and $$(\alpha/a^2)\ d\alpha+(\beta/b^2)\ d\beta+(\gamma/c^2)\ d\gamma=0. \quad ...(7)$$

Multiplying (6) by 1 and (7) by μ and adding and then equating to zero the coefficients of $d\alpha$, $d\beta$ and $d\gamma$, we get

$$\frac{\mu\alpha}{a^2}=0,\ \frac{b^4}{\beta^3}+\frac{\mu\beta}{b^2}=0,\ \frac{c^4}{\gamma^3}+\frac{\mu\gamma}{c^2}=0. \quad ...(8)$$

Multiplying these relations by α, β, γ respectively and adding, we have

$$\mu\left(\frac{\alpha^2}{a^2}+\frac{\beta^2}{b^2}+\frac{\gamma^2}{c^2}\right)+\frac{b^4}{\beta^2}+\frac{c^4}{\gamma^2}=0$$

or $$\mu.1+\lambda=0. \text{ using (4) and (5)}$$

or $$\mu=-\lambda.$$

Putting this value of μ in (8), we get

$$\frac{b^4}{\beta^3}-\frac{\lambda\beta}{b^2}=0, \quad \text{and} \quad \frac{c^4}{\gamma^3}-\frac{\lambda\gamma}{c^2}=0.$$

From these, we get $\lambda=b^6/\beta^4=c^6/\gamma^4$. ...(9)

Hence putting the values of β and γ from (9) in (4), we get

$$\lambda=\frac{b^4}{b^3/\sqrt{\lambda}}+\frac{c^4}{c^3/\sqrt{\lambda}}=\sqrt{\lambda}\ (b+c) \quad \text{or} \quad \sqrt{\lambda}=(b+c).$$

$\therefore$ From (3), the greatest value of the shortest distance is

$$=\frac{(b^2-c^2)}{\sqrt{\lambda}}=\frac{b^2-c^2}{b+c}=(b-c).$$

Proved.

Ex. 6. *The normal at P to the ellipsoid* $x^2/a^2+y^2/b^2+z^2/c^2=1$ *meets in Q and R the tangent planes to*

$$\frac{x^2}{a^2-k}+\frac{y^2}{b^2-k}+\frac{z^2}{c^2-k}=1$$

which are perpendicular to that normal. Prove that PQ·PR=k.

Solution. The equations of the given ellipsoids are

$$x^2/a^2+y^2/b^2+z^2/c^2=1 \quad ...(1)$$

and $$x^2/(a^2-k)+y^2/(b^2-k)+z^2/(c^2-k)=1. \quad ...(2)$$

The equations of the normal to the ellipsoid (1) at any point $P(\alpha, \beta, \gamma)$ on it are

$$\frac{x-\alpha}{p\alpha/a^2}=\frac{y-\beta}{p\beta/b^2}=\frac{z-\gamma}{p\gamma/c^2} \quad ..(3)$$

where $p\alpha/a^2$, $p\beta/b^2$, $p\gamma/c^2$ are the actual direction cosines and

$$\frac{1}{p^2}=\frac{\alpha^2}{a^4}+\frac{\beta^2}{b^4}+\frac{\gamma^2}{c^4}. \quad ...(4)$$

The equation of a plane perpendicular to the line (3) is given by

$$(p\alpha/a^2)\, x+(p\beta/b^2)\, y+(p\gamma/c^2)z=\lambda. \quad ...(5)$$

If this plane be a tangent plane to the ellipsoid (2), then applying the condition for tangency "$a^2l^2+b^2m^2+c^2n^2=p^2$" we have

$$(a^2-k).\frac{p^2\alpha^2}{a^4}+(b^2-k)\frac{p^2\beta^2}{b^4}+(c^2-k)\frac{p^2\gamma^2}{c^4}=\lambda^2.$$

or $$p^2\left(\frac{\alpha^2}{a^2}+\frac{\beta^2}{b^2}+\frac{\gamma^2}{c^2}\right)-kp^2\left(\frac{\alpha^2}{a^4}+\frac{\beta^2}{b^4}+\frac{\gamma^2}{c^4}\right)=\lambda^2$$

or $$p^2.1-k.1=\lambda^2$$

[∵ (α, β, γ) lies on (1) and also using (4)]

or $$\lambda=\pm\sqrt{(p^2-k)}.$$

Hence the equations of the two tangent planes to the ellipsoid (2) are

$$(p\alpha/a^2)\, x+(p\beta/b^2)\, y+(p\gamma/c^2)\, z=\sqrt{(p^2-k)} \quad ..(6)$$

and $$(p\alpha/a^2)\, x+(p\beta/b^2)\, y+(p\gamma/c^2)\, z=-\sqrt{(p^2-k)}. \quad ..(7)$$

The planes (6) and (7) given above are both perpendicular to the normal (3) through the point $P(\alpha, \beta, \gamma)$ and meet it in the points Q and R. Thus the distances PQ and PR are the perpendicular distances of the point $P(\alpha, \beta, \gamma)$ from the planes (6) and (7) respectively. Hence

$$PQ=\frac{(p\alpha/a^2).\alpha+(p\beta/b^2).\beta+(p\gamma/c^2).\gamma-\sqrt{(p^2-k)}}{\sqrt{\{(p\alpha/a^2)^2+(p\beta/b^2)^2+(p\gamma/c^2)^2\}}}$$

$$=\frac{p\,(\alpha^2/a^2+\beta^2/b^2+\gamma^2/c^2)-\sqrt{(p^2-k)}}{\sqrt{\{p^2\,(\alpha^2/a^4+\beta^2/b^4+\gamma^2/c^4)\}}}$$

$$=\frac{p.1-\sqrt{(p^2-k)}}{\sqrt{\{p^2.(1/p^2)\}}}$$ [$\because$ $\alpha^2/a^2+\beta^2/b^2+\gamma^2/c^2=1$ because $P\,(\alpha,\beta,\gamma)$ lies on (1) ; also using (4) in the denominator]

$$=p-\sqrt{(p^2-k)}.$$

Similarly $PR=p+\sqrt{(p^2-k)}$.

$\therefore$ $PQ.PR=\{p-\sqrt{(p^2-k)}\}.\{p+\sqrt{(p^2-k)}\}$

$=p^2-(p^2-k)=p^2-p^2+k=k.$ **Proved.**

Ex. 7. *Prove that the normals to* $x^2/a^2+y^2/b^2+z^2/c^2=1$ *at all points of its intersection with* $lyz+mzx+nxy=0$ *intersect the line*

$$\frac{a^2x}{l\,(a^2-b^2)(c^2-a^2)}=\frac{b^2y}{m(b^2-c^2)(a^2-b^2)}=\frac{c^2z}{n(c^2-a^2)\,(b^2-c^2)}.$$

Solution. Let (α,β,γ) be any point of intersection of the ellipsoid $x^2/a^2+y^2/b^2+z^2/c^2=1$ with the plane $lyz+mzx+nxy=0$, so that

$$\alpha^2/a^2+\beta^2/b^2+\gamma^2/c^2=1 \quad \text{and} \quad l\beta\gamma+m\gamma\alpha+n\alpha\beta=0. \qquad ...(1)$$

The equations of the normal at (α,β,γ) to the given ellipsoid are

$$\frac{x-\alpha}{\alpha/a^2}=\frac{y-\beta}{\beta/b^2}=\frac{z-\gamma}{\gamma/c^2}. \qquad ...(2)$$

The equations of the given line may be rewritten as

$$\frac{x}{l(a^2-b^2)(c^2-a^2)/a^2}=\frac{y}{m(b^2-c^2)(a^2-b^2)b^2}=\frac{z}{n(c^2-a^2)(b^2-c^2)/c^2} \qquad ...(3)$$

Now the lines (2) and (3) will intersect (*i.e.* will be coplanar) if

$$\begin{vmatrix} \alpha-0 & \beta-0 & \gamma-0 \\ \alpha/a^2 & \beta/b^2 & \gamma/c^2 \\ \frac{l}{a^2}(a^2-b^2)(c^2-a^2) & \frac{m}{b^2}(b^2-c^2)(a^2-b^2) & \frac{n}{c^2}(c^2-a^2)(b^2-c^2) \end{vmatrix}=0.$$

Multiplying column I by $a^2\,(b^2-c^2)$, column II by $b^2(c^2-a^2)$ and column III by $c^2\,(a^2-b^2)$ and then cancelling $(a^2-b^2)\,(b^2-c^2)\,(c^2-a^2)$ from the third row, the above condition for the coplanarity of the lines reduces to

$$\begin{vmatrix} a^2(b^2-c^2)\,\alpha & b^2(c^2-a^2)\,\beta & c^2(a^2-b^2)\,\gamma \\ (b^2-c^2)\,\alpha & (c^2-a^2)\,\beta & (a^2-b^2)\,\gamma \\ l & m & n \end{vmatrix}=0$$

or

$$\begin{vmatrix} a^2(b^2-c^2)\,\alpha & b^2(c^2-a^2)\,\beta & c^2(a^2-b^2)\,\gamma \\ (b^2-c^2)\,\alpha & (c^2-a^2)\,\beta & (a^2-b^2)\,\gamma \\ l\alpha\beta\gamma & m\alpha\beta\gamma & n\alpha\beta\gamma \end{vmatrix}=0.$$

Cancelling α, β and γ from first, second and third columns respectively, the condition becomes

$$\begin{vmatrix} a^2(b^2-c^2) & b^2(c^2-a^2) & c^2(a^2-b^2) \\ (b^2-c^2) & (c^2-a^2) & (a^2-b^2) \\ l\beta\gamma & m\gamma\alpha & n\alpha\beta \end{vmatrix}=0.$$

Adding second and third columns to the first column, the condition for coplanarity of the lines becomes

$$\begin{vmatrix} 0 & b^2(c^2-a^2) & c^2(a^2-b^2) \\ 0 & c^2-a^2 & a^2-b^2 \\ l\beta\gamma+m\gamma\alpha+n\alpha\beta & m\gamma\alpha & n\alpha\beta \end{vmatrix}=0.$$

or

$$\begin{vmatrix} 0 & b^2(c^2-a^2) & c^2(a^2-b^2) \\ 0 & c^2-a^2 & a^2-b^2 \\ 0 & m\gamma\alpha & n\alpha\beta \end{vmatrix}=0 \qquad \text{[using (1)]}$$

which is true since all entries in the first column are zero. Hence the lines are coplanar *i.e.*, they intersect.

Ex. 8. *Prove that two normals to the ellipsoid* $x^2/a^2+y^2/b^2+z^2/c^2=1$ *lie in the plane* $lx+my+nz=0$ *and the line joining their feet has direction cosines proportional to* $a^2(b^2-c^2)mn$, $b^2(c^2-a^2)\,nl$, $c^2(a^2-b^2)\,lm$. *Find also the co-ordinates of these points.*

Solution. The equation of the ellipsoid is

$$x^2/a^2+y^2/b^2+z^2/c^2=1. \qquad \ldots(1)$$

Let (α, β, γ) be any point on the ellipsoid (1) so that we have

$$\alpha^2/a^2+\beta^2/b^2+\gamma^2/c^2=1. \qquad \ldots(2)$$

The equations of the normal to the ellipsoid (1) at (α, β, γ) are

$$\frac{x-\alpha}{\alpha/a^2}=\frac{y-\beta}{\beta/b^2}=\frac{z-\gamma}{\gamma/c^2}. \quad ...(3)$$

Now if the normal *i.e.* line (3) lies in the given plane namely $lx+my+nz=0$, then we have

$$l\alpha+m\beta+n\gamma=0 \quad ...(4)$$

and

$$l(\alpha/a^2)+m(\beta/b^2)+n(\gamma/c^2)=0. \quad ...(5)$$

Solving the relations (4) and (5) for α, β, γ, we have

$$\frac{\alpha}{\frac{mn}{c^2}-\frac{mn}{b^2}}=\frac{\beta}{\frac{nl}{a^2}-\frac{nl}{c^2}}=\frac{\gamma}{\frac{lm}{b^2}-\frac{lm}{a^2}}$$

or

$$\frac{b^2c^2\alpha}{mn(b^2-c^2)}=\frac{c^2a^2\beta}{nl(c^2-a^2)}=\frac{a^2b^2\gamma}{lm(a^2-b^2)}$$

or

$$\frac{\alpha/a}{amn(b^2-c^2)}=\frac{\beta/b}{bnl(c^2-a^2)}=\frac{\gamma/c}{clm(a^2-b^2)}$$

$$=\frac{\sqrt{(\alpha^2/a^2+\beta^2/b^2+\gamma^2/c^2)}}{\sqrt{[\Sigma\{a^2m^2n^2(b^2-c^2)\}]}}=\pm\frac{1}{\lambda}$$

[using (2) and putting $\lambda=\sqrt{[\Sigma\{a^2m^2n^2(b^2-c^2)\}]}$]

or

$$\frac{\alpha}{a^2mn(b^2-c^2)}=\frac{\beta}{b^2nl(c^2-a^2)}=\frac{\gamma}{c^2lm(a^2-b^2)}=\pm\frac{1}{\lambda}. \quad ...(6)$$

Thus we have two sets of values of (α, β, γ) given by (6) and this shows that the equations (3) give two normals lying in the given plane namely $lx+my+nz=0$.

The co-ordinates of the two points are

$$(a^2mn(b^2-c^2)/\lambda,\ b^2nl(c^2-a^2)/\lambda,\ c^2lm(a^2-b^2)/\lambda)$$

and $(-a^2mn(b^2-c^2)/\lambda,\ -b^2nl(c^2-a^2)/\lambda,\ -c^2lm(a^2-b^2)/\lambda)$.

The direction cosines of the line joining these points are clearly proportional to

$$a^2mn(b^2-c^2),\ b^2nl(c^2-a^2),\ c^2lm(a^2-b^2).$$

Conjugate diameters.

Ex. 9. *If through a fixed point $H(\alpha, \beta, \gamma)$ perpendiculars HA, HB, HC are drawn to the conjugate semi-diameters OP, OQ and OR respectively of an ellipsoid, then prove that*

(*i*) $OP^2.HA^2+OQ^2.HB^2+OR^2.HC^2=$ *constant.*

(*ii*) *The plane through the feet of the perpendiculars passes through the point*

$$(a^2\alpha/(a^2+b^2+c^2),\ b^2\beta/(a^2+b^2+c^2),\ c^2\gamma/(a^2+b^2+c^2)).$$

Solution. Let the equation of the given ellipsoid be

$$x^2/a^2+y^2/b^2+z^2/c^2=1, \quad ...(1)$$

The centre of the ellipsoid (1) is $O(0, 0, 0)$.

Let the co-ordinates of the point P be (x_1, y_1, z_1). The equations of OP are

$$\frac{x-0}{x_1-0}=\frac{y-0}{y_1-0}=\frac{z-0}{z_1-0} \text{ or } \frac{x}{x_1}=\frac{y}{y_1}=\frac{z}{z_1}=r \text{ (say).} \quad \ldots(2)$$

The foot of the perpendicular HA from the fixed point H to OP is the point A and so the co-ordinates of A may be taken as (rx_1, ry_1, rz_1). Now since HA is perpendicular to OP, we have

$$(rx_1-\alpha).x_1+(ry_1-\beta).y_1+(rz_1-\gamma).z_1=0$$

or $$r=\frac{\alpha x_1+\beta y_1+\gamma z_1}{x_1^2+y_1^2+z_1^2}=\frac{\alpha x_1+\beta y_1+\gamma z_1}{OP^2}, \quad \ldots(3)$$

where $$OP^2=x_1^2+y_1^2+z_1^2. \quad \ldots(4)$$

Also $$HA^2=(rx_1-\alpha)^2+(ry_1-\beta)^2+(rz_1-\gamma)^2$$
$$=r^2(x_1^2+y_1^2+z_1^2)-2r(\alpha x_1+\beta y_1+\gamma z_1)+(\alpha^2+\beta^2+\gamma^2).$$

Putting the value of r from (3) and the value of $(x_1^2+y_1^2+z_1^2)$ from (4), we get

$$HA^2=\frac{(\alpha x_1+\beta y_1+\gamma z_1)}{OP^4}.OP^2-\frac{2.(\alpha x_1+\beta y_1+\gamma z_1)^2}{OP^2}+(\alpha^2+\beta^2+\gamma^2)$$

or $$HA^2.OP^2=(\alpha x_1+\beta y_1+\gamma z_1)^2-2(\alpha x_1+\beta y_1+\gamma z_1)^2+(\alpha^2+\beta^2+\gamma^2).OP^2$$

or $$HA^2.OP^2=OP^2.(\alpha^2+\beta^2+\gamma^2)-(\alpha x_1+\beta y_1+\gamma z_1)^2. \quad \ldots(5)$$

Again if the co-ordinates of Q and R be (x_2, y_2, z_2) and (x_3, y_3, z_3) respectively, then proceeding as above, we have

$$HB^2.OQ^2=OQ^2(\alpha^2+\beta^2+\gamma^2)-(\alpha x_2+\beta y_2+\gamma z_2)^2 \quad \ldots(6)$$

and $$HC^2.OR^2=OR^2.(\alpha^2+\beta^2+\gamma^2)-(\alpha x_3+\beta y_3+\gamma z_3)^2. \quad \ldots(7)$$

Adding the relations (5), (6) and (7) and using $OP^2+OQ^2+OR^2=a^2+b^2+c^2$, we have

$$HA^2.OP^2+HB^2.OQ^2+HC^2.OR^2$$
$$=(OP^2+OQ^2+OR^2)(\alpha^2+\beta^2+\gamma^2)-\alpha^2(x_1^2+x_2^2+x_3^2)$$
$$-\beta^2(y_1^2+y_2^2+y_3^2)-\gamma^2(z_1^2+z_2^2+z_3^2)$$
$$+2\alpha\beta(x_1y_1+x_2y_2+x_3y_3)+2\beta\gamma\,\Sigma\, y_1z_1+2\gamma\alpha\,\Sigma\, z_1x_1$$
$$=(a^2+b^2+c^2)(\alpha^2+\beta^2+\gamma^2)-\alpha^2a^2-\beta^2b^2-\gamma^2c^2$$

[using relations (4) and (5) of § 17 of this chapter]

=constant. This proves part (i) of the question.

Putting the value of r from (3) in the co-ordinates (rx_1, ry_1, rz_1) of the foot of the perpendicular A, the co-ordinates of the foot of the perpendicular A are

$$\left[\frac{x_1(\alpha x_1+\beta y_1+\gamma z_1)}{OP^2}, \frac{y_1(\alpha x_1+\beta y_1+\gamma z_1)}{OP^2}, \frac{z_1(\alpha x_1+\beta y_1+\gamma z_1)}{OP^2}\right]$$

In a similar way we find the co-ordinates of the feet of the perpendiculars B and C.

Let the equation of the plane through the points A, B and C be given by

$$lx+my+nz=p. \qquad ...(8)$$

If the plane (8) passes through the point A, we have

$$(\alpha x_1+\beta y_1+\gamma z_1)(lx_1+my_1+nz_1)=p.OP^2$$

or $$\alpha lx_1^2+\beta my_1^2+\gamma nz_1^2+(m\gamma+n\beta)\, y_1z_1+(n\alpha+l\gamma)\, z_1x_1 +(l\beta+m\alpha)\, x_1y_1=p.OP^2 \qquad ...(9)$$

Similarly if the plane (8) passes through the points B and C, we have

$$\alpha lx_2^2+\beta my_2^2+\gamma nz_2^2+(m\gamma+n\beta)\, y_2z_2+(n\alpha+l\gamma)\, z_2x_2 +(l\beta+m\alpha)\, x_2y_2=p.OQ^2 \qquad ...(10)$$

and $$\alpha lx_3^2+\beta my_3^2+\gamma nz_3^2+(m\gamma+n\beta)\, y_3z_3+(n\alpha+l\gamma)\, z_3x_3 +(l\beta+m\alpha)\, x_3y_3=p.OR^2. \qquad ...(11)$$

Adding the relations (9), (10) and (11) and using relations (4) and (5) of § 17 of this chapter, we have

$$\alpha la^2+\beta mb^2+\gamma nc^2+0+0+0=p\,(OP^2+OQ^2+OR^2)$$

or $$\alpha la^2+\beta mb^2+\gamma nc^2=p\,(a^2+b^2+c^2)$$

or $$l.\frac{\alpha a^2}{a^2+b^2+c^2}+m.\frac{\beta b^2}{a^2+b^2+c^2}+n.\frac{\gamma c^2}{a^2+b^2+c^2}=p.$$

This relation shows that the plane (8) passes through the point $\left(\frac{a^2\alpha}{a^2+b^2+c^2}, \frac{b^2\beta}{a^2+b^2+c^2}, \frac{c^2\gamma}{a^2+b^2+c^2}\right)$.

This proves the part (ii) of the question.

Ex. 10. *If the axes are rectangular, find the locus of the equal, conjugate diameters of the ellipsoid* $x^2/a^2+y^2/b^2+z^2/c^2=1$.

Solution. The equation of the given ellipsoid is

$$x^2/a^2+y^2/b^2+z^2/c^2=1. \qquad ...(1)$$

Let OP, OQ and OR be the equal conjugate semi-diameters of the ellipsoid (1), so that $OP=OQ=OR=r$, (say).

Let (x_1, y_1, z_1), (x_2, y_2, z_2) and (x_3, y_3, z_3) be the co-ordinates of the points P, Q, R. We have

$$OP=r \Rightarrow OP^2=r^2 \Rightarrow x_1^2+y_1^2+z_1^2=r^2. \qquad ...(2)$$

Similarly $$x_2^2+y_2^2+z_2^2=r^2 \qquad ...(3)$$

and $$x_3^2+y_3^2+z_3^2=r^2. \qquad ...(4)$$

Adding (2), (3) and (4), we get

$$a^2+b^2+c^2=3r^2 \qquad ...(5)$$

$$[\because\ \Sigma x_1^2=a^2,\ \Sigma y_1^2=b^2,\ \Sigma z_1^2=c^2]$$

Now let l, m, n be the d.c.'s of OP so that the co-ordinates of the point P are (lr, mr, nr). Since $P(lr, mr, nr)$ lies on the ellipsoid (1), we have

$$l^2r^2/a^2+m^2r^2/b^2+n^2r^2/c^2=1$$

or $\frac{l^2}{a^2}+\frac{m^2}{b^2}+\frac{n^2}{c^2}=\frac{1}{r^2}$ or $\frac{l^2}{a^2}+\frac{m^2}{b^2}+\frac{n^2}{c^2}=\frac{3(l^2+m^2+n^2)}{a^2+b^2+c^2}$ ...(6)

[Putting the value of r^2 from (5) and using the fact that $l^2+m^2+n^2=1$].

The relation (6) shows that the semi-diameter OP generates the cone *i.e.*, the locus of OP is the cone

$$\frac{x^2}{a^2}+\frac{y^2}{b^2}+\frac{z^2}{c^2}-\frac{3(x^2+y^2+z^2)}{a^2+b^2+c^2}=0$$

or $(x^2/a^2)(2a^2-b^2-c^2)+(y^2/b^2)(2b^2-c^2-a^2)$

$$+(z^2/c^2)(2c^2-a^2-b^2)=0.$$

Ex. 11. *Prove that the planes through a pair of equal conjugate diameters touches the cone*

$$\frac{x^2}{a^2(2a^2-b^2-c^2)}+\frac{y^2}{b^2(2b^2-c^2-a^2)}+\frac{z^2}{c^2(2c^2-a^2-b^2)}=0.$$

Solution. Let the equation of the ellipsoid be

$$x^2/a^2+y^2/b^2+z^2/c^2=1. \quad ...(1)$$

Now proceed exactly the same upto equation (5) of Ex. 10 above. Now consider the plane through OQ and OR and hence it is also the diametral plane to OP (since OP, OQ and OR are equal conjugate semi-diameters), and so its equation is given by

$$xx_1/a^2+yy_1/b^2+zz_1/c^2=0. \quad ...(6)$$

The direction cosines of the normal to the plane (6) are

$$x_1/a^2,\ y_1/b^2,\ z_1/c^2. \quad ...(7)$$

Now we are to prove that the plane (6) touches the given cone. The plane (6) will touch the given cone if the normal to the plane (6) is a generator of the reciprocal cone to the given cone.

The equation of the reciprocal cone to the given cone is

$$a^2(2a^2-b^2-c^2)x^2+b^2(2b^2-c^2-a^2)y^2+c^2(2c^2-a^2-b^2)z^2=0 \quad ...(8)$$

Therefore if the normal to the plane (6), whose d.c.'s are given by (7) is a generator of the reciprocal cone (8), we must have

$$a^2(2a^2-b^2-c^2)(x_1/a^2)^2+b^2(2b^2-c^2-a^2)(y_1/b^2)^2$$
$$+c^2(2c^2-a^2-b^2)(z_1/c^2)^2=0$$

or $2(x_1^2+y_1^2+z_1^2)-(b^2+c^2)\left(\frac{x_1^2}{a^2}\right)-(c^2+a^2)\left(\frac{y_1^2}{b^2}\right)$

$$-(a^2+b^2)\left(\frac{z_1^2}{c^2}\right)=0$$

or $2r^2-(3r^2-a^2)(x_1^2/a^2)-(3r^2-b^2)(y_1^2/b^2)-(3r^2-c^2)(z_1^2/c^2)=0$

[using (2) and (5)]

or $2r^2-3r^2(x_1^2/a^2+y_1^2/b^2+z_1^2/c^2)+(x_1^2+y_1^2+z_1^2)=0$

or $2r^2-3r^2(1)+r^2=0$ [$\because$ $P(x_1, y_1, z_1)$ lies on the ellipsoid (1)]

which is true.

Hence the planes through a pair OQ and OR of equal conjugate diameters touches the given cone.

Ex. 12. *Prove that the locus of the point of intersection of three tangent planes to $x^2/a^2+y^2/b^2+z^2/c^2=1$ which are parallel to conjugate diametral planes of $x^2/\alpha^2+y^2/\beta^2+z^2/\gamma^2=1$ is*

$$\frac{x^2}{\alpha^2}+\frac{y^2}{\beta^2}+\frac{z^2}{\gamma^2}=\frac{a^2}{\alpha^2}+\frac{b^2}{\beta^2}+\frac{c^2}{\gamma^2}.$$

Solution. The equations of the ellipsoids are given as

$$x^2/a^2+y^2/b^2+z^2/c^2=1 \quad ...(1)$$

and $$x^2/\alpha^2+y^2/\beta^2+z^2/\gamma^2=1. \quad ...(2)$$

Let OP, OQ and OR be the conjugate semi-diameters of the ellipsoid (2). Let (x_1, y_1, z_1), (x_2, y_2, z_2) and (x_3, y_3, z_3) be the co-ordinates of the extremities P, Q and R respectively.

The equation of the diametral plane of OP with respect to the ellipsoid (2) is

$$xx_1/\alpha^2+yy_1/\beta^2+zz_1/\gamma^2=0. \quad ...(3)$$

The equation of any plane parallel to the plane (3) is

$$xx_1/\alpha^2+yy_1/\beta^2+zz_1/\gamma^2=p_1, \text{ (say)} \quad ...(4)$$

If the plane (4) be a tangent plane to the ellipsoid (1), then

$$p_1^2=a^2(x_1^2/\alpha^4)+b^2(y_1^2/\beta^4)+c^2(z_1^2/\gamma^4) \quad ...(5)$$

[using the condition for tangency $p^2=a^2l^2+b^2m^2+c^2n^2$].

Similarly the equations of the other two tangent planes are

$$xx_2/\alpha^2+yy_2/\beta^2+zz_2/\gamma^2=p_2 \quad ...(6)$$

and $$xx_3/\alpha^2+yy_3/\beta^2+zz_3/\gamma^2=p_3 \quad ...(7)$$

where $$p_2^2=a^2(x_2^2/\alpha^4)+b^2(y_2^2/\beta^4)+c^2(z_2^2/\gamma^4) \quad ...(8)$$

and $$p_3^2=a^2(x_3^2/\alpha^4)+b^2(y_3^2/\beta^4)+c^2(z_3^2/\gamma^4). \quad ...(9)$$

Now to find the locus of the point of intersection of the tangent planes (4), (6) and (7), squaring and adding both sides of the equations (4), (6) and (7), we get

$$\sum \left\{\frac{x^2}{\alpha^4}(x_1^2+x_2^2+x_3^2)\right\}+2\sum\left\{\frac{xy}{\alpha^2\beta^2}(x_1y_1+x_2y_2+x_3y_3)\right\}$$
$$=\sum\left\{\frac{a^2}{\alpha^4}(x_1^2+x_2^2+x_3^2)\right\}$$

or $$\sum\left\{\frac{x^2}{\alpha^4}.\alpha^2\right\}+0=\sum\left\{\frac{a^2}{\alpha^4}.\alpha^2\right\} \quad [\because \Sigma x_1^2=\alpha^2, \Sigma x_1y_1=0]$$

or $$x^2/\alpha^2+y^2/\beta^2+z^2/\gamma^2=a^2/\alpha^2+b^2/\beta^2+c^2/\gamma^2.$$

This is the equation of the required locus.

Remark. In case $\alpha=\beta=\gamma$, the equation of the required locus becomes $x^2+y^2+z^2=a^2+b^2+c^2$ which is the equation of the **director sphere.**

Ex. 13. *P is any point on the ellipsoid $x^2/a^2+y^2/b^2+z^2/c^2=1$ and 2α, 2β are the principal axes of the section of the ellipsoid by the the diametral plane of OP. Prove that $OP^2=a^2+b^2+c^2-\alpha^2-\beta^2$ and $\alpha\beta p=abc$, where p is the perpendicular from O to the tangent plane at P.*

Solution. The ellipsoid is $x^2/a^2+y^2/b^2+z^2/c^2=1$ ...(1)

Let OQ and OR be the principal semi-axes of the section of the ellipsoid (1) by the diametral plane of OP, so that $OQ=\alpha$ and $OR=\beta$ (as given). Therefore, the conjugate semi-diameters of the ellipsoid (1) are OP, OQ and OR. Hence

$$OP^2+OQ^2+OR^2=a^2+b^2+c^2 \quad \text{[See § 18 (I), page 62]}$$

or $$OP^2=a^2+b^2+c^2-\alpha^2-\beta^2 \quad [\because OQ=\alpha, OR=\beta]$$

Now as given p=the length of the perpendicular from O on the tangent plane at P

=the length of the perpendicular from P on ΔOQR [Note]

$\therefore$ Volume of the tetrahedron (O, PQR)

$=\frac{1}{3}$ (area of ΔOQR)$\times$(perpendicular length from P on ΔOQR)

$=\frac{1}{3}.(\frac{1}{2}\alpha\beta)\,p$ (1)

Also volume of the tetrahedron (O, PQR)

$=\frac{1}{6}$ (volume of the parallelopiped whose edges are OP OQ, OR)

$=\frac{1}{6}(abc)$ [See § 18 (II) page 62] (2)

From (1) and (2), we get $\frac{1}{6}\alpha\beta p=\frac{1}{6}abc$ or $\alpha\beta p=abc$.

Ex. 14. *Prove that the two asymptotic lines can be drawn from a point P to a conicoid $ax^2+by^2+cz^2=1$ and they are at right angles if P lies on the cone*

$$a^2(b+c)x^2+b^2(c+a)y^2+c^2(a+b)z^2=0.$$

Solution. The conicoid is $ax^2+by^2+cz^2=1$. ...(1)

Let the point P be (α, β, γ). The equation of any line through the point P is

$$\frac{x-\alpha}{l}=\frac{y-\beta}{m}=\frac{z-\gamma}{n}=(r) \text{ say} \quad ...(2)$$

The co-ordinates of any point on the line (2) are $(lr+\alpha, mr+\beta, nr+\gamma)$. If this point lies on the conicoid (1), then

$$a(lr+\alpha)^2+b(mr+\beta)^2+c(nr+\gamma)^2=1$$

or $r^2(al^2+bm^2+cn^2)+2r(al\alpha+bm\beta+cn\gamma)+(a\alpha^2+b\beta^2+c\gamma^2-1)=0$. ...(3)

If the line (2) is an asymptotic line, then the value of r should be infinite and hence both the roots of the equation (3) should be infinite, the conditions for which are

$$al^2+bm^2+cn^2=0 \quad ...(4)$$

and $$al\alpha+bm\beta+cn\gamma=0. \quad ...(5)$$

Since the equation (3) is a quadratic equation in r, hence two asymptotic lines can be drawn from P to the conicoid (1). Let l_1, m_1, n_1 and l_2, m_2, n_2 be the direction cosines of these two asymptotic lines and these are clearly given by the roots of the equations (4) and (5). These lines will be perpendicular if

$$l_1l_2+m_1m_2+n_1n_2=0. \quad ...(6)$$

Now eliminating n between (4) and (5), we get

$$al^2+bm^2+c\left[-\frac{al\alpha+bm\beta}{c\gamma}\right]^2=0$$

or $ac(c\gamma^2+a\alpha^2)l^2+2(ac\alpha\beta)lm+bc(c\gamma^2+b\beta^2)m^2=0$

or $ac(c\gamma^2+a\alpha^2)(l/m)^2+2ac\alpha\beta(l/m)+bc(c\gamma^2+b\beta^2)=0$.

$\therefore$ The product of roots$=\dfrac{l_1}{m_1}\cdot\dfrac{l_2}{m_2}=\dfrac{bc(c\gamma^2+b\beta^2)}{ac(c\gamma^2+a\alpha^2)}$

or $\dfrac{l_1l_2}{bc(b\beta^2+c\gamma^2)}=\dfrac{m_1m_2}{ca(c\gamma^2+a\alpha^2)}=\dfrac{n_1n_2}{ab(a\alpha^2+b\beta^2)}$, by symmetry.

Substituting these values of l_1l_2, m_1m_2, n_1n_2 in (6), we have

$bc(b\beta^2+c\gamma^2)+ca(c\gamma^2+a\alpha^2)+ab(a\alpha^2+b\beta^2)=0$.

Hence the locus of $P(\alpha, \beta, \gamma)$ is

$bc(by^2+cz^2)+ca(cz^2+ax^2)+ab(ax^2+by^2)=0$.

or $$a^2(b+c)x^2+b^2(c+a)y^2+c^2(a+b)z^2=0.$$

Ex. 15. *Find the locus of the asymptotic line drawn from origin to the conicoid $ax^2+by^2+cz^2=1$.*

Solution. The conicoid is $ax^2+by^2+cz^2=1$ ...(1)

The equation of any line from the origin is

$$x/l=y/m=z/n=r \text{ (say)}. \quad ...(2)$$

Any point on the line (2) is (lr, mr, nr). If this point lies on the conicoid (1), then

$$a\,(lr)^2+b\,(mr)^2+c\,(nr)^2=1$$

or $$al^2+bm^2+cn^2=1/r^2. \qquad \text{...(3)}$$

If the line (2) be the asymptotic line, then r will be infinite and hence (3) gives

$$al^2+bm^2+cn^2=0. \qquad \text{...(4)}$$

Eliminating l, m, n between (2) and (4), the locus of the asymptote line drawn from the origin is given by

$$ax^2+by^2+cz^2=0.$$

Ex. 16. *Prove that the plane PQR touches a fixed sphere, where P, Q, R are the extremities of the conjugate semi-diameters of the ellipsoid* $x^2/a^2+y^2/b^2+z^2/c^2=1$.

Solution. Left as an exercise for the students.

Ex. 17. *If the normal at the point P to the ellipsoid* $x^2/a^2+y^2/b^2+z^2/c^2=1$ *meet the principal planes in the points L, M, N, show that*

$$PL/a^2=PM/b^2=PN/c^2.$$

2

The Paraboloids

§ 1. The elliptic paraboloid. The equation of the elliptic paraboloid is given by

$$x^2/a^2+y^2/b^2=2z/c. \quad ...(1)$$

The following facts are observed about the equation (1) :—

(i) We see that if the point $P(x_1, y_1, z_1)$ lies on the equation (1) then the point $Q(-x_1, y_1, z_1)$ also lies on it. Clearly the middle point of PQ *i.e.* $(0, y_1, z_1)$ lies on the yz-plane (*i.e.* the plane $x=0$).

The direction ratios of the line PQ are $2x_1, 0, 0$ *i.e.* 1, 0, 0 showing that the line PQ is perpendicular to the yz-plane (*i.e.* the plane $x=0$).

This proves that the yz-plane (i.e. $x=0$ plane) bisects all the chords of the surface (1) *which are perpendicular to it and the surface* (1) *is symmetrical with respect to the yz-plane.*

Similarly *we can show that the zx-plane (i.e. $y=0$ plane) bisects all the chords of the surface* (1) *which are perpendicular to it and the surface* (1) *is symmetrical with respect to the zx-plane.* These two planes namely $x=0$ and $y=0$ are called **principal planes.**

(ii) The section of the surface (1) by the plane $z=k$ is an ellipse whose equations are given by

$$x^2/a^2+y^2/b^2=2k/c, \; z=k. \quad ...(2)$$

The centre $(0, 0, k)$ of the ellipse (2) lies on the z-axis. As k increases *i.e.* the cutting plane $z=k$ recedes from the xy-plane, the ellipse (2) increases in size. For different values of k, we have different ellipses given by the equations (2). Thus the whole surface (1) may be supposed to be generated by the ellipses (2) as k varies.

(iii) If $c>0$, the surface (1) lies wholly above the xy-plane. If $c<0$, the surface (1) lies wholly below the xy-plane.

(iv) The sections of the surface (1) by the planes parallel to the yz-plane and zx-plane.

The sections of the surface (1) by the planes parallel to $x=0$ *i.e.* by the planes $x=k$ are given by

$$k^2/a^2+y^2/b^2=2z/c,\ x=k$$

or
$$y^2=\frac{2b^2}{c}\left(z-\frac{ck^2}{2a^2}\right),\ x=k. \quad \ldots(3)$$

These equations together represent parabolas with their vertices $(k, 0, ck^2/2a^2)$ lying on the parabola $x^2/a^2=2z/c,\ y=0$ which is clearly the section of the surface (1) by the plane $y=0$.

The length of the latus rectum of each of the parabolas (3) is $2b^2/c$ which is constant and hence the sections are all of the same size.

Hence it follows that the whole surface (1) may be determined by pushing the parabola

$$y^2=(2b^2/c)\ z,\ x=0$$

forwards and backwards perpendicular to its plane so that the vertex slides on the parabola

$$x^2=(2a^2/c)\ z,\ y=0.$$

Similarly it follows that the sections of the surface (1) by the planes parallel to the *zx*-plane (*i.e.* the plane $y=0$) are parabolas which are determined by pushing the parabola

$$x^2=(2a^2/c)\ z,\ y=0$$

so that the vertex slides on the parabola

$$y^2=(2b^2/c)\ z,\ x=0.$$

Hence in view of the above facts the rough sketch of the elliptic paraboloid (1) for the positive value of c is as shown in the figure below.

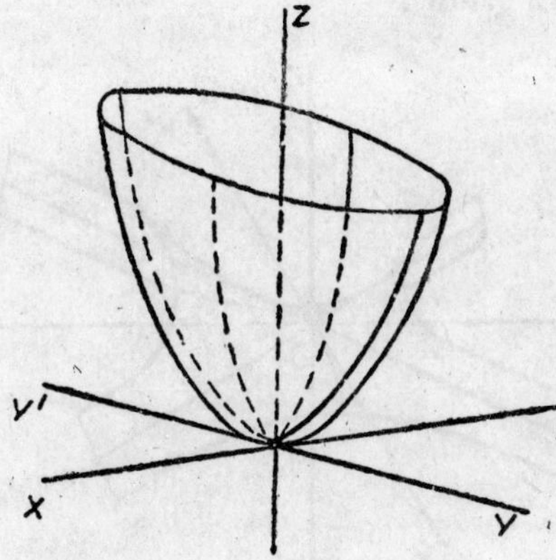

§ 2. **The hyperbolic paraboloid.** The equation of the hyperbolic paraboloid is given by

$$x^2/a^2-y^2/b^2=2z/c. \qquad ...(1)$$

The following facts are observed about the equation (1) :—

(i) Proceeding as in (i) of § 1, the surface (1) is symmetrical about the yz-plane (*i.e.* $x=0$ plane) and zx-plane (*i.e.* $y=0$ plane). The planes $x=0$ and $y=0$ are called the **principal planes.**

(ii) The sections of the surface (1) by the varying planes $z=k$ are given by

$$x^2/a^2-y^2/b^2=2k/c,\ z=k \qquad ...(2)$$

which are hyperbolas whose centres $(0, 0, k)$ lie on the z-axis, and asymptotes are the straight lines given by $y=\pm (b/a)\, x,\ z=k$. If k is positive the transverse and conjugate axes are parallel to the x-and y-axes respectively and increase with the increase of k. If k is negative, the transverse and conjugate axes are parallel to the y-and x-axes respectively. If $k=0$, the trace is the pair of straight lines given by $y=\pm(b/a)\, x,\ z=0$.

(iii) The section of the surface (1) by the plane $x=k$ is a parabola given by

$$k^2/a^2-y^2/b^2=2z/c,\ x=k \text{ or } y^2=-\frac{2b^2}{c}\left(z-\frac{ck^2}{2a^2}\right),\ x=k$$

which is a parabola open downwards.

The section of the surface (1) by the plane $y=k$ is a parabola open upwards and is given by

$$\frac{x^2}{a^2}-\frac{k^2}{b^2}=\frac{2z}{c},\ y=k \text{ i.e. } x^2=\frac{2a^2}{c}\left(z-\frac{ck^2}{2b^2}\right),\ y=k.$$

Hence in view of the above facts the rough sketch of the surface (1) is as shown below :—

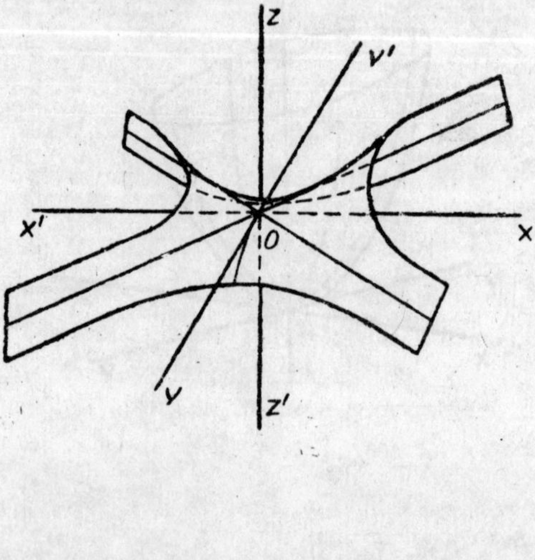

§ 3. The general equation

$$ax^2+by^2=2cz. \quad ...(1)$$

If a and b are both of the same sign then the general equation $ax^2+by^2=2cz$ represents elliptic paraboloid, and if a and b are of opposite signs then the general equation $ax^2+by^2=2cz$ represents a hyperbolic paraboloid.

Hence the various results proved in the chapter on the conicoids can be similarly proved here. We are giving below the various results :

(i) The points of intersection. The points of intersection of the paraboloid (1) with the line with d.c.'s l, m, n and passing through the point (α, β, γ) are given by

$$r^2 (al^2+bm^2)+2r (al\alpha+bm\beta-cn)+(a\alpha^2+b\beta^2-2c\gamma)=0. \quad ...(2)$$

This equation (2) being quadratic in r shows that every line cuts the paraboloid (1) in two points and the distances of these two points of intersection from the point (α, β, γ) are the two values of r given by the equation (2).

In particular if the line is parallel to the z-axis *i.e.* $l=m=0$, then one value of r is infinite [since the coefficient of r^2 becomes zero] and therefore a line parallel to the z-axis meets the paraboloid (1) in one point at an infinite distance from the point (α, β, γ), and in the other point P (say) at a finite distance r from the point (α, β, γ) given by

$$r=\frac{a\alpha^2+b\beta^2-2c\gamma}{2cn} \quad \text{[From (2) on putting } l=m=0]$$

All such lines are called **diameters** and the point P is called the **extremity of the diameter.**

(ii) The equation of the tangent plane at the point (α, β, γ) on the paraboloid (1) is

$$a\alpha x+b\beta y=c(\gamma+z). \quad ...(3)$$

(iii) The condition of tangency. If the plane $lx+my+nz=p$ touches the paraboloid (1), then the condition for tangency is

$$l^2/a+m^2/b+2np/c=0. \quad ...(4)$$

Also the **point of contact** is given by

$$(-lc/an, -mc/bn, -p/n). \quad ...(5)$$

Putting the value of p from (4) in $lx+my+nz=p$, we have

$$lx+my+nz=-\frac{c}{2n}\left(\frac{l^2}{a}+\frac{m^2}{b}\right)$$

or

$$2n(lx+my+nz)+c(l^2/a+m^2/b)=0. \quad ...(6)$$

The plane given by the equation (6) *will always touch the paraboloid* (1).

(iv) *To find the locus of the point of intersection of three mutually perpendicular tangent planes to the paraboloid*

$$ax^2+by^2=2cz.$$

Let the equations of the three mutually perpendicular tangent planes be [See equation (6) above]

$$\left.\begin{aligned} &2n_1\,(l_1x+m_1y+n_1z)+c\,(l_1^2/a+m_1^2/b)=0,\\ &2n_2\,(l_2x+m_2y+n_2z)+c\,(l_2^2/a+m_2^2/b)=0,\\ \text{and}\quad &2n_3\,(l_3x+m_3y+n_3z)+c\,(l_3^2/a+m_3^2/b)=0,\end{aligned}\right\}\quad ...(A)$$

where l_1, m_1, n_1 etc. are actual direction cosines. To find the required locus, we add the above three equations given by (A), and the required locus is given by

$$2z+c\,(1/a+1/b)=0$$

which is a plane perpendicular to the z-axis *i.e.* the axis of the paraboloid. [Note that the d.c.'s of the normal to the plane are 0, 0, 1].

(v) The equation of **the polar plane** of the point (α, β, γ) is given by

$$a\alpha x+b\beta y=c\,(\gamma+z). \quad ...(7)$$

(vi) **The locus of the chords which are bisected at the point** (α, β, γ) is given by

$$T=S_1$$

i.e. $$a\alpha x+b\beta y-c\,(\gamma+z)=a\alpha^2+b\beta^2-2c\gamma$$

i.e. $$a\alpha\,(x-\alpha)+b\beta\,(y-\beta)-c\,(z-\gamma)=0. \quad ...(8)$$

The plane (8) will meet the paraboloid (1) in a conic with its centre at the point (α, β, γ).

(vii) **Diametral plane.** *The locus of the middle points of a system of parallel chords is called a diametral plane.*

Let a system of parallel chords be parallel to the line $x/l=y/m=z/n$. The equation of the diametral plane of the line $x/l=y/m=z/n$ *i.e.* the locus of the middle points of the chords parallel to the line $x/l=y/m=z/n$ is given by

$$alx+bmy-cn=0. \quad ...(9)$$

Clearly the equation (9) of the diametral plane is parallel to the z-axis *i.e.* the axis of the paraboloid. *Hence it follows that all diametral planes are parallel to the axis of the paraboloid, and conversely every plane parallel to the axis of the paraboloid is a diametral plane.*

(viii) Conjugate diametral planes. *Two diametral planes are called conjugate if each bisects the chords parallel to the other.*

The diametral plane of the line

$$x/l = y/m = z/n \quad \text{...(i)}$$

is

$$alx + bmy - cn = 0. \quad \text{...(ii)}$$

Again the diametral plane of the other line

$$x/l' = y/m' = z/n' \quad \text{...(iii)}$$

is

$$al'x + bm'y - cn' = 0. \quad \text{...(iv)}$$

If the diametral planes (ii) and (iv) are conjugate then the line (iii) will be parallel to the diametral plane (ii) [or the line (i) will be parallel to the diametral plane (iv)], the condition for which is given by

$$all' + bmm' = 0. \quad \text{...(10)}$$

(ix) The equation of the enveloping cone with the point (α, β, γ) as its vertex is given by

$$SS_1 = T^2$$

i.e. $(ax^2 + by^2 - 2cz)(a\alpha^2 + b\beta^2 - 2c\gamma) = \{a\alpha x + b\beta y - c\,(z + \gamma)\}^2$ ...(11)

(x) The equation of the enveloping cylinder with its generators parallel to the line $x/l = y/m = z/n$ is given by

$$(ax^2 + by^2 - 2cz)\,(al^2 + bm^2) = (alx + bmy - cn)^2 \quad \text{...(12)}$$

SOLVED EXAMPLES (A)

Ex. 1 (a) *Prove that the plane* $8x - 6y - z = 5$ *touches the paraboloid* $x^2/2 - y^2/3 = z$ *and find the co-ordinates of the point of contact.*

Solution. The equation of the given paraboloid is

$$x^2/2 - y^2/3 = z. \quad \text{...(1)}$$

Comparing (1) with the standard equation $ax^2 + by^2 = 2cz$ of the paraboloid, we get $a = \frac{1}{2}$, $b = -\frac{1}{3}$, $c = \frac{1}{2}$.

Also comparing the given equation $8x - 6y - z = 5$ of the plane with $lx + my + nz = p$, we have $l = 8$, $m = -6$, $n = -1$, $p = 5$. Hence applying the condition of tangency namely

$$l^2/a + m^2/b + 2np/c = 0 \quad \text{[See equation (4), § 3]}$$

we have $64 \times 2 - 36 \times 3 - 2 \times 5 \times \frac{1}{2} = 0$, which is true. Hence the plane $8x - 6y - z = 5$ touches the paraboloid (1).

Let the co-ordinates of the point of contact be (α, β, γ), so that the equation of the tangent plane is [See equation (3), § 3]

$$\alpha x/2 - \beta y/3 = \tfrac{1}{2}\,(z + \gamma) \text{ or } 3\alpha x - 2\beta y - 3z = 3\gamma. \quad \text{...(2)}$$

But the equation of the given plane is

$$8x - 6y - z = 5. \quad \text{...(3)}$$

If the plane (3) touches the paraboloid (1) at the point (α, β, γ), then the planes (2) and (3) must be the same. Hence comparing the equations (2) and (3), we get

$$\frac{3\alpha}{8}=\frac{-2\beta}{-6}=\frac{-3}{-1}=\frac{3\gamma}{5} \text{ i.e. } \alpha=8, \beta=9, \gamma=5.$$

Hence the point of contact is (8, 9, 5).

Ex. 1 (b). *Show that the plane* $2x-4y-z+3=0$ *touches the paraboloid* $x^2-2y^2=3z$ *at the point* $(3, 3, -3)$.

Solution. Proceed as in Ex. 1 (a).

Ex. 2. *By completing the squares find the vertex of the paraboloid* $3x^2+2y^2-12z-6x+8y-13=0$.

Solution. The given equation can be written as

$$3(x^2-2x+1)+2(y^2+4y+4)=12(z+2).$$

or $$3(x-1)^2+2(y+2)^2=12(z+2)$$

Hence the given equation represents an elliptic paraboloid with its vertex at $(1, -2, -2)$.

Ex. 3. *Show that the equation to the two tangent planes to the surface* $ax^2+by^2=2z$ *which pass through the line*

$$u_1 \equiv l_1x+m_1y+n_1z-p_1=0 \quad u_2 \equiv l_2x+m_2y+n_2z-p_2=0$$

is $$u_1^2\left(\frac{l_2^2}{a}+\frac{m_2^2}{b}+2n_2p_2\right)-2u_1u_2(l_1l_2+m_1m_2+n_1p_2+n_2p_1)$$
$$+u_2^2\left(\frac{l_1^2}{a}+\frac{m_1^2}{b}+2n_1p_1\right)=0.$$

Solution. The equation of the given surface is

$$ax^2+by^2=2z. \qquad \ldots(1)$$

The equation of any plane through the given line $u_1=0$, $u_2=0$ is given by

$$u_1+\lambda u_2=0 \qquad \ldots(2)$$

or $$l_1x+m_1y+n_1z-p_1+\lambda(l_2x+m_2y+n_2z-p_2)=0$$

or $$(l_1+\lambda l_2)x+(m_1+\lambda m_2)y+(n_1+\lambda n_2)z=p_1+\lambda p_2. \qquad \ldots(3)$$

If the plane (3) touches the surface (1), then applying the condition for tangency

'$l^2/a+m^2/b+2np/c=0$', [See equation (4) of § 3]

we have $$\frac{(l_1+\lambda l_2)^2}{a}+\frac{(m_1+\lambda m_2)^2}{b}+\frac{2(n_1+\lambda n_2)(p_1+\lambda p_2)}{1}=0$$

or $$\left(\frac{l_1^2}{a}+\frac{m_1^2}{b}+2n_1p_1\right)+2\lambda\left(\frac{l_1l_2}{a}+\frac{m_1m_2}{b}+n_1p_2+n_2p_1\right)$$
$$+\lambda^2\left(\frac{l_2^2}{a}+\frac{m_2^2}{b}+2n_2p_2\right)=0. \qquad \ldots(4)$$

Now putting $\lambda=-u_1/u_2$ from (2) in (4), the required equation of the two tangent planes is given by

$$u_1^2\left(\frac{l_2^2}{a}+\frac{m_2^2}{b}+2n_2p_2\right)-2u_1u_2\left(\frac{l_1l_2}{a}+\frac{m_1m_2}{b}+n_1p_2+n_2p_1\right)$$
$$+u_2^2\left(\frac{l_1^2}{a}+\frac{m_1^2}{b}+2n_1p_1\right)=0.$$

Ex. 4. *Find the equation of the plane which cuts the paraboloid* $x^2-2y^2=3z$ *in a conic whose centre is* (1, 2, 3).

Solution. The equation of the given paraboloid is

$$x^2-2y^2=3z. \qquad ...(1)$$

The equation of the plane which cuts the paraboloid (1) in a conic with centre (1, 2, 3) is given by $T=S_1$,

i.e. $\quad 1.x-2.2y-\frac{3}{2}(z+3)=(1)^2-2(2)^2-3(3)$

or $\quad 2x-8y-3z=-23.$

Ex. 5. *Prove that the centre of the conic* $ax^2+by^2=2z$, $lx+my+nz=p$ *is the point* $\left(-\frac{l}{an}, -\frac{m}{bn}, \frac{k^2}{n^2}\right)$

where $\quad k^2=\frac{l^2}{a}+\frac{m^2}{b}+np.$

Solution. The given conic is the intersection of the paraboloid

$$ax^2+by^2=2z \qquad ...(1)$$

and the plane $\quad lx+my+nz=p. \qquad ...(2)$

Let the co-ordinates of the centre of the conic be (α, β, γ), so that the equation of the plane which cuts the paraboloid (1) in a conic with the centre at (α, β, γ) is given by $T=S_1$

i.e. $\quad a\alpha x+b\beta y-(z+\gamma)=a\alpha^2+b\beta^2-2\gamma$

or $\quad a\alpha x+b\beta y-z=a\alpha^2+b\beta^2-\gamma. \qquad ...(3)$

The equations (2) and (3) will represent the same plane and hence comparing, we get

$$\frac{l}{a\alpha}=\frac{m}{b\beta}=\frac{n}{-1}=\frac{p}{a\alpha^2+b\beta^2-\gamma}$$

or $\quad \alpha=-\frac{l}{an}, \beta=-\frac{m}{bn}, \gamma=a\alpha^2+b\beta^2+\frac{p}{n}$

i.e. $\quad \gamma=a\left(-\frac{l}{an}\right)^2+b\left(-\frac{m}{bn}\right)^2+\frac{p}{n}=\frac{(l^2/a+m^2/b+np)}{n^2}=\frac{k^2}{n^2},$

where $k^2=l^2/a+m^2/b+np.$

$\therefore$ The co-ordinates of the centre are

$$\left(-\frac{l}{an}, -\frac{m}{bn}, \frac{k^2}{n^2}\right).$$

Ex. 6 (a). *The plane* $10x-24y=21$ *is a diametral plane of the paraboloid* $5x^2-6y^2=7z$. *Find the equations to the chord through* (1, 2, 3) *which it bisects.*

Solution. The equation of the paraboloid is

$$5x^2-6y^2=7z. \qquad ...(1)$$

Let l, m, n be the d.c.'s of a system of parallel chords, so that the equation of its diametral plane with respect to the paraboloid (1) is

$$alx+bmy-cn=0 \qquad \text{[See § 3, part (vii)]}$$

i.e. $5lx-6my-\frac{1}{2}.7n=0$ or $10lx-12my-7n=0. \qquad ...(2)$

The equation (2) and the given equation $10x-24y=21$ should be the same. Comparing them, we have

$$\frac{10l}{10}=\frac{12m}{24}=\frac{7n}{21} \text{ or } \frac{l}{1}=\frac{m}{2}=\frac{n}{3}.$$

Hence the d.c.'s of the required chord are proportional to 1, 2, 3. Since it passes through the point (1, 2, 3), therefore its equations are

$$\frac{x-1}{1}=\frac{y-2}{2}=\frac{z-3}{3}.$$

Ex. 6(b). *Show that the equations of the chord through the point (4, 5, 6) which is bisected by the diametral plane $3x+4y=1$ of the paraboloid $5x^2+6y^2=2z$ are*

$$\frac{x-4}{9}=\frac{y-5}{10}=\frac{z-6}{15}.$$

Solution. Proceed exactly as in Ex. 6(a).

Ex. 6(c). *Find the direction cosines of chords of the paraboloid $2x^2+4y^2=9z$ bisected by the plane $x+y=1$.*

Solution. Clearly the plane $x+y=1 \qquad ...(1)$

is a diametral plane for the paraboloid

$$2x^2+4y^2=9z. \qquad ..(2)$$

Let l, m, n be the d.c.'s of a system of parallel chords, then the equation of the corresponding diametral plane is

$$alx+bmy-cn=0$$

or $2.lx+4.my-\frac{1}{2}9n=0$ or $4lx+8my-9n=0. \qquad ...(3)$

Comparing (1) and (3), we have

$$\frac{4l}{1}=\frac{8m}{1}=\frac{9n}{1} \text{ or } \frac{l}{18}=\frac{m}{9}=\frac{n}{8}.$$

∴ The d.c.'s of the required chords are proportional to 18, 9, 8.

Ex. 7(a). *Prove that the diametral planes $x+3y=3$, $2x-y=1$ are conjugate diametral planes for the paraboloid $2x^2+3y^2=4z$.*

Solution. The equation of the paraboloid is

$$2x^2+3y^2=4z. \qquad ...(1)$$

The equations of the diametral planes are given as

$$x+3y=3 \quad ...(2), \quad \text{and} \quad 2x-y=1. \qquad ...(3)$$

We know [See § 3, part (viii)] that two diametral planes are called conjugate if each biscets the chords parallel to the other.

Let the plane (3) bisect chords parallel to a line whose d.c.'s are l, m, n. Then the plane (3) should be the same as the diametral plane

$$alx+bmy-cn=0 \quad i.e. \quad 2lx+3my-2n=0. \qquad ...(4)$$

Comparing (3) and (4), we get

$$\frac{2l}{2}=\frac{3m}{-1}=\frac{2n}{1} \quad \text{or} \quad \frac{l}{6}=\frac{m}{-2}=\frac{n}{3}.$$

$\therefore$ l, m, n are proportional to 6, -2, 3.

Hence the plane (2) should be parallel to the line whose d.c.'s are proportional to 6, -2, 3.

$\therefore$ We should have $1.6+3.(-2)+0.3=0$ or $6-6=0$, which is true.

Hence the given diametral planes (2) and (3) are conjugate.

Ex. 7(b). *Show that the diametral planes* $3x-4y=7$ *and* $2x+3y=4$ *are conjugate diametral planes for the parboloid*

$$x^2+2y^2=4z.$$

Solution. Proceed exactly as in Ex. 7(a) or apply the result of § 3, part (viii).

Ex. 8. *Find the locus of the perpendicular from* (α, β, γ) *to its polar plane with respect to the paraboloid* $x^2/a^2+y^2/b^2=2z$.

Solution. The equation of the polar plane of (α, β, γ) w.r.t. the paraboloid $x^2/a^2+y^2/b^2=2z$ is

$$\alpha x/a^2+\beta y/b^2=z+\gamma. \qquad ...(1)$$

Let the equations of any line through the point (α, β, γ) be

$$\frac{x-\alpha}{l}=\frac{y-\beta}{m}=\frac{z-\gamma}{n}. \qquad ...(2)$$

If the line (2) be perpendicular to the polar plane (1), then the line (2) is parallel to the normal of the plane (1) and so we have

$$\frac{\alpha/a^2}{l}=\frac{\beta/b^2}{m}=\frac{-1}{n}=\lambda, \text{ (say)}.$$

$$\therefore \quad \frac{\alpha}{l}=\lambda a^2, \ \frac{\beta}{m}=\lambda b^2, \ \lambda=-\frac{1}{n}$$

i.e. $$\frac{\alpha}{l}-\frac{\beta}{m}=\lambda(a^2-b^2); \text{ and } \lambda=-\frac{1}{n}$$

i.e. $$\frac{\alpha}{l}-\frac{\beta}{m}=-\frac{a^2-b^2}{n}. \quad \text{...(3)}$$

Eliminating l, m, n between (2) and (3), the required locus of the perpendicular (2) is given by

$$\frac{\alpha}{x-\alpha}-\frac{\beta}{y-\beta}+\frac{a^2-b^2}{z-\gamma}=0.$$

Ex. 9. *Two perpendicular tangent planes to the paraboloid $x^2/a^2+y^2/b^2=2z$ intersect in a line lying on the plane $x=0$. Show that the line touches the parabola*

$$y^2=(a+b)(2z+a),\ x=0.$$

Solution. The equation of the paraboloid is

$$x^2/a+y^2/b=2z. \quad \text{.. (1)}$$

Let the two tangent planes intersect in a line lying on the plane $x=0$ given by

$$my+nz=p,\ x=0. \quad \text{.. (2)}$$

The equation of any plane through the line (2) is given by

$$my+nz-p+\lambda x=0 \text{ or } \lambda x+my+nz=p. \quad \text{...(3)}$$

The plane (3) must be tangent plane to the parabo oid (1) and hence we have [By equation (4) of § 3 (iii)]

$$a\lambda^2+bm^2+2np=0. \quad \text{...(4)}$$

This being a quadratic equation in λ gives two values of λ, say, λ_1 and λ_2.

$$\therefore \quad \lambda_1\lambda_2=(bm^2+2np)/a.$$

Hence the equation (3) gives two tangent planes for two values of λ. The d.r.'s of the normals of these two tangent planes are λ_1, m, n and λ_2, m, n. If these tangent planes be perpendicular, then

$$\lambda_1\lambda_2+m.m+n.n=0$$

or $$(bm^2+2np)/a+m^2+n^2=0$$

or $$(a+b)m^2+an^2+2np=0. \quad \text{...(5)}$$

Now in order to prove that the line (2) touches a parabola, we should show that the envelope of (2) under condition (5) is the parabola in question.

Putting the value of p from (2) in (5), the equations of the line (2) are

$$(a+b)m^2+an^2+2n(my+nz)=0,\ x=0$$

or $$(a+b)(m/n)^2+2y(m/n)+(a+2z)=0,\ x=0. \quad \text{...(6)}$$

The first of these two equations being a quadratic in the parameter m/n, the equation of the envelope is given by the discriminant of (6) equated to zero

i.e. by $$4y^2-4.(a+b)(a+2z)=0,\ x=0$$

i.e. by $$y^2=(a+b)(a+2z),\ x=0.$$ **Proved.**

Ex. 10. *Tangent planes at two points P and Q of a paraboloid meet on the line CD. Prove that the plane through CD and middle of PQ is parallel to the axis of the paraboloid.*

Solution. Let the equation of the paraboloid be

$$ax^2+by^2=2z. \qquad ...(1)$$

Let the co-ordinates of the points P and Q on (1) be (x_1, y_1, z_1) and (x_2, y_2, z_2) respectively, so that, we have

$$ax_1^2+by_1^2-2z_1=0,\ ax_2^2+by_2^2-2z_2=0. \qquad ...(2)$$

The equations of the tangent planes at the points P and Q are

$$ax_1x+by_1y-(z+z_1)=0 \qquad (3)$$

$$ax_2x+by_2y-(z+z_2)=0. \qquad (4)$$

The tangent planes (3) and (4) intersect in the line CD. The equation of any plane through the line CD *i.e.* through the line of intersection of the planes (3) and (4) is given by

$$\{ax_1x+by_1y-(z+z_1)\}+\lambda\{ax_2x+by_2y-(z+z_2)\}=0. \qquad ...(5)$$

If (5) passes through the middle point of PQ *i.e.* through the point $\left(\frac{x_1+x_2}{2}, \frac{y_1+y_2}{2}, \frac{z_1+z_2}{2}\right)$ we have

$$[\tfrac{1}{2}ax_1(x_1+x_2)+\tfrac{1}{2}by_1(y_1+y_2)-\tfrac{1}{2}(z_1+z_2)-z_1]$$
$$+\lambda[\tfrac{1}{2}ax_2(x_1+x_2)+by_2(y_1+y_2)-\tfrac{1}{2}(z_1+z_2)-z_2]=0$$

or $$[(ax_1^2+by_1^2-2z_1)+ax_1x_2+by_1y_2-(z_1+z_2)]$$
$$+\lambda[(ax_2^2+by_2^2-2z_2)+ax_1x_2+by_1y_2-(z_1+z_2)]=0.$$

Using the relations (2), the above equation in λ becomes

$$[ax_1x_2+by_1y_2-(z_1+z_2)]+\lambda[ax_1x_2+by_1y_2-(z_1+z_2)]=0$$

giving, $$\lambda=-1.$$

Putting the value of λ in (5), we get

$$ax_1x+by_1y-(z+z_1)-ax_2x-by_2y+(z+z_2)=0$$

or $$a(x_1-x_2)x+b(y_1-y_2)y-(z_1-z_2)=0.$$

The plane given by this equation is clearly parallel to the z-axis *i.e.* the axis of the paraboloid (1).

Ex. 11. *Show that the locus of the tangents from a point (α, β, γ) to the paraboloid $ax^2+by^2=2z$ is given by*

$$(ax^2+by^2-2z)\,(a\alpha^2+b\beta^2-2\gamma)=(a\alpha x+b\beta y-z-\gamma)^2$$

and hence deduce the locus of the points from which three mutually perpendicular tangents can be drawn to the paraboloid.

Solution. The equation of the given paraboloid is

$$S \equiv ax^2+by^2-2z=0. \qquad \ldots(1)$$

Clearly we are required to find the equation of the enveloping cone with its vertex at (α, β, γ) and so the locus of the tangents *i.e.* the enveloping cone is given by

$$SS_1=T^2$$

i.e. $\quad (ax^2+by^2-2z)\,(a\alpha^2+b\beta^2-2\gamma)=(a\alpha x+b\beta y-z-\gamma)^2. \qquad \ldots(2)$

Now if the cone (2) has three mutually perpendicular generators, then we have

the coefficient of x^2 + the coeffi. of y^2 + the coeffi. of $z^2=0$

or $\quad \{a\,(a\alpha^2+b\beta^2-2\gamma)-a^2\alpha^2\}+\{b\,(a\alpha^2+b\beta^2-2\gamma)-b^2\beta^2\}-1=0$

or $\quad ab\beta^2-2a\gamma+ab\alpha^2-2b\gamma-1=0$

or $\quad ab(\alpha^2+\beta^2)-2\,(a+b)\,\gamma-1=0.$

$\therefore$ The required locus of (α, β, γ) is

$$ab\,(x^2+y^2)-2\,(a+b)\,z-1=0.$$

§ 4. The normal.

(A) *To find the equations of the normal at any point (α, β, γ) of the paraboloid $ax^2+by^2=2cz$.*

The equation of the paraboloid is

$$ax^2+by^2=2cz. \qquad \ldots(1)$$

The equation of the tangent plane at any point (α, β, γ) of the paraboloid (1) is

$$a\alpha x+b\beta y-cz=c\gamma. \qquad \ldots(2)$$

The direction ratios of the normal to the plane (2) are

$$a\alpha,\ b\beta,\ -c.$$

Now the normal at (α, β, γ) to the paraboloid (1) is a line perpendicular to the tangent plane (2) and passing through the point (α, β, γ). Hence its equations are given by

$$\frac{x-\alpha}{a\alpha}=\frac{y-\beta}{b\beta}=\frac{z-\gamma}{-c} \qquad \ldots(3)$$

(B) *To prove that five normals can be drawn from a given point (x', y', z') to a paraboloid.*

Let the equation of the paraboloid be

$$ax^2+by^2=2cz. \qquad \ldots(1)$$

Let (α, β, γ) be a point on (1) so that

$$a\alpha^2+b\beta^2=2c\gamma. \qquad ...(2)$$

The equations of the normal at (α, β, γ) to (1) are

$$\frac{x-\alpha}{a\alpha}=\frac{y-\beta}{b\beta}=\frac{z-\gamma}{-c}. \qquad ...(3)$$

If the normal (3) passes through the given point (x', y', z'), we get

$$\frac{x'-\alpha}{a\alpha}=\frac{y'-\beta}{b\beta}=\frac{z'-\gamma}{-c}=\lambda \text{ (say)}$$

or $$x'=\alpha+a\alpha\lambda,\ y'=\beta+b\beta\lambda,\ z'=\gamma-c\lambda$$

or $$\alpha=x'/(1+a\lambda),\ \beta=y'/(1+b\lambda),\ \gamma=z'+c\lambda.$$

Putting these values of α, β, γ in (2), we get

$$\frac{ax'^2}{(1+a\lambda)^2}+\frac{by'^2}{(1+b\lambda)^2}=2c\,(z'+c\lambda). \qquad ...(4)$$

The equation (4) is clearly of fifth degree in λ and hence gives five values of λ. Further, corresponding to these five values of λ, we get five points (α, β, γ) on the paraboloid (1), and the five normals at these five points all pass through the point (x', y', z').

Hence we conclude that from a given point five normals can be drawn to a paraboloid.

§ 5. Cubic curve through the feet of the normals.

To prove that the five feet of normals from any point (x', y', z') *to the paraboloid lie on a cubic curve.*

Let the equation of the paraboloid be

$$ax^2+by^2=2cz \qquad ...(1)$$

Let (α, β, γ) be a point on (1) so that the normal at (α, β, γ) passes through (x', y', z') and hence proceeding as in § 4 (B) above, we have

$$\alpha=\frac{x'}{1+a\lambda},\ \beta=\frac{y'}{1+b\lambda},\ \gamma=z'+c\lambda.$$

Consider a curve whose parametric equations (in the parameter λ) are given by

$$x=\frac{x'}{1+a\lambda},\ y=\frac{y'}{1+b\lambda},\ z=z'+c\lambda. \qquad (2)$$

The five values of the parameter λ are given by the equation (4) of § 4 (B) above and corresponding to each value of λ, we have a point on the curve (2).

Now consider a plane $Ax+By+Cz+D=0$. The points of intersection of this plane with the curve (2) are given by

$$\frac{Ax'}{1+a\lambda}+\frac{By'}{1+b\lambda}+C\,(z'+c\lambda)+D=0$$

which is clearly a cubic in λ and hence gives three values of λ. This shows that the curve (2) meets the plane in three points and hence the curve given by (2) is the required cubic curve.

SOLVED EXAMPLES (B)

Ex. 1. *Show that the feet of the normals from the point* (x', y', z') *to the paraboloid* $x^2+y^2=2az$ *lie on the sphere*

$$x^2+y^2+z^2-z\,(a+z')-\tfrac{1}{2}\,(y/y')\,(x'^2+y'^2)=0.$$

Solution. The equation of the paraboloid is

$$x^2+y^2=2az. \qquad \text{...(1)}$$

Let (α, β, γ) be a point on (1) so that

$$\alpha^2+\beta^2=2a\gamma. \qquad \text{...(2)}$$

The equations of the normal at (α, β, γ) to (1) are

$$\frac{x-\alpha}{\alpha}=\frac{y-\beta}{\beta}=\frac{z-\gamma}{-a}. \qquad \text{...(3)}$$

If the normal (3) passes through (x', y', z'), we get

$$\frac{x'-\alpha}{\alpha}=\frac{y'-\beta}{\beta}=\frac{z'-\gamma}{-a}=\lambda \text{ (say)}.$$

From these, we get

$$\alpha=x'/(1+\lambda),\ \beta=y'/(1+\lambda),\ \gamma=z'+a\lambda. \qquad \text{...(4)}$$

Therefore the equations of the cubic curve on which lie the feet of the normals from (x', y', z') are given by

$$x=\frac{x'}{1+\lambda},\ y=\frac{y'}{1+\lambda},\ z=z'+a\lambda, \qquad \text{...(5)}$$

where λ is the parameter. The values of the parameter λ giving the feet of the normals are obtained by putting the values of α, β, γ from (4) in (2) and so are given by

$$\frac{x'^2}{(1+\lambda)^2}+\frac{y'^2}{(1+\lambda)^2}=2a\,(z'+a\lambda)$$

or

$$(x'^2+y'^2)-2a\,(z'+a\lambda)\,(1+\lambda)^2=0. \qquad \text{...(6)}$$

The feet of the normals will lie on the given sphere if the values of x, y, z from (5) satisfy the equation of the given sphere

i.e. if

$$\frac{x'^2}{(1+\lambda)^2}+\frac{y'^2}{(1+\lambda)^2}+(z'+a\lambda)^2-(z'+a\lambda)\,(a+z')$$
$$-\frac{y'}{2\,(1+\lambda)\,y'}\,(x'^2+y'^2)=0$$

i.e. if

$$\frac{x'^2+y'^2}{2(1+\lambda)^2}\,\{2-(1+\lambda)\}+(z'+a\lambda)\,\{(z'+a\lambda)-(a+z')\}=0$$

i.e. if $\dfrac{(1-\lambda)}{2(1+\lambda)^2}[(x'^2+y'^2)-2a(z'+a\lambda)(1+\lambda)^2]=0$

which is true in view of (6). Hence proved.

Ex. 2. *Prove that in general three normals can be drawn from a given point to the paraboloid of revolution $x^2+y^2=2az$, but if the point lies on the surface $27a(x^2+y^2)+8(a-z)^3=0$ two of them coincide.*

Solution. Let the given point be (x', y', z'). Proceeding exactly as in Ex. 1 upto the equation (6). we have

$$F(\lambda)\equiv(x'^2+y'^2)-2a(z'+a\lambda)(1+\lambda)^2=0. \qquad ...(6)$$

This being a cubic equation in λ gives three values of λ, so that corresponding to each value of λ we get a point (α, β, γ) on the paraboloid (1) the normal at which passes through the point (x', y', z').

Hence it follows that in general three normals can be drawn from a given point (x', y', z') to the paraboloid (1).

Now it is required to find the locus of the point (x', y', z') under the condition that two of the normals coincide (*i.e.* two values of λ are equal).

We know that the condition for the equation $F(\lambda)=0$ to have two equal roots is found by eliminating λ between $F(\lambda)=0$ and $F'(\lambda)=0$.

Differentiating (6) w.r.t. λ, we get

$$F'(\lambda)\equiv-2a\{a(1+\lambda)^2+(z'+a\lambda).2(1+\lambda)\}=0$$

or $\quad (1+\lambda)\{a(1+\lambda)+2(z'+a\lambda)\}=0$

or $\quad 3a\lambda+(a+2z')=0$, since $\lambda\neq-1$

or $\quad \lambda=-(a+2z')/(3a)$.

Putting this value of λ in (6), we get

$$(x'^2+y'^2)-2a\{z'-\tfrac{1}{3}(a+2z')\}\{1-(2z'+a)/(3a)\}^2=0$$

or $\quad 27a(x'^2+y'^2)+8(a-z')^3=0.$

$\therefore$ The required locus of (x', y', z') is given by

$$27a(x^2+y^2)+8(a-z)^3=0.$$

Ex. 3. *Show that the normals from (x', y', z') to the paraboloid $ax^2+by^2=2cz$ lie on the cone*

$$\frac{x'}{x-x'}-\frac{y'}{y-y'}+c\frac{(1/a-1/b)}{z-z'}=0.$$

Or

Find the equation of the cone through the five feet of the normals drawn from (x', y', z') to the paraboloid $ax^2+by^2=2cz$.

Solution. The equation of the paraboloid is

$$ax^2+by^2=2cz. \quad ..(1)$$

If (α, β, γ) be a point on (1), then the equations of the normal at (α, β, γ) are

$$\frac{x-\alpha}{a\alpha}=\frac{y-\beta}{b\beta}=\frac{z-\gamma}{-c}.$$

If it passes through (x', y', z'), we get

$$\frac{x'-\alpha}{a\alpha}=\frac{y'-\beta}{b\beta}=\frac{z'-\gamma}{-c}=\lambda \text{ (say)}.$$

$$\therefore \quad \alpha=x'/(1+a\lambda),\ \beta=y'/(1+b\lambda),\ \gamma=z'+c\lambda. \quad ...(2)$$

There are five points like (α, β, γ) the normals at which pass through (α, β, γ). [See § 4 (B)]

Now the equations of any line through (x', y', z') are

$$\frac{x-x'}{l}=\frac{y-y'}{m}=\frac{z-z'}{n}. \quad ...(3)$$

If (3) is a normal to the paraboloid (1) at the point (α, β, γ) then we clearly have $l=a\alpha,\ m=b\beta,\ n=-c$

or $$l=\frac{ax'}{1+a\lambda},\ m=\frac{by'}{1+b\lambda},\ n=-c \text{ [using (2)]}$$

or $$\frac{ax'}{l}=1+a\lambda,\ \frac{by'}{m}=1+b\lambda,\ \frac{c}{n}=-1.$$

To eliminate λ, multiplying these relations by $b, -a$ and $(b-a)$ respectively and adding, we have

$$\frac{abx'}{l}-\frac{aby'}{m}+\frac{c\,(b-a)}{n}=b\,(1+a\lambda)-a\,(1+b\lambda)-(b-a)$$

or $$\frac{abx'}{l}-\frac{aby'}{m}+\frac{c\,(b-a)}{n}=0.$$

Dividing by ab, we get

$$\frac{x'}{l}-\frac{y'}{m}+\frac{c\,(1/a-1/b)}{n}=0. \quad ...(4)$$

Eliminating l, m, n between (3) and (4), we get the locus of the normal (3). Hence the normal (3) lies on the cone

$$\frac{x'}{x-x'}-\frac{y'}{y-y'}+\frac{c.\,(1/a-1/b)}{z-z'}=0. \quad ..(5)$$

Ex. 4. *Prove that the normals from (x', y', z') to the paraboloid $x^2/a^2+y^2/b^2=2z$ lie on the cone*

$$\frac{x'}{x-x'}-\frac{y'}{y-y'}+\frac{a^2-b^2}{z-z'}=0.$$

Solution. Relplacing a by $1/a^2$, b by $1/b^2$ and c by 1 in Ex. 3 above, the required cone is obtained.

Ex. 5. *Show that the cubic curve through the five feet of the normals drawn to a paraboloid from any point* (x', y', z') *lies on the cone through the five concurrent normals.*

Solution. The equation of the cone through the five feet of normals is given by [as found in Ex. 3 above]

$$\frac{x'}{x-x'}-\frac{y'}{y-y'}+c\,\frac{(1/a-1/b)}{z-z'}=0. \quad ...(1)$$

Also the equations of the cubic curve through the five feet of the normals are given by

$$x=\frac{x'}{1+a\lambda},\ y=\frac{y'}{1+b\lambda},\ z=z'+c\lambda.$$

[See equation (2), § 5].

Putting these values of x, y, z in (1), we see that the equation (1) is satisfied. Hence proved.

3

Generating Lines

§ 1. Introduction. We know that the cones and cylinders are the surfaces which are generated by a moving straight line. Similarly the *hyperboloid of one sheet* and *hyperbolic paraboloid* can be generated by a moving straight line. Such surfaces are called **ruled surfaces.** "*A ruled surface is defined as a surface which is generated by the motion of one parameter family of straight lines and the straight line itself is called its generating line, generator or ruling.*"

§ 2 (A). The generating lines of a hyperboloid of one sheet.

The equation of the hyperboloid of one sheet is

$$x^2/a^2+y^2/b^2-z^2/c^2=1. \qquad \text{...(1)}$$

The equation (1) may be rewritten as

$$x^2/a^2-z^2/c^2=1-y^2/b^2$$

or $$\left(\frac{x}{a}-\frac{z}{c}\right)\left(\frac{x}{a}+\frac{z}{c}\right)=\left(1-\frac{y}{b}\right)\left(1+\frac{y}{b}\right) \qquad \text{...(2)}$$

From equation (2) it follows that the hyperboloid of one sheet is the locus of the line whose equations are given by

$$\frac{x}{a}-\frac{z}{c}=\lambda\left(1-\frac{y}{b}\right), \frac{x}{a}+\frac{z}{c}=\frac{1}{\lambda}\left(1+\frac{y}{b}\right) \qquad \text{...(3)}$$

where λ is a variable parameter. The equations given by (3) are the equations of one parameter (λ parameter) family of straight lines and hence the hyperboloid of one sheet is a ruled surface.

In a similar manner one parameter (μ parameter) family of straight lines given by the equations

$$\frac{x}{a}-\frac{z}{c}=\mu\left(1+\frac{y}{b}\right), \frac{x}{a}+\frac{z}{c}=\frac{1}{\mu}\left(1-\frac{y}{b}\right) \qquad \text{...(4)}$$

also generate the hyperboloid of one sheet given by (1). By giving different values to λ and μ it follows clearly that the equations given by (3) and (4) can never be made identical. Hence the systems of straight lines given by equations (3) and (4) are two distinct systems of generating lines. The system given by (3) is called the λ-system and that given by (4) is called the μ-system.

§ 2 (B). Properties of the generating lines of hyperboloid of one sheet.

(I) *One generator each of λ-and μ-systems passes through every point of the hyperboloid.*

The equation of hyperboloid of one sheet is

$$x^2/a^2+y^2/b^2-z^2/c^2=1. \qquad \text{...(1)}$$

Let the co-ordinates of any point on (1) be (α, β, γ), so that we have

$$\alpha^2/a^2+\beta^2/b^2-\gamma^2/c^2=1. \qquad \text{...(2)}$$

A generator of the λ-system is given by

$$\frac{x}{a}-\frac{z}{c}=\lambda\left(1-\frac{y}{b}\right), \frac{x}{a}+\frac{z}{c}=\frac{1}{\lambda}\left(1+\frac{y}{b}\right) \qquad \text{...(3)}$$

We observe clearly that the generator (3) will pass through the point (α, β, γ) if and only if the value of λ is

$$\left(\frac{\alpha}{a}-\frac{\gamma}{c}\right)\Big/\left(1-\frac{\beta}{b}\right) \text{ or } \left(1+\frac{\beta}{b}\right)\Big/\left(\frac{\alpha}{a}+\frac{\gamma}{c}\right) \qquad \text{...(4)}$$

If we put the values of λ given by (4) and the co-ordinates of the point (α, β, γ) in the equations (3), then one equation is obviously satisfied and the other equation gives

$$\left(\frac{\alpha}{a}-\frac{\gamma}{c}\right)\left(\frac{\alpha}{a}+\frac{\gamma}{c}\right)=\left(1-\frac{\beta}{b}\right)\left(1+\frac{\beta}{b}\right)$$

or $$\frac{\alpha^2}{a^2}-\frac{\gamma^2}{c^2}=1-\frac{\beta^2}{b^2} \text{ or } \frac{\alpha^2}{a^2}+\frac{\beta^2}{b^2}-\frac{\gamma^2}{c^2}=1,$$

which is true by virtue of (2).

Hence we conclude that if λ has either of the values given by (4), the corresponding line of the λ-system will pass through the point (α, β, γ).

Similarly we can show that if the value of μ is equal to

$$\left(\frac{\alpha}{a}-\frac{\gamma}{c}\right)\Big/\left(1+\frac{\beta}{b}\right) \text{ or } \left(1-\frac{\beta}{b}\right)\Big/\left(\frac{\alpha}{a}+\frac{\gamma}{c}\right)$$

then one member of the μ-system *i.e.*

$$\frac{x}{a}-\frac{z}{c}=\mu\left(1+\frac{y}{b}\right), \frac{x}{a}+\frac{z}{c}=\frac{1}{\mu}\left(1-\frac{y}{b}\right)$$

will pass through the point (α, β, γ).

(II) *No two generators of the same system intersect.*

Let λ_1 and λ_2 be two different values of λ. Corresponding to these values of λ, the equations of the two generators of the λ-system are given by

$$\left.\begin{aligned} x/a-z/c&=\lambda_1\,(1-y/b) \quad ...(1)\\ x/a+z/c&=(1/\lambda_1)\,(1+y/b) \quad ...(2)\end{aligned}\right\}$$

and

$$\left.\begin{aligned} x/a-z/c&=\lambda_2\,(1-y/b) \quad ...(3)\\ x/a+z/c&=(1/\lambda_2)\,(1+y/b) \quad ...(4)\end{aligned}\right\}.$$

Now subtracting equation (3) from equation (1), we get

$$(\lambda_1-\lambda_2)\,(1-y/b)=0 \Rightarrow 1-y/b=0, \text{ since } \lambda_1\neq\lambda_2$$
$$\Rightarrow y=b. \quad ...(5)$$

Again subtracting equation (4) from equation (2), we get

$$(1/\lambda_1-1/\lambda_2)\,(1+y/b)=0 \Rightarrow 1+y/b=0 \text{ since } \lambda_1\neq\lambda_2$$
$$\Rightarrow y=-b. \quad ...(6)$$

The values of y given by (5) and (6) are distinct and hence the four equations of the two generators are inconsistent, and therefore, it follows that the two generators of the same system do not intersect.

Note 1. In a similar manner the above statement can be proved for the generators of the μ-system.

Note 2. From the properties I and II we conclude that through each point of a hyperboloid of one sheet one and only one generator of each system passes.

(III) *Any generator of the λ-system intersects any generator of the μ-system.*

Or *Any two generators of the different systems intersect.*

The equations of any generator of the λ-system are

$$\frac{x}{a}-\frac{z}{c}=\lambda\left(1-\frac{y}{b}\right) \quad ...(1), \quad \frac{x}{a}+\frac{z}{c}=\frac{1}{\lambda}\left(1+\frac{y}{b}\right) \quad ...(2)$$

The equations of any generator of the μ-system are

$$\frac{x}{a}-\frac{z}{c}=\mu\left(1+\frac{y}{b}\right) \quad ...(3), \quad \frac{x}{a}+\frac{z}{c}=\frac{1}{\mu}\left(1-\frac{y}{b}\right). \quad ...(4)$$

Now we shall solve these equations.

From (2) and (4), we get

$$\frac{1}{\lambda}\left(1+\frac{y}{b}\right)=\frac{1}{\mu}\left(1-\frac{y}{b}\right) \text{ or } \frac{y}{b}=\frac{\lambda-\mu}{\lambda+\mu} \quad ...(5)$$

Putting this value of y/b in (2) and (3), we get

$$\frac{x}{a}+\frac{z}{c}=\frac{2}{\lambda+\mu} \quad \text{and} \quad \frac{x}{a}-\frac{z}{c}=\frac{2\lambda\mu}{\lambda+\mu}.$$

Solving these, $\dfrac{x}{a}=\dfrac{1+\lambda\mu}{\lambda+\mu}$, $\dfrac{z}{c}=\dfrac{1-\lambda\mu}{\lambda+\mu}$. ...(6)

Clearly the equation (1) is satisfied by these values of x, y, z given by equations (5) and (6). Hence any two generators of the different systems intersect and the point of intersection is

$$\left(a.\frac{1+\lambda\mu}{\lambda+\mu},\ b.\frac{\lambda-\mu}{\lambda+\mu},\ c.\frac{1-\lambda\mu}{\lambda+\mu}\right). \qquad ...(7)$$

Furthermore, for all values of λ and μ, the co-ordinates of the point given by (7) satisfy the equation of the hyperboloid of one sheet namely $x^2/a^2+y^2/b^2-z^2/c^2=1$, and hence the parametric equations of the hyperboloid of one sheet are given by

$$x=a.\frac{1+\lambda\mu}{\lambda+\mu},\ y=b.\frac{\lambda-\mu}{\lambda+\mu},\ z=c.\frac{1-\lambda\mu}{\lambda+\mu}. \qquad ...(8)$$

Corollary. *The tangent plane at a point of a hyperboloid of one sheet meets the hyperboloid in two generators through that point.*

For all values of k and k' the equations

$$\frac{x}{a}-\frac{z}{c}-\lambda\left(1-\frac{y}{b}\right)+k\left[\left(\frac{x}{a}+\frac{z}{c}\right)-\frac{1}{\lambda}\left(1+\frac{y}{b}\right)\right]=0,$$

and $$\left(\frac{x}{a}-\frac{z}{c}\right)-\mu\left(1+\frac{y}{b}\right)+k'\left[\left(\frac{x}{a}+\frac{z}{c}\right)-\frac{1}{\mu}\left(1-\frac{y}{b}\right)\right]=0$$

give two planes—one through a generator of the λ-system and the other through a generator of the μ-system.

These planes become identical for $k=k'=\lambda\mu$ and the equation of any of them in that case is

$$\left(\frac{x}{a}-\frac{z}{c}\right)-\lambda\left(1-\frac{y}{b}\right)+\lambda\mu\left[\left(\frac{x}{a}+\frac{z}{c}\right)-\frac{1}{\lambda}\left(1+\frac{y}{b}\right)\right]=0$$

or $$\frac{x}{a}(1+\lambda\mu)+\frac{y}{b}(\lambda-\mu)-\frac{z}{c}(1-\lambda\mu)=0$$

or $$\frac{x}{a}.\frac{1+\lambda\mu}{\lambda+\mu}+\frac{y}{b}.\frac{\lambda-\mu}{\lambda+\mu}-\frac{z}{c}.\frac{1-\lambda\mu}{\lambda+\mu}=0. \qquad ...(9)$$

Thus the plane given by the equation (9) contains one generator of the λ-system and one generator of the μ-system. This plane is also the tangent plnne to the hyperboloid of one sheet $x^2/a^2+y^2/b^2-z^2/c^2=1$ at the point of intersection

$$\left(a\frac{1+\lambda\mu}{\lambda+\mu},\ b\frac{\lambda-\mu}{\lambda+\mu},\ c\frac{1-\lambda\mu}{\lambda+\mu}\right)$$

of these two generators.

We have proved in property I that one generator each of λ-system and μ-system passes through every point of the hyperboloid. Hence in view of the above facts, we conclude that the tangent plane at a point of a hyperboloid of one sheet meets the hyperboloid in two generators through that point one belonging to each system.

§ 3. Perpendicular generators. *To find the locus of the point of intersection of two perpendicular generators of hyperboloid of one sheet.*

The equation of the hyperboloid is

$$x^2/a^2+y^2/b^2-z^2/c^2=1. \qquad \ldots(1)$$

The equations of any generator of the λ-system are

$$\frac{x}{a}-\frac{z}{c}=\lambda\left(1-\frac{y}{b}\right),\ \frac{x}{a}+\frac{z}{c}=\frac{1}{\lambda}\left(1+\frac{y}{b}\right)$$

or
$$\frac{x}{a}+\frac{\lambda}{b}y-\frac{z}{c}=\lambda,\ \frac{x}{a}-\frac{1}{\lambda b}y+\frac{z}{c}=\frac{1}{\lambda}$$

or
$$\frac{x}{a}+\frac{\lambda y}{b}-\frac{z}{c}=\lambda,\ \frac{\lambda x}{a}-\frac{1}{b}y+\frac{\lambda z}{c}=1.$$

Let l_1, m_1, n_1 be the d.c.'s of this generator, so that we have

$$\frac{l_1}{a}+\lambda\frac{m_1}{b}-\frac{n_1}{c}=0,\ \lambda\frac{l_1}{a}-\frac{m_1}{b}+\lambda\frac{n_1}{c}=0.$$

Solving, we get $\dfrac{l_1/a}{1-\lambda^2}=\dfrac{m_1/b}{2\lambda}=\dfrac{n_1/c}{1+\lambda^2}$ $\qquad \ldots(2)$

The equations of any generator of the μ-system are

$$\frac{x}{a}-\frac{z}{c}=\mu\left(1+\frac{y}{b}\right),\ \frac{x}{a}+\frac{z}{c}=\frac{1}{\mu}\left(1-\frac{y}{b}\right)$$

If l_2, m_2, n_2 be the d.c.'s of this generator, then proceeding as above, we get

$$\frac{l_2/a}{1-\mu^2}=\frac{m_2/b}{-2\mu}=\frac{n_2/c}{1+\mu^2} \qquad \ldots(3)$$

If the two generators given above are perpendicular, then we have

$$l_1l_2+m_1m_2+n_1n_2=0. \qquad \ldots(4)$$

Putting proportionate values from (2) and (3) in (4), we have

$$a^2(1-\lambda^2)(1-\mu^2)-4b^2\lambda\mu+c^2(1+\lambda^2)(1+\mu^2)=0$$

or
$$a^2(1+\lambda^2\mu^2-\lambda^2-\mu^2)-b^2(4\lambda\mu)+c^2(1+\lambda^2\mu^2+\lambda^2+\mu^2)=0$$

or
$$a^2\{(1+\lambda\mu)^2-(\lambda^2+\mu^2+2\lambda\mu)\}-b^2\{(\lambda+\mu)^2-(\lambda-\mu)^2\}$$
$$+c^2\{(1-\lambda\mu)^2+(\lambda^2+\mu^2+2\lambda\mu)\}=0$$

or
$$a^2(1+\lambda\mu)^2-a^2(\lambda+\mu)^2+b^2(\lambda-\mu)^2-b^2(\lambda+\mu)^2$$
$$+c^2(1-\lambda\mu)^2+c^2(\lambda+\mu)^2=0$$

or $$a^2(1+\lambda\mu)^2+b^2(\lambda-\mu)^2+c^2(1-\lambda\mu)^2=(a^2+b^2-c^2)(\lambda+\mu)^2$$

or $$a^2\left\{\frac{1+\lambda\mu}{\lambda+\mu}\right\}^2+b^2\left\{\frac{\lambda-\mu}{\lambda+\mu}\right\}^2+c^2\left\{\frac{1-\lambda\mu}{\lambda+\mu}\right\}^2=a^2+b^2-c^2.$$

Hence the locus of the point of intersection of two perpendicular generators *i.e.* of the point

$$\left(a.\frac{1+\lambda\mu}{\lambda+\mu},\ b.\frac{\lambda-\mu}{\lambda+\mu},\ c.\frac{1-\lambda\mu}{\lambda+\mu}\right)$$

[See result (7) of § 2 (B), property III]

is given by

$$x^2+y^2+z^2=a^2+b^2-c^2.$$

This is called the director sphere.

Hence the required locus is the curve of intersection of the hyperboloid and the director sphere.

§ 4. *To show that if three points of a straight line lie on a conicoid then the straight line lies wholly on the conicoid.*

Let the equations of a straight line be

$$\frac{x-\alpha}{l}=\frac{y-\beta}{m}=\frac{z-\gamma}{n}=r \text{ (say)}. \qquad \text{...(1)}$$

Let the equation of a conicoid of second degree be

$$F(x, y, z)=0. \qquad \text{...(2)}$$

The co-ordinates of any point on the line (1) are $(lr+\alpha, mr+\beta, nr+\gamma)$. If this point lies on the conicoid (2), then we shall get a quadratic equation in r and let it be of the form given by

$$Ar^2+Br+C=0. \qquad \text{...(3)}$$

Now if the three points of the line (1) lie on the conicoid (2), then the equation (3) is satisfied for three distinct values of r and hence the relation (3) should be an identity, and therefore

$$A=B=C=0.$$

But then the equations (3) is satisfied for all values of r, showing that every point of the line (1) lies on the conicoid (2) *i.e.* the straight line (1) lies wholly on the conicoid.

§ 5. *To find the conditions that the straight line*

$$\frac{x-\alpha}{l}=\frac{y-\beta}{m}=\frac{z-\gamma}{n}$$

is a generator of the conicoid $ax^2+by^2+cz^2=1$.

The equations of the given conicoid and the line are

$$ax^2+by^2+cz^2=1, \qquad \text{...(1)}$$

and $$\frac{x-\alpha}{l}=\frac{y-\beta}{m}=\frac{z-\gamma}{n}=r \text{ (say)}, \qquad \text{...(2)}$$

The co-ordinates of any point on the line (2) are $(lr+\alpha, mr+\beta, nr+\gamma)$. If this point lies on the conicoid (1), then we have

$$a(lr+\alpha)^2+b(mr+\beta)^2+c(nr+\gamma)^2=1$$

or $$(al^2+bm^2+cn^2)r^2+2(al\alpha+bm\beta+cn\gamma)r$$
$$+(a\alpha^2+b\beta^2+c\gamma^2-1)=0 \quad ...(3)$$

The line (2) will be a generator of the conicoid (1), if this line lies wholly on (1) and for this the equation (3) should be an identity in r, the conditions for which are given by

$$a\alpha^2+b\beta^2+c\gamma^2=1, \quad ...(4)$$

$$al\alpha+bm\beta+cn\gamma=0, \quad ...(5)$$

and $$al^2+bm^2+cn^2=0. \quad ...(6)$$

These conditions show the following facts :

The condition (4) shows that the point (α, β, γ) on the line should also lie on the conicoid (1).

The condition (5) states that the generating line with d.c.'s l, m, n lies on the plane $a\alpha x+b\beta y+c\gamma z=1$ which is the equation of the tangent plane at the point (α, β, γ) on the conicoid (1).

The condition (6) shows that the lines parallel to the generating lines having their d.c.'s as l, m, n and passing through the centre (0, 0, 0) of the conicoid (1) *i.e.* the lines whose equations are $x/l=y/m=z/n$ generate the cone

$$ax^2+by^2+cz^2=0. \quad ...(7)$$

The cone given by the equation (7) is called the *asymptotic cone.*

Note. The equation (6) is of second degree in l, m, n and hence it follows from equations (4), (5) and (6) that through any point (α, β, γ) of a central conicoid, we can draw two straight lines which lie wholly on the conicoid. The direction ratios of these generating lines are given by the equations (5) and (6).

SOLVED EXAMPLES (A)

Ex. 1. (a). *Find the equations of the generators of the hyperboloid* $x^2/a^2+y^2/b^2-z^2/c^2=1$ *which pass through the point* $(a \cos \alpha, b \sin \alpha, 0)$.

Solution. The equation of the hyperboloid is

$$x^2/a^2+y^2/b^2-z^2/c^2=1. \quad ...(1)$$

Let l, m, n be the direction cosines of the generator. Then the equations of the generator through the point $(a \cos \alpha, b \sin \alpha, 0)$ are

$$\frac{x-a\cos\alpha}{l}=\frac{y-b\sin\alpha}{m}=\frac{z-0}{n}=r \text{ (say)}. \quad ...(2)$$

Any point on (2) is $(lr+a\cos\alpha, mr+b\sin\alpha, nr)$. If it lies on the hyperboloid (1), we have

$$\frac{(lr+a\cos\alpha)^2}{a^2}+\frac{(mr+b\sin\alpha)^2}{b^2}-\frac{n^2r^2}{c^2}=1$$

or $$r^2\left[\frac{l^2}{a^2}+\frac{m^2}{b^2}-\frac{n^2}{c^2}\right]+2\left(\frac{l\cos\alpha}{a}+\frac{m\sin\alpha}{b}\right)r=0. \quad ...(3)$$

If the line (2) is a generator, it will lie wholly on the hyperboloid (1) and for this the relation (3) will be satisfied for all values of r *i.e.* (3) will be an identity in r, the conditions for which are

$$l^2/a^2+m^2/b^2-n^2/c^2=0 \quad ...(4)$$

and $$l\cos\alpha/a+m\sin\alpha/b=0$$

or $$\frac{l}{a\sin\alpha}=\frac{m}{-b\cos\alpha}=k \text{ (say)}. \quad ..(5)$$

Putting the values of l and m from (5) in (4), we get

$$k^2(\sin^2\alpha+\cos^2\alpha)-n^2/c^2=0 \text{ or } n=\pm ck. \quad ...(6)$$

From (5) and (6), we get

$$\frac{l}{a\sin\alpha}=\frac{m}{-b\cos\alpha}=\frac{n}{\pm c}=k.$$

Puting these values of l, m, n in (2), the required equations of the generators are

$$\frac{x-a\cos\alpha}{a\sin\alpha}=\frac{y-b\sin\alpha}{-b\cos\alpha}=\frac{z}{\pm c}.$$

Ex. 1(b). *Find the equations to the generators of the hyperboloid $x^2/a^2+y^2/b^2-z^2/c^2=1$, through any point on the principal elliptic section $x^2/a^2+y^2/b^2-z^2/c^2=1$, $z=0$ by the plane $z=0$.*

Solution. Any point on the principal elliptic section of the hyperboloid is $(a\cos\alpha, b\sin\alpha, 0)$. Now this question is the same as Ex. 1(a) above.

Ex. 2. *Find the equations to the generating lines of the hyperboloid $x^2/4+y^2/9-z^2/16=1$ which pass through the points* $(2, 3, -4)$ *and* $(2, -1, 4/3)$.

Solution. The equation of the hyperboloid is

$$x^2/4+y^2/9-z^2/16=1. \quad ...(1)$$

Let l, m, n be the d.c.'s of the generator. Hence the equations of the generator through the point $(2, 3, -4)$ are given by

$$\frac{x-2}{l}=\frac{y-3}{m}=\frac{z+4}{n}=r \text{ (say).} \qquad ...(2)$$

Any point on (2) is $(lr+2, \; mr+3, \; nr-4)$. If it lies on (1), we get

$$\frac{1}{4}(lr+2)^2+\frac{1}{9}(mr+3)^2-\frac{1}{16}(nr-4)^2=1$$

or $$r^2\left(\frac{l^2}{4}+\frac{m^2}{9}-\frac{n^2}{16}\right)+2\left(\frac{l}{2}+\frac{m}{3}+\frac{n}{4}\right)=0. \qquad ...(3)$$

If the line (2) is a generator then (3) is an identity in r, the conditions for which are

$$\frac{l^2}{4}+\frac{m^2}{9}-\frac{n^2}{16}=0 \qquad ...(4)$$

and $$\frac{l}{2}+\frac{m}{3}+\frac{n}{4}=0. \qquad ...(5)$$

Eliminating n between (4) and (5), we get

$$\frac{l^2}{4}+\frac{m^2}{9}-\left(\frac{l}{2}+\frac{m}{3}\right)^2=0 \quad \text{or} \quad lm=0.$$

Hence either $l=0$ or $m=0$.

If $l=0$, then from (5)

$$m/3+n/4=0 \quad \text{or} \quad m/3=n/-4.$$

Hence the d.c.'s of one generator are given by

$$l/0=m/3=n/-4. \qquad ...(6)$$

If $m=0$, then from (5) $\frac{l}{2}+\frac{n}{4}=0$ or $\frac{l}{1}=\frac{n}{-2}$.

Hence the d.c.'s of the other generator are given by

$$l/1=m/0=n/-2. \qquad ...(7)$$

Thus the equations of the two generators through the point $(2, 3, -4)$ are obtained by putting the values of l, m, n from (6) and (7) in (2) and are given by

$$\frac{x-2}{0}=\frac{y-3}{3}=\frac{z+4}{-4} \text{ and } \frac{x-2}{1}=\frac{y-3}{0}=\frac{z+4}{-2}.$$

Proceeding similarly as above the equations of the two generators through the point $(2, -1, 4/3)$ are given by

$$\frac{x-2}{3}=\frac{y+1}{6}=\frac{z-\frac{4}{3}}{10} \text{ and } \frac{x-2}{0}=\frac{y+1}{3}=\frac{z-\frac{4}{3}}{-4}.$$

Ex. 3. *Find the equations of the generating lines of the hyperboloid $yz+2zx+3xy+6=0$ which pass through the point $(-1, 0, 3)$.*

Solution. Proceeding exactly as in Ex. 2 above, the two pairs of values of l, m, n are given by

$$\frac{l}{0}=\frac{m}{1}=\frac{n}{0}, \text{ and } \frac{l}{1}=\frac{m}{-1}=\frac{n}{3}.$$

Hence the equations of the required generators are

$$x+1=0, z-3=0 \text{ and } \frac{x+1}{1}=\frac{y}{-1}=\frac{z-3}{3}.$$

Ex. 4. *CP, CQ are any two conjugate semi-diameters of the ellipse $x^2/a^2+y^2/b^2=1$, $z=c$. CP′, CQ′ are the conjugate semi-diameters of the ellipse $x^2/a^2+y^2/b^2=1$, $z=-c$, drawn in the same directions as CP and CQ. Prove that the hyperboloid $\frac{2x^2}{a^2}+\frac{2y^2}{b^2}-\frac{z^2}{c^2}=1$ is generated by either PQ′ or P′Q.*

Solution. Since CP and CQ are the conjugate semi-diameters of the ellipse $x^2/a^2+y^2/b^2=1$, $z=c$, so that the co-ordinates of the extremities P and Q are

$P\equiv(a \cos \alpha, b \sin \alpha, c)$ and $Q\equiv(-a \sin \alpha, b \cos \alpha, c)$.

Similarly the co-ordinates of the extremities P' and Q' on $x^2/a^2+y^2/b^2=1$, $z=-c$ are

$P'\equiv(a \cos \alpha, b \sin \alpha, -c)$ and $Q'\equiv(-a \sin \alpha, b \cos \alpha, -c)$.

The equations to the line joining the points P and Q' i.e of the line PQ' are

$$\frac{x-a \cos \alpha}{-a \sin \alpha-a \cos \alpha}=\frac{y-b \sin \alpha}{b \cos \alpha-b \sin \alpha}=\frac{z-c}{-c-c}$$

or
$$\frac{(x/a)-\cos \alpha}{-(\sin \alpha+\cos \alpha)}=\frac{(y/b)-\sin \alpha}{\cos \alpha-\sin \alpha}=\frac{(z/c)-1}{-2}=r, \text{ (say)}.$$

From these, we have

$$x/a=\cos \alpha-r (\cos \alpha+\sin \alpha), \quad \ldots(1)$$

$$y/b=\sin \alpha-r (\cos \alpha-\sin \alpha), \quad \ldots(2)$$

and
$$z/c=1-2r. \quad \ldots(3)$$

Squaring (1) and (2) and adding, we have

$$x^2/a^2+y^2/b^2=1+r^2 (1+1)-2r (1)$$

[using $\cos^2 \alpha+\sin^2 \alpha=1$]

or
$$2 (x^2/a^2+y^2/b^2)=4r^2-4r+2$$
$$=(1-2r)^2+1$$
$$=z^2/c^2+1, \text{ using (3)}.$$

$\therefore$ the line PQ' generates the hyperboloid

$$2x^2/a^2+2y^2/b^2-z^2/c^2=1.$$

Similarly proceeding as above, we can prove that the line $P'Q$ also generates the given hyperboloid.

Ex. 5. *Show that the projections of the generators of a hyperboloid on co-ordinate planes are tangents to the sections of the hyperboloid by these respective planes.*

Solution. Let the equation of the hyperboloid be

$$x^2/a^2+y^2/b^2-z^2/c^2=1. \qquad ...(1)$$

The equations of a generator of the hyperboloid (1) are given by [See Ex. 1 (a) above]

$$\frac{x-a\cos\alpha}{a\sin\alpha}=\frac{y-b\sin\alpha}{-b\cos\alpha}=\frac{z}{c}. \qquad ...(2)$$

Now consider the co-ordinate plane *XOY i e.*, the plane $z=0$. The section of the hyperboloid (1) by the plane $z=0$ is

$$x^2/a^2+y^2/b^2=1,\ z=0. \qquad ...(3)$$

Again the projection of the generator (2) on the $z=0$ plane is

$$\frac{x-a\cos\alpha}{a\sin\alpha}=\frac{y-b\sin\alpha}{-b\cos\alpha},\ z=0$$

or $$\frac{x}{a\sin\alpha}-\frac{\cos\alpha}{\sin\alpha}=-\frac{y}{b\cos\alpha}+\frac{\sin\alpha}{\cos\alpha},z=0$$

or $$\frac{x}{a\sin\alpha}+\frac{y}{b\cos\alpha}=\frac{1}{\sin\alpha\cos\alpha},\ z=0$$

or $$(x/a)\cos\alpha+(y/b)\sin\alpha=1,\ z=0. \qquad ...(4)$$

These are clearly the equations of a tangent line to the section (3) of the hyperboloid at the point $(a\cos\alpha, b\sin\alpha, 0)$. Note that the first of the equations (4) *i.e.* $(x/a)\cos\alpha+(y/b)\sin\alpha=1$ is the equation of the plane through the generator and perpendicular to the plane $z=0$.

Again consider the co-ordinate plane *ZOX i.e.*, the plane $y=0$. The section of hyperboloid by the plane $y=0$ is

$$x^2/a^2-z^2/c^2=1,\ y=0. \qquad ...(5)$$

The projection of the generator (2) on the plane $y=0$ is

$$\frac{x-a\cos\alpha}{a\sin\alpha}=\frac{z}{c},\ y=0$$

or $$\frac{x}{a}\sec\alpha-\frac{z}{c}\tan\alpha=1,\ y=0. \qquad ...(6)$$

The equation $(x/a)\sec\alpha-(z/c)\tan\alpha=1$ represents the plane through the generator perpendicular to the plane $y=0$. Clearly the equations (6) represent the straight line which is tangent to the section (5) of the hyperboloid at the point $(a\sec\alpha, 0, c\tan\alpha)$.

In a similar manner the result follows for the co-ordinate plane $x=0$.

Ex. 6. *Prove that if two generators of the hyperboloid* $x^2/a^2+y^2/b^2-z^2/c^2=1$ *through the points P* $(a \cos \alpha, b \sin \alpha, 0)$ *and* $Q(a \cos \beta, b \sin \beta, 0)$ *intersect at right angles, their projections on the plane* $z=0$ *intersect at an angle* θ, *where*

$$\tan \theta=(ab/c^2) \sin (\alpha-\beta).$$

Solution. The equation of the hyperboloid is

$$x^2/a^2+y^2/b^2-z^2/c^2=1. \qquad \ldots(1)$$

The equations of the generator of (1) through the point $P(a \cos \alpha, b \sin \alpha, 0)$ belonging to the one system of generators [See Ex. 1(a) above] are

$$\frac{x-a \cos \alpha}{a \sin \alpha}=\frac{y-b \sin \alpha}{-b \cos \alpha}=\frac{z}{c}. \qquad \ldots(2)$$

Also the equations of the generator of (1) through the point $Q(a \cos \beta, b \sin \beta, 0)$ belonging to the other system of generators are

$$\frac{x-a \cos \beta}{a \sin \beta}=\frac{y-b \sin \beta}{-b \cos \beta}=\frac{z}{-c}. \qquad \ldots(3)$$

If the generators (2) and (3) are at right angles, then using the condition $l_1l_2+m_1m_2+n_1n_2=0$, we have

$$a^2 \sin \alpha \sin \beta+b^2 \cos \alpha \cos \beta-c^2=0. \qquad \ldots(4)$$

Now we know that the projections of the generators (2) and (3) on the plane $z=0$ are tangents to the ellipse $x^2/a^2+y^2/b^2=1$, $z=0$ [*i.e.* to the section of (1) by the plane $z=0$] at the points P and Q. Therefore the projections of (2) and (3) on the plane $z=0$ are respectively given by

$$(x/a) \cos \alpha+(y/b) \sin \alpha=1,\ z=0 \qquad \ldots(5)$$

and

$$(x/a) \cos \beta+(y/b) \sin \beta=1,\ z=0. \qquad \ldots(6)$$

The slopes m_1 and m_2 of the lines (5) and (6) lying in the plane $z=0$ are given by

$m_1=-(b \cos \alpha)/(a \sin \alpha)$ and $m_2=-(b \cos \beta)/(a \sin \beta)$.

The angle θ between (5) and (6) is given by

$$\tan \theta=\frac{m_1-m_2}{1+m_1m_2} \text{ or } \tan \theta=\frac{-\frac{b}{a}\left\{\frac{\cos \alpha}{\sin \alpha}-\frac{\cos \beta}{\sin \beta}\right\}}{1+\frac{b^2}{a^2}\cdot\frac{\cos \alpha}{\sin \alpha}\cdot\frac{\cos \beta}{\sin \beta}}$$

or $$\tan\theta=\frac{-ab\,[\sin\beta\cos\alpha-\cos\beta\sin\alpha]}{a^2\sin\alpha\sin\beta+b^2\cos\alpha\cos\beta}$$

$$=\frac{ab\sin(\alpha-\beta)}{c^2}\quad\text{[using (4)].}$$ **Proved.**

Ex. 7. *Show that the perpendiculars from the origin on the generator of the hyperboloid* $x^2/a^2+y^2/b^2-z^2/c^2=1$ *lie on the cone*

$$\frac{a^2(b^2+c^2)^2}{x^2}+\frac{b^2(c^2+a^2)^2}{y^2}-\frac{c^2(a^2-b^2)^2}{z^2}=0.$$

Solution. The equation of the hyperboloid is

$$x^2/a^2+y^2/b^2-z^2/c^2=1. \qquad \ldots(1)$$

The equations of the generator of (1) belonging to one system and passing through any point $(a\cos\alpha, b\sin\alpha, 0)$ on the principal elliptic section $x^2/a^2+y^2/b^2=1$, $z=0$ are given by

$$\frac{x-a\cos\alpha}{a\sin\alpha}=\frac{y-b\sin\alpha}{-b\cos\alpha}=\frac{z}{c}. \qquad \ldots(2)$$

[See Ex. 1(a) above]

The equations to any line through the origin are

$$x/l=y/m=z/n. \qquad \ldots(3)$$

If (2) and (3) are perpendicular, then we have

$$al\sin\alpha-bm\cos\alpha+cn=0. \qquad \ldots(4)$$

The lines (2) and (3) will intersect *i.e.* they will be coplanar if

$$\begin{vmatrix} a\cos\alpha & b\sin\alpha & 0 \\ a\sin\alpha & -b\cos\alpha & c \\ l & m & n \end{vmatrix}=0$$

or $$a\cos\alpha\,(-bn\cos\alpha-cm)-b\sin\alpha\,(an\sin\alpha-cl)=0$$

or $$-abn\,(\cos^2\alpha+\sin^2\alpha)-acm\cos\alpha+bcl\sin\alpha=0$$

or $$lbc\sin\alpha-mac\cos\alpha-nab=0. \qquad \ldots(5)$$

Solving the relations (4) and (5) for $\sin\alpha$ and $\cos\alpha$, we have

$$\frac{\sin\alpha}{mnab^2+mnac^2}=\frac{\cos\alpha}{nlbc^2+nlba^2}=\frac{1}{-lmca^2+lmcb^2}.$$

$$\therefore\quad \sin\alpha=-\frac{na(b^2+c^2)}{lc(a^2-b^2)},\ \cos\alpha=-\frac{nb(c^2+a^2)}{mc(a^2-b^2)}.$$

Squaring and adding *i.e.* eliminating α, we have

$$\frac{n^2a^2(b^2+c^2)^2}{l^2c^2(a^2-b^2)^2}+\frac{n^2b^2(c^2+a^2)^2}{m^2c^2(a^2-b^2)^2}=1$$

or $$\frac{a^2}{l^2}(b^2+c^2)^2+\frac{b^2}{m^2}(c^2+a^2)^2=\frac{c^2}{n^2}(a^2-b^2)^2.$$

Hence the line (3) lies on the cone

$$\frac{a^2(b^2+c^2)^2}{x^2}+\frac{b^2(c^2+a^2)^2}{y^2}-\frac{c^2(a^2-b^2)^2}{z^2}=0.$$

A similar result can be proved by taking generators of the other system.

Ex. 8. *Show that the points of intersection P, Q of the generators of opposite systems drawn through the point A(a cos α, b sin α, 0), B(a cos β, b sin β, 0) of the principal elliptic section of the hyperboloid* $x^2/a^2+y^2/b^2-z^2/c^2=1$ *are*

$$\left(\frac{a\cos\frac{1}{2}(\alpha+\beta)}{\cos\frac{1}{2}(\alpha-\beta)}, \frac{b\sin\frac{1}{2}(\alpha+\beta)}{\cos\frac{1}{2}(\alpha-\beta)}, \pm\frac{c\sin\frac{1}{2}(\alpha-\beta)}{\cos\frac{1}{2}(\alpha-\beta)}\right).$$

Hence show that if A and B are extremities of semi-conjugate diameters, the loci of the points P and Q are the ellipses

$$x^2/a^2+y^2/b^2=2,\ z=\pm c.$$

Solution. Let the co-ordinates of one of the two points of intersection of the generators, say of the point P be (x_1, y_1, z_1). The equation of the tangent plane to the hyperboloid

$$x^2/a^2+y^2/b^2-z^2/c^2=1$$

at the point (x_1, y_1, z_1) on it is

$$xx_1/a^2+yy_1/b^2-zz_1/c^2=1. \qquad (1)$$

The tangent plane (1) meets the plane $z=0$ in the line which is given by

$$xx_1/a^2+yy_1/b^2=1,\ z=0. \qquad ...(2)$$

The equations of the line joining the points A $(a\cos\alpha, b\sin\alpha, 0)$ and B $(a\cos\beta, b\sin\beta, 0)$ are

$$(x/a)\cos\tfrac{1}{2}(\alpha+\beta)+(y/b)\sin\tfrac{1}{2}(\alpha+\beta)=\cos\tfrac{1}{2}(\alpha-\beta),\ z=0. \qquad ..(3)$$

The lines given by the equations (2) and (3) are the same. Hence comparing these equations, we have

$$\frac{x_1/a}{\cos\frac{1}{2}(\alpha+\beta)}=\frac{y_1/b}{\sin\frac{1}{2}(\alpha+\beta)}=\frac{1}{\cos\frac{1}{2}(\alpha-\beta)}. \qquad ...(4)$$

Since the point P (x_1, y_1, z_1) lies on the given hyperboloid, we have

$$x_1^2/a^2+y_1^2/b^2-z_1^2/c^2=1. \qquad ...(5)$$

Putting the values of x_1/a and y_1/b from (4) in (5), we get

$$\frac{\cos^2\frac{1}{2}(\alpha+\beta)}{\cos^2\frac{1}{2}(\alpha-\beta)}+\frac{\sin^2\frac{1}{2}(\alpha+\beta)}{\cos^2\frac{1}{2}(\alpha-\beta)}-\frac{z_1^2}{c^2}=1$$

or

$$\frac{1}{\cos^2\frac{1}{2}(\alpha-\beta)}-\frac{z_1^2}{c^2}=1$$

or $\quad z_1^2/c^2=\sec^2 \frac{1}{2}(\alpha-\beta)-1 \quad$ or $\quad z_1^2/c^2=\tan^2 \frac{1}{2}(\alpha-\beta)$

or $\quad z_1/c=\pm\sin \frac{1}{2}(\alpha-\beta)/\cos \frac{1}{2}(\alpha-\beta)$. ...(6)

Hence from (4) and (6) the co-ordinates of the required points of intersection P and Q are

$$\left(\frac{a\cos \frac{1}{2}(\alpha+\beta)}{\cos \frac{1}{2}(\alpha-\beta)}, \frac{b\sin \frac{1}{2}(\alpha+\beta)}{\cos \frac{1}{2}(\alpha-\beta)}, \pm\frac{c\sin \frac{1}{2}(\alpha-\beta)}{\cos \frac{1}{2}(\alpha-\beta)}\right). \quad ...(7)$$

Second part. If the points A and B are the extremities of the semi-conjugate diameters, then we have $\alpha-\beta=\frac{1}{2}\pi$.

$\therefore \quad x_1^2/a^2+y_1^2/b^2=1/\cos^2 \frac{1}{2}(\alpha-\beta),\ z_1=\pm c\tan \frac{1}{2}(\alpha-\beta)$

or $\quad x_1^2/a^2+y_1^2/b^2=1/\cos^2 \frac{1}{4}\pi,\ z_1=\pm c\tan \frac{1}{4}\pi$

or $\quad x_1^2/a^2+y_1^2/b^2=2,\ z_1=\pm c$.

Therefore, the loci of the points P and Q are

$$x^2/a^2+y^2/b^2=2,\ z=\pm c.$$ **Proved.**

Ex. 9. *The generators through P of $x^2/a^2+y^2/b^2-z^2/c^2=1$ meet the principal elliptic section at A and B. If the median of the triangle APB through P is parallel to the fix d plane $lx+my+nz=0$, show that P lies on the surface $z(lx+my)+n(c^2+z^2)=0$.*

Solution. The principal elliptic section of the hyperboloid $x^2/a^2+y^2/b^2-z^2/c^2=1$ by the plane $z=0$ (say) is $x^2/a^2+y^2/b^2=1$, $z=0$. The co-ordinates, of the points A and B on this section are $A(a\cos\alpha, b\sin\alpha, 0)$ and $B(a\cos\beta, b\sin\beta, 0)$. Let P be (x_1, y_1, z_1).

Proceeding as in Ex. 8 above, the values of x_1, y_1, z_1 are given by (4) and (6) of Ex. 8.

Now if M is the mid. point of AB then

$M\equiv(\frac{1}{2}a(\cos\alpha+\cos\beta), \frac{1}{2}b(\sin\alpha+\sin\beta), 0)$

i.e. $\quad M\equiv(a\cos \frac{1}{2}(\alpha+\beta)\cos \frac{1}{2}(\alpha-\beta),$
$\quad b\sin \frac{1}{2}(\alpha+\beta)\cos \frac{1}{2}(\alpha-\beta), 0)$.

$\therefore$ The direction ratios of the median PM are

$x_1-a\cos \frac{1}{2}(\alpha+\beta)\cos \frac{1}{2}(\alpha-\beta),$
$\quad y_1-b\sin \frac{1}{2}(\alpha+\beta)\cos \frac{1}{2}(\alpha-\beta),\ z_1-0$

or $\quad x_1-x_1\cos^2 \frac{1}{2}(\alpha-\beta),\ y_1-y_1\cos^2 \frac{1}{2}(\alpha-\beta),\ z_1$

[using (4) of Ex. 8]

or $\quad x_1\sin^2 \frac{1}{2}(\alpha-\beta),\ y_1\sin^2 \frac{1}{2}(\alpha-\beta),\ z_1$

or $\quad x_1, y_1, z_1\operatorname{cosec}^2 \frac{1}{2}(\alpha-\beta)$, or $x_1, y_1, z_1\{1+\cot^2 \frac{1}{2}(\alpha-\beta)\}$

or $\quad x_1, y_1, z_1\{1+c^2/z_1^2\}$, [using (6) of Ex. 8]

It is given that the median PM is parallel to the plane $lx+my+nz=0$. Hence we have

$$lx_1+my_1+nz_1(1+c^2/z_1^2)=0.$$

$\therefore$ The locus of $P(x_1, y_1, z_1)$ is the surface

$$lx+my+nz(1+c^2/z^2)=0.$$

Ex. 10 *The generators through points on the principal elliptic section of the hyperboloid $x^2/a^2+y^2/b^2-z^2/c^2=1$, such that eccentric angle of one is double that of the other, intersect on the curve given by* $x=a(1-3t^2)/(1+t^2)$, $y=bt(3-t^2)/(1+t^2)$, $z=\pm ct$.

Solution. The principal elliptic section of the hyperboloid $x^2/a^2+y^2/b^2-z^2/c^2=1$ by the plane $z=0$ (say) is $x^2/a^2+y^2/b^2=1$, $z=0$. The co-ordinates of the two points A and B on it are $A(a\cos\alpha\ b\sin\alpha, 0)$ and $B(a\cos\beta, b\sin\beta, 0)$. Let P and Q be the points of intersection of the generators of the opposite systems through A and B. Let (x_1, y_1, z_1) be the co-ordinates of any of the points P or Q.

Proceeding as in Ex. 8 above, we have [See equations (4) and (6)]

$$\frac{x_1}{a}=\frac{\cos\frac{1}{2}(\alpha+\beta)}{\cos\frac{1}{2}(\alpha-\beta)}, \frac{y_1}{b}=\frac{\sin\frac{1}{2}(\alpha+\beta)}{\cos\frac{1}{2}(\alpha-\beta)}, \frac{z_1}{c}=\pm\frac{\sin\frac{1}{2}(\alpha-\beta)}{\cos\frac{1}{2}(\alpha-\beta)}.$$

According to the given condition $\beta=2\alpha$.

Also taking $\tan\frac{1}{2}\alpha=t$, we have

$$\frac{x_1}{a}=\frac{\cos(\frac{1}{2}.3\alpha)}{\cos\frac{1}{2}\alpha}=\frac{4\cos^3\frac{1}{2}\alpha-3\cos\frac{1}{2}\alpha}{\cos\frac{1}{2}\alpha}=4\cos^2\tfrac{1}{2}\alpha-3$$

or $$x_1=a\left\{\frac{4-3\sec^2\frac{1}{2}\alpha}{\sec^2\frac{1}{2}\alpha}\right\}=a\left\{\frac{4-3(1+\tan^2\frac{1}{2}\alpha)}{1+\tan^2\frac{1}{2}\alpha}\right\}=\frac{a(1-3t^2)}{1+t^2}.$$

Also $$\frac{y_1}{b}=\frac{\sin(\frac{1}{2}.3\alpha)}{\cos\frac{1}{2}\alpha}=\frac{3\sin\frac{1}{2}\alpha-4\sin^3\frac{1}{2}\alpha}{\cos\frac{1}{2}\alpha}$$

or $$y_1=b\tan\tfrac{1}{2}\alpha(3-4\sin^2\tfrac{1}{2}\alpha)=b\tan\tfrac{1}{2}\alpha\left\{\frac{3\sec^2\frac{1}{2}\alpha-4\tan^2\frac{1}{2}\alpha}{\sec^2\frac{1}{2}\alpha}\right\}$$
$$=bt(3-t^2)/(1+t^2),$$

and $z_1=\pm c\tan\frac{1}{2}\alpha=\pm ct$.

$\therefore$ The locus of (x_1, y_1, z_1) *i.e.* the curve on which the generators intersect is

$$x=a(1-3t^2)/(1+t^2),\ y=bt(3-t^2)/(1+t^2),\ z=\pm ct.$$

Ex. 11. *If the generators through a point P of the hyperboloid $x^2/a^2+y^2/b^2-z^2/c^2=1$ meet the principal elliptic section in two points such that the eccentric angle of one is three times that of the other, prove that P lies on the curve of intersection of the hyperboloid with the cylinder $y^2(c^2+z^2)=4b^2z^2$.*

Also if the difference of the eccentric angles is 2θ, then show that the locus of P is the curve of intersection of the hyperboloid with the cone

$$x^2/a^2+{}^2/b^2=(z^2/c^2)\operatorname{cosec}^2\theta.$$

Solution. Here we are given that $\beta=3\alpha$. Proceeding as in Ex. 10 above, we have

$$\frac{x_1}{a}=\frac{\cos 2\alpha}{\cos \alpha}, \quad ...(1)$$

$$\frac{y_1}{b}=\frac{\sin 2\alpha}{\cos \alpha}=\frac{2 \sin \alpha \cos \alpha}{\cos \alpha}=2 \sin \alpha \text{ or } y_1=2b \sin \alpha \quad ...(2)$$

and $$z_1=\pm c \tan \alpha=\pm c \sin \alpha/\cos \alpha$$

or $$z_1=\pm(cy_1)/(2b \cos \alpha), \text{ using (2)}. \quad ...(3)$$

$\therefore$ From (2) and (3), we get

$$\sin \alpha=y_1/(2b) \text{ and } \cos \alpha=cy_1/(2bz_1).$$

Eliminating α, we have

$$\frac{y_1^2}{4b^2}+\frac{c^2y_1^2}{4b^2z_1^2}=1 \text{ or } y_1^2\,(c^2+z_1^2)=4b^2z_1^2.$$

$\therefore$ The point P lies on the curve of intersection of the given hyperboloid with the cylinder

$$y^2\,(c^2+z^2)=b^2z^2.$$

Second part. If $\alpha-\beta=2\theta$ *i.e.* $\frac{1}{2}(\alpha-\beta)=\theta$, then we have

$$\frac{x_1}{a}=\frac{\cos \frac{1}{2}(\alpha+\beta)}{\cos \theta}, \frac{y_1}{b}=\frac{\sin \frac{1}{2}(\alpha+\beta)}{\cos \theta}, \frac{z_1}{c}=\pm \tan \theta.$$

$$\therefore \frac{x_1^2}{a^2}+\frac{y_1^2}{b^2}=\frac{\cos^2 \frac{1}{2}(\alpha+\beta)+\sin^2 \frac{1}{2}(\alpha+\beta)}{\cos^2 \theta}=\frac{1}{\cos^2 \theta}$$

or $$\frac{x_1^2}{a^2}+\frac{y_1^2}{b^2}=\frac{1}{\cos^2 \theta}\cdot\left(\pm\frac{z_1}{c \tan \theta}\right)^2$$

or $$\frac{x_1^2}{a^2}+\frac{y_1^2}{b^2}=\frac{z_1^2 \operatorname{cosec}^2 \theta}{c^2}.$$

Hence P lies on the curve of intersection of the given hyperboloid with the cone

$$x^2/a^2+y^2/b^2=(z^2/c^2) \operatorname{cosec}^2 \theta.$$

Ex. 12. *If the generators through P a point on the hyperboloid $x^2/a^2+y^2/b^2-z^2/c^2=1$ whose centre is O, meet the plane $z=0$ in A and B and the volume of the tetrahedron $OAPB$ is constant and equal to $abc/6$, show that P lies on one of the planes $z=\pm c$.*

Solution. The equation of the hyperboloid is

$$x^2/a^2+y^2/b^2-z^2/c^2=1.$$

The co-ordinates of its centre O are $(0, 0, 0)$. The co-ordinates of the points A, B and P [See Ex. 8 above] are

$$A\,(a \cos \alpha, b \sin \alpha, 0),\ B\,(a \cos \beta, b \sin \beta, 0) \text{ and}$$

$$P\left(\frac{a \cos \frac{1}{2}(\alpha+\beta)}{\cos \frac{1}{2}(\alpha-\beta)}, \frac{b \sin \frac{1}{2}(\alpha+\beta)}{\cos \frac{1}{2}(\alpha-\beta)}, \pm\frac{c \sin \frac{1}{2}(\alpha-\beta)}{\cos \frac{1}{2}(\alpha-\beta)}\right)$$

Hence the volume V of the tetrahedron $OAPB$ is given by

$$V=\pm\frac{1}{6}\begin{vmatrix} a\cos\alpha & b\sin\alpha & 0 \\ a\cos\beta & b\sin\beta & 0 \\ \dfrac{a\cos\frac{1}{2}(\alpha+\beta)}{\cos\frac{1}{2}(\alpha-\beta)} & \dfrac{b\sin\frac{1}{2}(\alpha+\beta)}{\cos\frac{1}{2}(\alpha-\beta)} & \pm\dfrac{c\sin\frac{1}{2}(\alpha-\beta)}{\cos\frac{1}{2}(\alpha-\beta)}\end{vmatrix}$$

or $\quad V=\frac{1}{6}\,abc\tan\frac{1}{2}(\alpha-\beta)\{\cos\alpha\sin\beta-\sin\alpha\cos\beta\}.$

$\therefore\quad \frac{1}{6}\,abc=\frac{1}{6}\,abc\tan\frac{1}{2}(\alpha-\beta)\sin(\alpha-\beta)$

[$\because$ as given, $V=\frac{1}{6}\,abc$]

or $\quad 1=2\sin^2\frac{1}{2}(\alpha-\beta)$, or $\operatorname{cosec}^2\frac{1}{2}(\alpha-\beta)=2$

or $\quad 1+\cot^2\frac{1}{2}(\alpha-\beta)=2$, or $\cot^2\frac{1}{2}(\alpha-\beta)=1$

or $\quad \tan^2\frac{1}{2}(\alpha-\beta)=1$

or $\quad z^2/c^2=1$ [$\because$ $z=\pm c\tan\frac{1}{2}(\alpha-\beta)$ for the point P]

or $\quad z=\pm c.$ **Proved.**

Ex. 13. *Show that in general two generators of the hyperboloid* $x^2/a^2+y^2/b^2-z^2/c^2=1$ *can be drawn to cut a given generator at right angles. Also show that if they meet the plane* $z=0$ *in* P *and* Q, PQ *touches the ellipse*

$$\frac{x^2}{a^6}+\frac{y^2}{b^6}=\frac{c^4}{a^4b^4}.$$

Solution. Proceeding as in § 3, the d.c.'s of a generator of the λ-system are proportional to

$$a(1-\lambda^2),\ 2b\lambda,\ c(1+\lambda^2)$$

and those of a generator of the μ-system are proportional to

$$a(1-\mu^2),\ -2b\mu,\ c(1+\mu^2).$$

If these generators are at right angles, then we have

$$a^2(1-\mu^2)(1-\lambda^2)-4b^2\mu\lambda+c^2(1+\mu^2)(1+\lambda^2)=0. \quad \text{...(1)}$$

Now suppose the μ-generator is given so that μ is a constant and hence the equation (1) is a quadratic in λ. This shows that there are two generators of the λ-system which are at right angles to a generator of the μ-system. Let the generators of the λ-system cut the plane $z=0$ in the points $P(a\cos\alpha,\ b\sin\alpha,\ 0)$ and $Q(a\cos\beta,\ b\sin\beta,\ 0)$. The equations of these generators belonging to the λ system through the points P and Q are given by [See Ex. 1(a) above]

$$\frac{x-a\cos\alpha}{a\sin\alpha}=\frac{y-b\sin\alpha}{-b\cos\alpha}=\frac{z}{c}, \quad \text{...(2)}$$

and

$$\frac{x-a\cos\beta}{a\sin\beta}=\frac{y-b\sin\beta}{-b\cos\beta}=\frac{z}{c}. \quad \text{...(3)}$$

Also the equations of the generator belonging to the μ-system and passing through the point, say $(a \cos \theta, b \sin \theta, 0)$, are

$$\frac{x-a \cos \theta}{a \sin \theta}=\frac{y-b \sin \theta}{-b \cos \theta}=\frac{z}{-c}. \quad \text{.. (4)}$$

The generators (2) and (3) both intersect the generator given by (4) at right angles and hence we have

$$a^2 \sin \alpha \sin \theta+b^2 \cos \alpha \cos \theta-c^2=0,$$

and $$a^2 \sin \beta \sin \theta+b^2 \cos \beta \cos \theta-c^2=0.$$

Solving these last two relations, we have

$$\frac{a^2 \sin \theta}{-\cos \alpha+\cos \beta}=\frac{b^2 \sin \theta}{-\sin \beta+\sin \alpha}=\frac{c^2}{\sin \alpha \cos \beta-\cos \alpha \sin \beta}$$

or $$\frac{a^2 \sin \theta}{2 \sin \frac{1}{2}(\alpha+\beta) \sin \frac{1}{2}(\alpha-\beta)}=\frac{b^2 \cos \theta}{2 \cos \frac{1}{2}(\alpha+\beta) \sin \frac{1}{2}(\alpha-\beta)}$$

$$=\frac{c^2}{2 \sin \frac{1}{2}(\alpha-\beta) \cos \frac{1}{2}(\alpha-\beta)}$$

or $$\frac{a^2 \sin \theta}{\sin \frac{1}{2}(\alpha+\beta)}=\frac{b^2 \cos \theta}{\cos \frac{1}{2}(\alpha+\beta)}=\frac{c^2}{\cos \frac{1}{2}(\alpha-\beta)}=\frac{1}{k} \text{ (say).} \quad \text{...(5)}$$

Now the equations of the line joining the points P and Q are

$$(x/a) \cos \tfrac{1}{2}(\alpha+\beta)+(y/b) \sin \tfrac{1}{2}(\alpha+\beta)=\cos \tfrac{1}{2}(\alpha-\beta), z=0.$$

Putting the values from (5), the above equations to the line PQ become

$$(x/a)\, kb^2 \cos \theta+(y/b)\, ka^2 \sin \theta=kc^2, z=0$$

or $$(x/a^3) \cos \theta+(y/b^3) \sin \theta=(c^2/a^2b^2), z=0. \quad \text{...(6)}$$

$[\because k \neq 0]$

Now it is required to find the envelope of (6) and so differentiating (6) w.r.t. 'θ', we get

$$-(x/a^3) \sin \theta+(y/b^3) \cos \theta=0, z=0. \quad \text{...(7)}$$

Squaring (6) and (7) and then adding, the equations of the envelope of the line PQ [or in other words the curve which the line PQ alwaye touches] are given by

$$\frac{x^2}{a^6}+\frac{y^2}{b^6}=\frac{c^4}{a^4b^4}, z=0$$

which are the equations of an ellipse.

Ex. 14. *Show that the shortest distances between generators of the same system drawn at the ends of diameters of principal elliptic section of the hyperboloid* $x^2/a^2+y^2/b^2-z^2/c^2=1$ *lie on the surfaces whose equations are*

$$\frac{cxy}{x^2+y^2}=\pm\frac{abz}{a^2-b^2}.$$

Solution. The equation of the hyperboloid is

$$x^2/a^2+y^2/b^2-z^2/c^2=1. \qquad \text{...(1)}$$

The principal elliptic section of (1) by the plane $z=0$ is

$$x^2/a^2+y^2/b^2=1,\ z=0. \qquad \text{...(2)}$$

Let PQ be any diameter of (2), so that if the co-ordinates of the extremity P are $(a \cos \alpha, b \sin \alpha, 0)$ then those of Q are $(a \cos (\pi+\alpha), b \sin (\pi+\alpha), 0)$.

The equations of the generator through P are

$$\frac{x-a \cos \alpha}{a \sin \alpha}=\frac{y-b \sin \alpha}{-b \cos \alpha}=\frac{z}{c}. \qquad \text{...(3)}$$

Replacing α by $\alpha+\pi$ in (3), the equations of the generator belonging to the system through Q are

$$\frac{x+a \cos \alpha}{-a \sin \alpha}=\frac{y+b \sin \alpha}{b \cos \alpha}=\frac{z}{c} \qquad \text{...(4)}$$

Let l, m, n be the d.c.'s of the line of shortest distance between the generators (3) and (4). Since the line of shortest distance is perpendicular to both (3) and (4), we have

$$la \sin \alpha-mb \cos \alpha+cn=0,$$

and $$-la \sin \alpha+mb \cos \alpha+cn=0.$$

Solving these relations, we have

$$\frac{l}{2bc \cos \alpha}=\frac{m}{2ac \sin \alpha}=\frac{n}{0},$$

or $$\frac{l}{b \cos \alpha}=\frac{m}{a \sin \alpha}=\frac{n}{0}. \qquad \text{...(5)}$$

Now the equations of the line of shortest distance are

$$\begin{vmatrix} x-a \cos \alpha & y-b \sin \alpha & z \\ a \sin \alpha & -b \cos \alpha & c \\ b \cos \alpha & a \sin \alpha & 0 \end{vmatrix}=0 \text{ and } \begin{vmatrix} x+a \cos \alpha & y+b \sin \alpha & z \\ -a \sin \alpha & b \cos \alpha & c \\ b \cos \alpha & a \sin \alpha & 0 \end{vmatrix}=0.$$

Expanding both the determinants with respect to the last column, we have

$$z\,(a^2 \sin^2 \alpha+b^2 \cos^2 \alpha)-c\,\{(x-a \cos \alpha)\, a \sin \alpha - (y-b \sin \alpha)\, b \cos \alpha\}=0 \qquad \text{...(6)}$$

and $$z\,(-a^2 \sin^2 \alpha-b^2 \cos^2 \alpha)-c\,\{(x+a \cos \alpha)\, a \sin \alpha - (y+b \sin \alpha)\, b \cos \alpha\}=0$$

i.e. $$z\,(a^2 \sin^2 \alpha+b^2 \cos^2 \alpha)+c\,\{(x+a \cos \alpha)\, a \sin \alpha - (y+b \sin \alpha)\, b \cos \alpha\}=0 \qquad \text{...(7)}$$

Thus the line of shortest distance is given by the planes (6) and (7). To find the locus of the line of shortest distance we are to eliminate the parameter 'α' between (6) and (7). For this we proceed as follows :

Subtracting (6) from (7), we have

$c\{2ax \sin\alpha - 2by \cos\alpha\} = 0$, or $\tan\alpha = (by/ax)$. ...(8)

Adding (6) and (7), we get

$$2z(a^2 \sin^2\alpha + b^2\cos^2\alpha) + c.\{2a^2 \sin\alpha\cos\alpha - 2b^2 \sin\alpha\cos\alpha\} = 0$$

or $z(a^2\tan^2\alpha + b^2) + c(a^2 - b^2)\tan\alpha = 0$, dividing by $2\cos^2\alpha$

or $z\left(\dfrac{b^2y^2}{x^2} + b^2\right) + c(a^2 - b^2).\dfrac{by}{ax} = 0$, substituting for $\tan\alpha$ from (8)

or $b^2z(x^2+y^2)/x^2 + bc(a^2 - b^2)y/(ax) = 0$

or $$\frac{cxy}{x^2+y^2} = -\frac{abz}{a^2-b^2}. \quad ...(9)$$

In a similar manner if we consider the shortest distance between the generators of the other system, the locus of shortest distance is given by

$$\frac{cxy}{x^2+y^2} = \frac{abz}{a^2-b^2} \text{ [Simply replace } c \text{ by } -c]. \quad ...(10)$$

From (9) and (10), the required locus is

$$\frac{cxy}{x^2+y^2} = \pm\frac{abz}{a^2-b^2}.$$

Ex. 15. *Show that the equations to the generating lines through the point (θ, ϕ) on the hyperboloid $x^2/a^2 + y^2/b^2 - z^2/c^2 = 1$ are*

$$\frac{x - a\cos\theta\sec\phi}{a\sin(\theta\pm\phi)} = \frac{y - b\sin\theta\sec\phi}{-b\cos(\theta\pm\phi)} = \frac{z - c\tan\phi}{\pm c}.$$

Solution. The equation of the hyperboloid is

$$x^2/a^2 + y^2/b^2 - z^2/c^2 = 1. \quad ...(1)$$

The co-ordinates of any point $P(\theta, \phi)$ on (1) are

$$(a\cos\theta\sec\phi,\ b\sin\theta\sec\phi,\ c\tan\phi).$$

The equation of the tangent plane at P to (1) is

$$(x/a)\cos\theta\sec\phi + (y/b)\sin\theta\sec\phi - (z/c)\tan\phi = 1. \quad ...(2)$$

Its intersection with the plane $z=0$ is the line given by

$$(x/a)\cos\theta\sec\phi + (y/b)\sin\theta\sec\phi = 1,\ z=0$$

or $$(x/a)\cos\theta + (y/b)\sin\theta = \cos\phi,\ z=0. \quad ...(3)$$

We know that the generating lines through the point P are the lines of intersection of the hyperboloid (1) with the tangent plane (2),

Now the principal elliptic section of (1) by the plane $z=0$ is

$$x^2/a^2 + y^2/b^2 = 1,\ z=0. \quad ...(4)$$

Let the line (3) meet the elliptic section (4) in the points A $(a \cos \alpha, b \sin \alpha, 0)$ and B $(a \cos \beta, b \sin \beta, 0)$. The equations to the line AB are

$$(x/a) \cos \tfrac{1}{2} (\alpha+\beta)+(y/b) \sin \tfrac{1}{2} (\alpha+\beta)=\cos \tfrac{1}{2} (\alpha-\beta),\ z=0. \quad ...(5)$$

The equations (3) and (5) should represent the same line and hence comparing them, we have

$$\theta=\tfrac{1}{2} (\alpha+\beta) \text{ and } \phi=\tfrac{1}{2} (\alpha-\beta). \quad ...(6)$$

Solving the equations (6), we get $\alpha=\theta+\phi$, $\beta=\theta-\phi$.

Therefore, PA and PB are the two generators through the point P and to find their equations, we are to determine their direction ratios.

The d.r.'s of PA are

$$a (\cos \alpha-\cos \theta \sec \phi),\ b (\sin \alpha-\sin \theta \sec \phi),\ c (0-\tan \phi)$$

or $$a \{\cos (\theta+\phi)-\cos \theta/\cos \phi\},\ b \{\sin (\theta+\phi)-\sin \theta/\cos \phi\},\ -c \sin \phi/\cos \phi.$$

Now multiplying throughout by $\cos \phi/\sin \phi$, the d.r.'s of PA are

$$a \left\{\frac{\cos (\theta+\phi) \cos \phi-\cos \theta}{\sin \phi}\right\},\ b \left\{\frac{\sin (\theta+\phi) \cos \phi-\sin \theta}{\sin \phi}\right\},\ -c$$

or $$a \left\{\frac{\cos \theta \cos^2 \phi-\sin \theta \sin \phi \cos \phi-\cos \theta}{\sin \phi}\right\},$$
$$b \left\{\frac{\sin \theta \cos^2 \phi+\cos \theta \sin \phi \cos \phi-\sin \theta}{\sin \phi}\right\},\ -c$$

or $$a \left\{\frac{-\sin \theta \sin \phi \cos \phi-\cos \theta (1-\cos^2 \phi)}{\sin \phi}\right\},$$
$$b \left\{\frac{\sin \phi \cos \theta \cos \phi-\sin \theta (1-\cos^2 \phi)}{\sin \phi}\right\},\ -c$$

or $$-a \{\sin \theta \cos \phi+\cos \theta \sin \phi\},\ b \{\cos \theta \cos \phi-\sin \theta \sin \phi\},\ -c$$

or $$a \sin (\theta+\phi),\ -b \cos (\theta+\phi),\ c.$$

$\therefore$ the equations to the generator PA are

$$\frac{x-a \cos \theta \sec \phi}{a \sin (\theta+\phi)}=\frac{y-b \sin \theta \sec \phi}{-b \cos (\theta+\phi)}=\frac{z-c \tan \phi}{c}.$$

Proceeding in a similar way for the d.r.'s of PB, we see that d.r.'s of PB are

$$a \sin (\theta-\phi),\ -b \cos (\theta-\phi),\ -c.$$

Hence the equations to the generator PB are

$$\frac{x-a \cos \theta \sec \phi}{a \sin (\theta-\phi)}=\frac{y-b \sin \theta \sec \phi}{-b \cos (\theta-\phi)}=\frac{z-c \tan \phi}{-c}.$$

Proved.

Ex. 16. *Prove that the angle α between the generators through any point P on the hyperboloid $x^2/a^2+y^2/b^2-z^2/c^2=1$ is given by*

$$\tan \alpha=\frac{2\,abc}{p\,(a^2+b^2-c^2-OP^2)},$$

where p is the length of perpendicular from the centre on the tangent plane at P.

Hence or otherwise, find the locus of the point of intersection of perpendicular generators.

Solution. The co-ordinates of the centre O are $(0, 0, 0)$ and those of the point P are $(a \cos \theta \sec \phi, b \sin \theta \sec \phi, c \tan \phi)$.

$\therefore \quad OP^2=(a^2 \cos^2 \theta+b^2 \sin^2 \theta+c^2 \sin^2 \phi)/\cos^2 \phi. \quad ...(1)$

The equation of the tangent plane at the point P is

$(x/a) \cos \theta \sec \phi+(y/b) \sin \theta \sec \phi-(z/c) \sin \phi \sec \phi=1. \quad ...(2)$

$\therefore \quad p=$ the length of perpendicular from $O\,(0, 0, 0)$ to (2)

$=1/[\cos^2 \theta \sec^2 \phi/a^2+\sin^2 \theta \sec^2 \phi/b^2+\sin^2 \theta \sec^2 \phi/c^2]^{1/2}$

or $\quad (abc/p) \cos \phi=[b^2c^2 \cos^2 \theta+c^2a^2 \sin^2 \theta+a^2b^2 \sin^2 \phi]^{1/2} \quad ...(3)$

The d.r.'s of the two generators through P are [See Ex. 15 above]

$a \sin (\theta+\phi), -b \cos (\theta+\phi), c$; and $a \sin (\theta-\phi), -b \cos (\theta-\phi), -c$.

$\therefore$ The angle α between these generators is given by

$$\tan \alpha=\frac{\sqrt{[\Sigma\,(l_1m_2-m_1l_2)^2]}}{l_1l_2+m_1m_2+n_1n_2} \quad ...(4)$$

For the sake of convenience let us calculate Nr. and Dr. separately. We have

$(\text{Nr})^2=[-ab\,\{\sin (\theta+\phi) \cos (\theta-\phi)-\cos (\theta+\phi) \sin (\theta-\phi)\}]^2$
$+[bc\,\{\cos (\theta+\phi)+\cos (\theta-\phi)\}]^2+[ca\,\{\sin (\theta+\phi)+\sin (\theta-\phi)\}]^2$
$=a^2b^2 \sin^2 2\phi+b^2c^2\,(2 \cos \theta \cos \phi)^2+c^2a^2\,(2 \sin \theta \cos \phi)^2.$

$\therefore \quad \text{Nr}=\sqrt{(4 \cos^2 \phi)}\,\{a^2b^2 \sin^2 \phi+b^2c^2 \cos^2 \theta+c^2a^2 \sin^2 \theta\}^{1/2}$
$=2 \cos \phi.(abc/p) \cos \phi,$ using (3)
$=(2abc/p) \cos^2 \phi.$

Also $\text{Dr.}=a^2 \sin (\theta+\phi) \sin (\theta-\phi)+b^2 \cos (\theta+\phi) \cos (\theta-\phi)-c^2$
$=a^2\,(\sin^2 \theta-\sin^2 \phi)+b^2\,(\cos^2 \theta-\sin^2 \phi)-c^2$
$=a^2\,(\cos^2 \phi-\cos^2 \theta)+b^2\,(\cos^2 \phi-\sin^2 \theta)-c^2$
$=(a^2+b^2) \cos^2 \phi-c^2 \cos^2 \phi.\sec^2 \phi-(a^2 \cos^2 \theta+b^2 \sin^2 \theta)$
$=\cos^2 \phi\,[a^2+b^2-c^2\,(1+\tan^2 \phi)$
$-(a^2 \cos^2 \theta+b^2 \sin^2 \theta)/\cos^2 \phi]$
$=\cos^2 \phi\,[a^2+b^2-c^2-\{a^2 \cos^2 \theta+b^2 \sin^2 \theta+c^2 \sin^2 \phi\}/\cos^2 \phi]$
$=\cos^2 \phi\,[a^2+b^2-c^2-OP^2],$ using (1).

$\therefore\quad \tan\alpha=\dfrac{2abc}{p\,(a^2+b^2-c^2-OP^2)}$, on putting the values of Nr. and Dr. in (4).

If $\alpha=90°$ *i.e.* the generators intersect at right angles, then

$$a^2+b^2-c^2-OP^2=0 \quad \text{or} \quad OP^2=a^2+b^2-c^2$$

or $x^2+y^2+z^2=a^2+b^2-c^2$, which is the required locus.

Ex. 17. *The normals to* $x^2/a^2+y^2/b^2-z^2/c^2=1$ *at points of a generator meet the plane* $z=0$ *at points lying on a straight line and for different generators of the same system this line touches a fixed conic*

$$\frac{a^2x^2}{(a^2+c^2)^2}+\frac{b^2y^2}{(b^2+c^2)^2}=1,\ z=0.$$

Solution. Proceed yourself.

Ex. 18. *Show that the tangent planes to* $x^2/a^2+y^2/b^2-z^2/c^2=1$ *which are parallel to the tangent planes to*

$$\frac{b^2c^2x^2}{c^2-b^2}+\frac{c^2a^2y^2}{c^2-a^2}+\frac{a^2b^2z^2}{a^2+b^2}=0$$

meet the surface in perpendicular generators.

Solution. We know that the tangent plane at a point P of a hyperboloid meets it in two generators through P. Also from § 3, we know that the locus of the point of intersection of the two perpendicular generators is the director sphere whose equation is given by

$$x^2+y^2+z^2=a^2+b^2-c^2. \qquad \ldots(1)$$

Therefore the tangent plane at any point P ($a\cos\theta\sec\phi$, $b\sin\theta\sec\phi$, $c\tan\phi$) on the hyperboloid will cut the hyperboloid in perpendicular generators through P if P lies on (1) *i.e.* we show that

$$a^2\cos^2\theta\sec^2\phi+b^2\sin^2\theta\sec^2\phi+c^2\tan^2\phi=a^2+b^2-c^2.$$

Now complete the solution.

Ex. 19. *If A and A' are the extremities of the major axis of the principal elliptic section and any generator meets two generators of the same system through A and A' respectively in P and P', prove that*

$$AP\,.\,A'P'=b^2+c^2.$$

Solution. Let the equation of the hyperboloid be

$$x^2/a^2+y^2/b^2-z^2/c^2=1.$$

The point of intersection of a generator of the λ-system with a generator of the μ-system is [See § 2 (B), part III]

$$(a\,(1+\lambda\mu/(\lambda+\mu),\ b\,(\lambda-\mu)/(\lambda+\mu),\ c(1-\lambda\mu)/(\lambda+\mu)). \qquad \ldots(1)$$

The extremities A and A' of the major axis of the principal elliptic section are $A\ (a, 0, 0)$ and $A'\ (-a, 0, 0)$. Thus the y and z co-ordinates of both these extremities are zero. This shows that for these extremities $\lambda-\mu=0$ and $1-\lambda\mu=0$. Hence for these extremities $\lambda=\mu$ and $1-\lambda^2=0$ *i.e.* $\lambda=\pm 1$.

The value $\lambda=1$ gives the extremity A and the value $\lambda=-1$ gives the extremity A'.

First consider the generator through the extremity $A\ (a, 0, 0)$ given by $\lambda=1$. Putting $\lambda=1$ in (1), the co-ordinates of the point of intersection P of this generator with a generator of the μ-system are given by

$$(a,\ b\ (1-\mu)/(1+\mu),\ c\ (1-\mu)/(1+\mu))$$

or $$(a,\ bt,\ ct), \text{ where } t=(1-\mu)/(1+\mu).$$

$$\therefore\ AP^2=(a-a)^2+(bt-0)^2+(ct-0)^2=(b^2+c^2)\ t^2. \qquad \text{...(2)}$$

Again consider the generator through the extremity $A'\ (-a, 0, 0)$ given by $\lambda=-1$. Putting $\lambda=-1$ in (1), the co-ordinates of the point of intersection P' of this generator with a generator of the μ-system are given by

$$(-a,\ b\ (1+\mu)/(1-\mu),\ -c\ (1+\mu)/(1-\mu) \quad \text{or} \quad (-a,\ b/t,\ c/t).$$

$$\therefore\ A'P'^2=(b^2+c^2)/t^2. \qquad \text{...(3)}$$

Multiplying (2) and (3), we get

$$AP^2 . A'P'^2=(b^2+c^2)^2$$

i.e. $$AP . A'P'=b^2+c^2.$$

Note. In Ex. 19, if we take the extremities B and B' of the minor axis instead of the extremities A and A' of the major axis, we have $BP . B'P'=b^2+c^2$.

Ex. 20. *Show that the equations*

$$y-\lambda z+\lambda+1=0,\ (\lambda+1)\ x+y+\lambda=0$$

represent for different values of λ *generators of one system of the hyperboloid* $yz+zx+xy+1=0$ *and find the equations to the generators of the other system.*

Solution. The given equations may be written as

$$y+1=\lambda\ (z-1), \text{ and } x+1=(-1/\lambda)\ (x+y). \qquad \text{..(1)}$$

Eliminating λ between the equations (1), we have

$$(y+1)\ (x+1)=-(z-1)\ (x+y)$$

or $$xy+yz+zx+1=0,$$

which is the equation of the given hyperboloid. Hence the equations (1) represent the generators of the λ-system.

Now the generators of the other system (*i.e.* μ-system) are given by

$$y+1=\mu\,(x+y),\ x+1=-(1/\mu)\,(z-1)$$

or $$\mu x+(\mu-1)\,y-1=0,\ \mu x+z-1+\mu=0.$$ **Ans.**

§ 6 (A). The generating lines of a hyperbolic paraboloid.

The equation of the hyperbolic paraboloid is

$$x^2/a^2-y^2/b^2=2z. \qquad \ldots(1)$$

The equation (1) may be rewritten as

$$(x/a+y/b)\,(x/a-y/b)=2z. \qquad \ldots(2)$$

From the equation (2) it follows that the hyperboloic paraboloid is the locus of a line whose equations are given by

$$x/a-y/b=\lambda z,\ x/a+y/b=2/\lambda \qquad \ldots(3)$$

where λ is a variable parameter. The equations given by (3) are the equations of a one parameter (λ parameter) family of straight lines and hence the hyperbolic paraboloid is a ruled surface.

In a similar manner the hyperbolic paraboloid can also be generated by the following μ-system of family of straight lines whose equations are given by

$$x/a-y/b=2/\mu,\ x/a+y/b=\mu z. \qquad \ldots(4)$$

The families of straight lines given by (3) and (4) are respectively called the λ-system and μ-system of generators.

§ 6 (B). Properties of generators of a hyperboloid.

(I) *One generator each of λ-and μ-systems passes through every point of the hyperbolic paraboloid.*

For its proof proceed exactly as in § 2 (B), part (I).

(II) *No two generators of the same system intersect.*

For its proof proceed exactly as in § 2 (B), part (II).

(III) *Any generator of the λ-system intersects any generator of the μ-system.*

The equations of any generator of the λ-system are

$$x/a-y/b=\lambda z \quad \ldots(1), \qquad x/a+y/b=2/\lambda. \qquad \ldots(2)$$

The equations of any generator of the μ-system are

$$x/a-y/b=2/\mu \quad \ldots(3), \qquad x/a+y/b=\mu z. \qquad \ldots(4)$$

Now we shall solve these equations.

From (2) and (4), we have $2/\lambda=\mu z$ *i.e.* $z=2/(\lambda\mu)$.

Adding and subtracting (2) and (3), we get

$$\frac{2x}{a}=\frac{2}{\lambda}+\frac{2}{\mu} \quad \text{or} \quad x=a\left(\frac{\lambda+\mu}{\lambda\mu}\right)$$

and $$\frac{2y}{b}=\frac{2}{\lambda}-\frac{2}{\mu} \quad \text{or} \quad y=b\left(\frac{\mu-\lambda}{\lambda\mu}\right)$$

The values of x, y, z obtained above obviously satisfy the equation (1). Hence the point of intersection is

$$\left(a.\ \frac{\lambda+\mu}{\lambda\mu},\ b.\ \frac{\mu-\lambda}{\lambda\mu},\ \frac{2}{\lambda\mu}\right). \qquad ...(5)$$

The co-ordinates of the point given by (5), for all values of λ and μ, satisfy the equation of the hyperbolic paraboloid namely the equation $x^2/a^2-y^2/b^2=2z$. Therefore, the parametric equations of the hyperbolic paraboloid are given by

$$x=a\ \frac{\lambda+\mu}{\lambda\mu},\ y=b\ \frac{\mu-\lambda}{\lambda\mu},\ z=\frac{2}{\lambda\mu}. \qquad ...(6)$$

(IV) *The tangent plane at any point of a hyperbolic paraboloid meets it in two generators through that point.*

For its proof proceed as in corollary to § 2 (B), part (III).

§ 7. Perpendicular generators. *To find the locus of the point of intersection of two perpendicular generators of a hyperbolic paraboloid.*

The equation of the hyperbolic paraboloid is

$$x^2/a^2-y^2/b^2=2z. \qquad ...(1)$$

The equations of any generator of the λ-system are

$$x/a-y/b=\lambda z,\ x/a+y/b=2/\lambda$$

or
$$x/a-y/b-\lambda z=0,\ x/a+y/b+0.z-2/\lambda=0.$$

If l_1, m_1, n_1 be the d.c.'s of this generator, then we have

$$l_1/a-m_1/b-\lambda n_1=0,\ l_1/a+m_1/b+0.n_1=0.$$

Solving, we get $\dfrac{l_1}{a\lambda}=\dfrac{m_1}{-b\lambda}=\dfrac{n_1}{2}$. ...(2)

The equations of any generator of the μ-system are

$$x/a-y/b=2/\mu,\ x/a+y/b=\mu z.$$

If l_2, m_2, n_2 be its d.c.'s, then proceeding as above, we have

$$\frac{l_2}{a\mu}=\frac{m_2}{b\mu}=\frac{n_2}{2}. \qquad ...(3)$$

If these two generators intersect at right angles, then

$$l_1l_2+m_1m_2+n_1n_2=0$$

or $a^2\lambda\mu-b^2\lambda\mu+4=0$ *i.e.* $(a^2-b^2)\lambda\mu+4=0$

or $(a^2-b^2).(2/z)+4=0$ [$\because$ $z=2/\lambda\mu$, for the point of intersection; see result (6) of § 6 (B), part III]

or $a^2-b^2+2z=0$. ...(4)

Hence the required locus is the curve given by the intersection of (1) by the plane (4).

§ 8. *To show that the generators of the λ-and μ-systems of the hyperbolic paraboloid $x^2/a^2-y^2/b^2=2z/c$ are parallel to the planes $x/a\pm y/b=0$.*

A generator of the λ-system is given by

$$x/a-y/b=\lambda z,\ x/a+y/b=2/\lambda.$$

It lies in the plane $x/a+y/b=2/\lambda$ which is parallel to the plane $x/a+y/b=0$ for all values of λ. Hence all the generators of the hyperbolic paraboloid that belong to the λ-system are parallel to the plane $x/a+y/b=0$.

Similarly the generators of the μ-system are all parallel to the plane $x/a-y/b=0$.

SOLVED EXAMPLES (B)

Ex. 1. *Planes are drawn through the origin O and the generators through any point P of the paraboloid given by $x^2-y^2=az$. Prove that the angle between them is $\tan^{-1}(2r/a)$ where r is the length of OP.*

Solution. The equations of the two generators may be taken as

$$x-y=\lambda z,\ x+y=a/\lambda \qquad \text{...(1)}$$

and
$$x-y=a/\mu,\ x+y=\mu z. \qquad \text{...(2)}$$

The equation of any plane through the generator (1) is

$$x-y-\lambda z+k\,(x+y-a/\lambda)=0.$$

If it passes through (0, 0, 0), then $k=0$.

∴ The equation of the above plane is

$$x-y-\lambda z=0. \qquad \text{...(3)}$$

In a similar way the equations of the plane through the origin and the generator (2) is $x+y-\mu z=0.$ ...(4)

Let θ be the angle between the planes (3) and (4).

Then $$\cos\theta=\frac{(1).(1)+(-1)(1)+(-\lambda)(-\mu)}{\sqrt{(1+1+\lambda^2)}\sqrt{(1+1+\mu^2)}}.$$

$$\therefore\ \sec^2\theta=(2+\lambda^2)(2+\mu^2)/(\lambda^2\mu^2)$$

or
$$1+\tan^2\theta=(2+\lambda^2)(2+\mu^2)/(\lambda^2\mu^2)$$

or
$$\tan^2\theta=(2\lambda^2+2\mu^2+4)/(\lambda^2\mu^2). \qquad \text{...(5)}$$

The point P in the question is the point of intersection of the generators (1) and (2) and therefore is given by

$$P\left(\frac{a}{2}\cdot\frac{\lambda+\mu}{\lambda\mu},\ \frac{a}{2}\cdot\frac{\mu-\lambda}{\lambda\mu},\ \frac{a}{\lambda\mu}\right).$$

$$\therefore\ r=OP=\sqrt{\left[\frac{a^2}{4}\left(\frac{\lambda+\mu}{\lambda\mu}\right)^2+\frac{a^2}{4}\left(\frac{\mu-\lambda}{\lambda\mu}\right)^2+\frac{a^2}{\lambda^2\mu^2}\right]}$$

$$=(a/2\lambda\mu)\sqrt{\{2\lambda^2+2\mu^2+4\}}=(a/2)\tan\theta, \qquad \text{using (5).}$$

Hence $\tan\theta=(2r/a)$ or $\theta=\tan^{-1}(2r/a)$.

Ex. 2. *Find the locus of the perpendiculars from the vertex of the paraboloid $x^2/a^2-y^2/b^2=2z$ to the generators of one system.*

Solution. The equations of any generator of the λ-system are

$$x/a-y/b=\lambda z,\ x/a+y/b=2/\lambda. \qquad ...(1)$$

The d.c.'s of this line are proportional to $a\lambda$, $-b\lambda$, 2.

[See § 7]

The vertex of the paraboloid is (0, 0, 0). The equations of any line through the vertex are

$$x/l=y/m=z/n=r \text{ (say)}. \qquad ...(2)$$

If the line (2) is perpendicular to the generator (1), then we have

$$a\lambda l-b\lambda m+2n=0. \qquad ...(3)$$

Suppose the line (2) meets the generator (1) in the point (lr, mr, nr). Putting the co-ordinates of this point in the first of the equations (1), we have

$$l/a-m/b=n\lambda \quad \text{or} \quad \lambda=(lb-ma)/(abn).$$

Putting this value of λ in (3), we get

$$(al-bm)(lb-ma)/(abn)+2n=0$$

or
$$abl^2-a^2lm-b^2lm+abm^2+2abn^2=0$$

or
$$l^2+m^2+2n^2-\frac{(a^2+b^2)lm}{ab}=0.$$

Hence for varying values of l, m, n, the locus of the perpendicular (2) is given by

$$x^2+y^2+2z^2-\{(a^2+b^2)/(ab)\}xy=0.$$

Similarly considering the μ-system of generators, the locus is given by

$$x^2+y^2+2z^2+\{(a^2+b^2)/(ab)\}xy=0.$$

$\therefore$ The required locus is

$$x^2+y^2+2z^2\pm\{(a^2+b^2)/(ab)\}xy=0.$$

Ex. 3. *The point of intersection of the generators of $xy=az$ which are inclined at a constant angle α, lie on the curve of intersection of the paraboloid and the hyperboloid*

$$x^2+y^2-z^2\tan^2\alpha+a^2=0.$$

Solution. The equation of the given paraboloid is

$$xy=az. \qquad ...(1)$$

The two generators of the λ-and μ-systems can be taken as

$$x=a\lambda,\ y=z/\lambda \qquad ...(2)$$

and
$$x=z/\mu,\ y=a\mu. \qquad ...(3)$$

The symmetrical forms of (2) and (3) are respectively given by

$$\frac{x-a\lambda}{0}=\frac{y}{1}=\frac{z}{\lambda} \text{ and } \frac{x}{1}=\frac{y-a\mu}{0}=\frac{z}{\mu}.$$

The angle α between these generators is given by

$$\cos\alpha=\frac{0.1+1.0+\lambda\mu}{\sqrt{(1+\lambda^2)}\sqrt{(1+\mu^2)}} \quad \text{or} \quad \sec^2\alpha=\frac{(1+\lambda^2)(1+\mu^2)}{\lambda^2\mu^2}$$

or $$1+\tan^2\alpha=\frac{1+\lambda^2+\mu^2+\lambda^2\mu^2}{\lambda^2\mu^2} \quad \text{or} \quad \tan^2\alpha=\frac{1+\lambda^2+\mu^2}{\lambda^2\mu^2}$$

or $$1+\lambda^2+\mu^2=\lambda^2\mu^2\tan^2\alpha. \qquad ...(4)$$

The point of intersection of the generators (2) and (3) is

$$x=a\lambda,\ y=a\mu,\ z=a\lambda\mu.$$

$$\therefore \quad \lambda=x/a,\ \mu=y/a,\ \lambda\mu=z/a. \qquad ...(5)$$

Eliminating λ, μ and $\lambda\mu$ between (4) and (5), we have

$$1+x^2/a^2+y^2/a^2=(z^2/a^2)\tan^2\alpha$$

or $$x^2+y^2-z^2\tan^2\alpha+a^2=0. \qquad ...(6)$$

The point of intersection also lies on (1). Hence the required locus is the curve of intersection of the surfaces (1) and (6).

Ex. 4. *Show that the polar lines with respect to the sphere $x^2+y^2+z^2=a^2$ of the generators of the quadric $x^2-y^2=2az$ all lie on the quadric $x^2-y^2=-2az$.*

Solution. Any generator of $x^2-y^2=2az$ belonging to the λ-system is $x-y=\lambda z$, $x+y=2a/\lambda$.

Its symmetrical form is

$$\frac{x-a/\lambda}{1}=\frac{y-a/\lambda}{-1}=\frac{z}{2/\lambda}=r \text{ (say)}. \qquad ...(1)$$

The polar plane of any point $(r+a/\lambda,\ -r+a/\lambda,\ 2r/\lambda)$ on the generator (1) with respect to the given sphere $x^2+y^2+z^2=a^2$ is

$$x(r+a/\lambda)+y(-r+a/\lambda)+z(2r/\lambda)=a^2$$

or $$r(x-y+2z/\lambda)+a(x/\lambda+y/\lambda-a)=0.$$

$\therefore$ The polar line of the λ-generator is

$$x-y+2z/\lambda=0,\ x/\lambda+y/\lambda-a=0$$

or $$x-y=-2z/\lambda,\ (x+y)/\lambda=a.$$

Eliminating λ between these equations, we get

$$(x-y)/a=-2z/(x+y) \quad \text{or} \quad x^2-y^2=-2az,$$

which is the required quadric on which the polar lines lie.

Ex. 5. *Show that the equations to the generators through the point "r, θ" on the hyperbolic paraboloid $x^2/a^2-y^2/b^2=2z$ are*

$$\frac{x-ar\cos\theta}{a}=\frac{y-br\sin\theta}{\pm b}=\frac{z-\frac{1}{2}r^2\cos 2\theta}{r(\cos\theta\mp\sin\theta)}.$$

Solution. Any point "r, θ" on the given hyperbolic paraboloid is given by

$$x=ar\cos\theta,\ y=br\sin\theta,\ z=\tfrac{1}{2}r^2\cos 2\theta. \quad \ldots(1)$$

The generators of λ-and μ-systems are given by

$$x/a-y/b=\lambda z,\ x/a+y/b=2/\lambda \quad \ldots(2)$$

and

$$x/a-y/b=2/\mu,\ x/a+y/b=\mu z. \quad (3)$$

Their d.r.'s are given by [see § 7]

$$\frac{l}{a}=\frac{m}{-b}=\frac{n}{2/\lambda} \text{ and } \frac{l}{a}=\frac{m}{b}=\frac{n}{2/\mu}.$$

If the λ-generator passes through the point (1) then

$x/a+y/b=2/\lambda$ gives $2/\lambda=r(\cos\theta+\sin\theta)$.

And if the μ-generator passes through the point (1), then

$x/a-y/b=2/\mu$ gives $2/\mu=r(\cos\theta-\sin\theta)$.

Hence the direction ratios of the two generators of the opposite systems passing through the point (1) are

$$a,\ -b,\ r(\cos\theta+\sin\theta) \text{ and } a,\ b,\ r(\cos\theta-\sin\theta).$$

$\therefore$ The equations of the two generators through the point "r, θ" given by (1) are

$$\frac{x-ar\cos\theta}{a}=\frac{y-br\sin\theta}{-b}=\frac{z-\frac{1}{2}r^2\cos 2\theta}{r(\cos\theta+\sin\theta)}$$

and

$$\frac{x-ar\cos\theta}{a}=\frac{y-br\sin\theta}{b}=\frac{z-\frac{1}{2}r^2\cos 2\theta}{r(\cos\theta-\sin\theta)}.$$

Ex. 6. *Show that the angle between generating lines of $x^2/a^2-y^2/b^2=2z$ through (x, y, z) is given by*

$$\tan\theta=ab\left(1+\frac{x^2}{a^4}+\frac{y^2}{b^4}\right)^{1/2}\left(z+\frac{a^2-b^2}{2}\right)^{-1}.$$

Solution. Proceeding as in § 6 (B), part III, the point of intersection (x, y, z) of the two generators of λ-and μ-systems is given by

$$x=a\left(\frac{\lambda+\mu}{\lambda\mu}\right),\ y=b\left(\frac{\mu-\lambda}{\lambda\mu}\right),\ z=\frac{2}{\lambda\mu}. \quad (1)$$

Also their d.r.'s are $a\lambda$, $-b\lambda$, 2 and $a\mu$, $b\mu$, 2. [See § 7].

If θ is the angle between these generators, then

$$\tan\theta=\frac{[\Sigma(m_1n_2-m_2n_1)^2]^{1/2}}{l_1l_2+m_1m_2+n_1n_2}$$

or

$$\tan\theta=\frac{[(-2b\lambda-2b\mu)^2+(2a\mu-2a\lambda)^2+(2ab\lambda\mu)^2]^{1/2}}{a^2\lambda\mu-b^2\lambda\mu+4}$$

$$=\frac{\left[4b^2\left(\frac{\lambda+\mu}{\lambda\mu}\right)^2+4a^2\left(\frac{\mu-\lambda}{\lambda\mu}\right)^2+4a^2b^2\right]^{1/2}}{(a^2-b^2)+4/\lambda\mu}$$

$$=\frac{[4b^2(x^2/a^2)+4a^2(y^2/b^2)+4a^2b^2]^{1/2}}{(a^2-b^2)+2z}, \text{ using (1)}$$

$$=2ab\,[x^2/a^4+y^2/b^4+1]^{1/2}/\{(a^2-b^2)+2z\}$$

$$=ab\left(1+\frac{x^2}{a^4}+\frac{y^2}{b^4}\right)^{1/2}\left(z+\frac{a^2-b^2}{2}\right)^{-1}.$$

Ex. 7. *The generators of the paraboloid $x^2/a-y^2/b=4z$ are drawn through the point $(\alpha, 0, \gamma)$. Prove that the angle between them is* $\cos^{-1}\left(\dfrac{a-b+\gamma}{a+b+\gamma}\right)$

Solution. Let the equations of any line through $(\alpha, 0, \gamma)$ be

$$\frac{x-\alpha}{l}=\frac{y-0}{m}=\frac{z-\gamma}{n}=r \text{ (say)}. \quad \ldots(1)$$

Any point on (1) is $(\alpha+lr, mr, \gamma+nr)$. If it lies on the given paraboloid $x^2/a-y^2/b=4z$, we have

$$(\alpha+lr)^2/a-(mr)^2/b=4(\gamma+nr)$$

or $$r^2\,(l^2/a-m^2/b)+2r\,(\alpha l/a-2n)+(\alpha^2/a-4\gamma)=0. \quad \ldots(2)$$

If the line (1) is a generator, it wholly lies on the given paraboloid so that (2) is an identity in r and consequently we have

$$l^2/a-m^2/b=0,\ \alpha l/a-2n=0,\ \alpha^2/a=4\gamma. \quad \ldots(3)$$

From the first and the second of the results (3),

$$\frac{l}{\sqrt{a}}=\frac{m}{\pm\sqrt{b}}=\frac{2n\sqrt{a}}{\alpha}$$

or $$\frac{l}{2a}=\frac{m}{\pm 2\sqrt{(ab)}}=\frac{n}{\alpha}.$$

Hence the d.c.'s of the two generators through $(\alpha, 0, \gamma)$ are proportional to $2a,\ 2\sqrt{(ab)},\ \alpha$ and $2a,\ -2\sqrt{(ab)},\ \alpha$.

If θ is the angle between the generators, we have

$$\cos\theta=\frac{4a^2-4ab+\alpha^2}{4a^2+4ab+\alpha^2}, \text{ or } \cos\theta=\frac{4a^2-4ab+4a\gamma}{4a^2+4ab+4a\gamma}, \text{ using (3)}$$

or $$\cos\theta=\frac{a-b+\gamma}{a+b+\gamma} \text{ or } \theta=\cos^{-1}\left(\frac{a-b+\gamma}{a+b+\gamma}\right).$$

Ex. 8. *Prove that the projections of the generators of a hyperboloid on any principal plane are tangents to the section by the plane.*

Solution. Let the equation of the hyperboloid be

$$x^2/a^2-y^2/b^2=2z. \quad \ldots(1)$$

The λ-and μ-generators of (1) are

$$x/a-y/b=\lambda z,\ x/a+y/b=2/\lambda \quad \ldots(2)$$

and $$x/a-y/b=2/\mu,\ x/a+y/b=\mu z. \quad \ldots(3)$$

The projections of these generators on the *YOZ* piane *i.e.* the plane $x=0$ are given by

$$x=0,\ 2y/b=2/\lambda-\lambda z$$

and

$$x=0,\ 2y/b=\mu z-2/\mu.$$

These may be rewritten as

$$x=0,\ bz\lambda^2+2y\lambda-2b=0$$

and

$$x=0,\ bz\mu^2-2y\mu-2b=0.$$

∴ The envelope of the projections on the plane $x=0$ is

$$x=0,\ (2y)^2-4.(bz)\,(-2b)=0$$

[Note that the envelope is given by $B^2-4AC=0$]

or

$$x=0,\ y^2=-2b^2z. \qquad ...(4)$$

Also the projection of the surface (1) on the plane $x=0$ is

$$x=0,\ y^2=-2b^2z \qquad ...(5)$$

which is the same as (4).

Thús the projections of the generators of a hyperboloid on a principal plane are tangents to the section of the surface by the principal plane.

In a similar way the projections on the principal planes $y=0$ and $z=0$ can be considered.

Ex. 9. *Find the equations to the generators of the paraboloid* $(x+y+z)\,(2x+y-z)=6z$, *which pass through the point* (1, 1, 1).

Solution. The two generators of the given surface belonging to the λ-and μ-systems are given by

$$x+y+z=\lambda z,\ 2x+y-z=6/\lambda \qquad ...(1)$$

and

$$x+y+z=6/\mu,\ 2x+y-z=\mu z. \qquad ...(2)$$

If these pass through (1, 1, 1), we have $\lambda=3$, $\mu=2$.

Hence the two generators of the opposite systems are

$$x+y-2z=0,\ 2x+y-z=2 \qquad ...(3)$$

and

$$x+y+z=3,\ 2x+y-3z=0. \qquad ...(4)$$

The d.r.'s of (3) and (4) are respectively given by $-1, 3, 1$ and $-4, 5, 1$. Since (3) and (4) both pass through the point (1, 1, 1), their equations in symmetrical forms are given by

$$\frac{x-1}{-1}=\frac{y-1}{3}=\frac{z-1}{1} \text{ and } \frac{x-1}{-4}=\frac{y-1}{5}=\frac{z-1}{1}.$$

4

The plane Sections of Conicoids

§ 1. Introduction.

We have already seen that all plane sections of a conicoid are conics and also that sections by parallel planes are similar and similarly situated conics. Further, we know that the orthogonal projections of parabolas, ellipses or hyperbolas are another parabolas, ellipses or hyperbolas respectively. We can find the nature of the section of a conicoid by a plane by finding the equations of the projection of the section on any one of the co-ordinate planes. If the plane passes through the centre of the conicoid then the section of the conicoid is called a **Central plane section** otherwise the section is called simply a plane section.

§ 2. Nature of a plane section.

To determine the nature of a plane section of a central conicoid.

Let the equation of the central conicoid be given by

$$ax^2+by^2+cz^2=1 \quad \text{...(1)}$$

and the equation of the plane be $lx+my+nz=p$. ...(2)

The equation of the cylinder passing through the section of the conicoid (1) by the plane (2) and having its generators parallel to z-axis is obtained by eliminating z between (1) and (2) and is therefore given by

$$ax^2+by^2+c\,\{(p-lx-my)/n\}^2=1$$

or $$x^2\,(an^2+cl^2)+2clmxy+y^2\,(bn^2+cm^2)-2cplx-2cpmy$$
$$+(cp^2-n^2)=0. \quad \text{...(3)}$$

The plane $z=0$ being perpendicular to the generators of the cylinder (3) cuts it in the conic given by

$$z=0,\ x^2\,(an^2+cl^2)+2clmxy+y^2\,(bn^2+cm^2)-2cplx$$
$$-2cpmy+(cp^2-n^2)=0. \quad \text{...(4)}$$

The conic given by (4) represents the projection of the given section on the plane $z=0$.

*We know that in two dimensional geometry the general equation of the second degree namely

$$ax^2+2hxy+by^2+2gx+2fy+c=0$$

represents a hyperbola, a parabola or an ellipse according as

$$h^2-ab >, =, \text{ or } < 0.$$

Thus the projection given by (4) and *hence the given section is a hyperbola, a parabola or an ellipse according as*

$$c^2l^2m^2-(an^2+cl^2)(bn^2+cm^2) >, =, \text{ or } < 0$$

i.e. $$bcl^2+cam^2+abn^2 <, =, \text{ or } > 0.$$

§ 3. Lengths and direction ratios of the axes of a central section. *To find the lengths and direction ratios of the axes of a central section of a central conicoid.*

Let the equation of the conicoid be $ax^2+by^2+cz^2=1$ .. (1)
and the equation of a plane passing through the centre (0, 0, 0) [*i.e.* central plane] be $lx+my+nz=0$. ...(2)

If λ, μ, ν are the d.c.'s of a semi-diameter of the conicoid (1) of length r, then its equations are

$$x/\lambda=y/\mu=z/\nu=r. \quad ...(3)$$

The point $(\lambda r, \mu r, \nu r)$ which is the extremity of the semi-diameter (3), lies on the conicoid (1). Therefore

$$a\lambda^2r^2+b\mu^2r^2+c\nu^2r^2=1=\lambda^2+\mu^2+\nu^2 \quad [\because \lambda^2+\mu^2+\nu^2=1]$$

or $$\lambda^2(ar^2-1)+\mu^2(br^2-1)+\nu^2(cr^2-1)=0. \quad ...(4)$$

$\therefore$ the semi-diameters (3) of length r are the generators of the cone

$$x^2(ar^2-1)+y^2(br^2-1)+z^2(cr^2-1)=0. \quad ...(5)$$

The plane (2) cuts the above cone (5) in two semi-diameters of length r of the conic given by (1) and (2). When r becomes the length of either of the semi-axes of the conic, the two equal generators coincide along one of the axes of the conic. Therefore the plane (2) should touch the cone (5) along the generator of contact (*i.e.* along one of the axes), the condition for which is

$$\frac{l^2}{ar^2-1}+\frac{m^2}{br^2-1}+\frac{n^2}{cr^2-1}=0 \quad (5')$$

or $$r^4(bcl^2+cam^2+abn^2)-r^2\{(b+c)l^2+(c+a)m^2+(a+b)n^2\}$$
$$+(l^2+m^2+n^2)=0. \quad ...(6)$$

The roots of this quadratic equation in r^2 give the squares of the semi-axes of the section *i.e.* of the conic given by (1) and (2).

---

* See authors' book on "Analytical Geometry of two dimensions".

Now if $2r$ is the length and λ, μ, ν the d.c.'s of an axis of the conic section, the plane (2) touches the cone (5) along this axis namely the line $x/\lambda=y/\mu=z/\nu$. Hence the plane (2) is identical with the tangent plane to the cone (5) namely

$$\lambda x\ (ar^2-1)+\mu y\ (br^2-1)+\nu z\ (cr^2-1)=0 \qquad ...(7)$$

at any point $(\lambda r, \mu r, \nu r)$ on $x/\lambda=y/\mu=z/\nu$. Comparing (2) and (7), we have

$$\lambda\ (ar^2-1)/l=\mu\ (br^2-1)/m=\nu\ (cr^2-1)/n \qquad ...(8)$$

which give the direction ratios of the two axes for two values of r^2 given by (6).

Corollary 1. The area of the central plane section. If the central plane section is an ellipse, the lengths of whose semi-axes are r_1 and r_2, then its area is given by

$$\pi r_1 r_2=\pi\left\{\frac{l^2+m^2+n^2}{bcl^2+cam^2+abn^2}\right\}^{1/2}. \qquad ...(9)$$

We can put the area of this plane section in one other form also as explained below.

The equation of the tangent plane to the conicoid (1) which is parallel to the plane (2) is

$$lx+my+nz=\sqrt{\{l^2/a+m^2/b+n^2/c\}}$$

or $$lx+my+nz=\sqrt{(bcl^2+cam^2+abn^2)}/\sqrt{(abc)}.$$

Let p be the length of the perpendicular from the centre (0, 0, 0) of the conicoid to this plane.

Then $p=\dfrac{\sqrt{(bcl^2+cam^2+abn^2)}}{\sqrt{(abc)}.\sqrt{(l^2+m^2+n^2)}}$, so that

$$\left\{\frac{l^2+m^2+n^2}{bcl^2+cam^2+abn^2}\right\}^{1/2}=\frac{1}{p\sqrt{(abc)}}$$

Putting this value in (9), the area of the central plane section is also $$=\frac{\pi}{p\sqrt{(abc)}}. \qquad ...(10)$$

Corollary 2. If the conicoid be the ellipsoid $x^2/a^2+y^2/b^2+z^2/c^2=1$, then replacing a, b, c by $1/a^2, 1/b^2, 1/c^2$ respectively in the equation (6) above, the quadratic equation in r^2 giving the squares of the semi-axes of the plane section is given by

$$r^4\ (a^2l^2+b^2m^2+c^2n^2)-r^2\ \{a^2\ (b^2+c^2)\ l^2$$
$$+b^2\ (c^2+a^2)\ m^2+c^2\ (a^2+b^2)\ n^2\}+a^2b^2c^2\ \ (l^2+m^2+n^2)=0. \qquad ...(11)$$

The equations (8) giving the d.r.'s λ, μ, ν of an axis of length $2r$ become

$$\frac{\lambda\,(r^2-a^2)}{a^2 l}=\frac{\mu\,(r^2-b^2)}{b^2 m}=\frac{\nu\,(r^2-c^2)}{c^2 n}. \quad ...(12)$$

Also the area of the central plane section becomes

$$\pi abc\left\{\frac{l^2+m^2+n^2}{a^2l^2+b^2m^2+c^2n^2}\right\}^{1/2} \text{ or } \frac{\pi abc}{p} \quad ...(13)$$

where p has the same meaning as defined above.

Corollary 3. The condition for the section to be a rectangular hyperbola. If the central plane section is a rectangular hyperbola then r_1^2 and r_2^2 are equal in magnitude but opposite in sign *i.e.* $r_1^2+r_2^2=0$. Hence from the equation (6) above the required condition is given by

$$(b+c)\,l^2+(c+a)\,m^2+(a+b)\,n^2=0. \quad ...(14)$$

The condition (14) clearly shows that the normal $x/l=y/m=z/n$ to the plane (2) is a generator of the cone

$$(b+c)\,x^2+(c+a)\,y^2+(a+b)\,z^2=0.$$

Therefore the plane (2) is the tangent plane to the reciprocal cone $\quad x^2/(b+c)+y^2/(c+a)+z^2/(a+b)=0. \quad ...(15)$

Thus we conclude that "*the section of the conicoid* (1) *by any tangent plane to the cone* (15) *is a rectangular hyperbola.*"

SOLVED EXAMPLES (A)

Ex. 1. *Prove that the axes of the section of the conicoid* $ax^2+by^2+cz^2=1$ *by the plane* $lx+my+nz=0$ *lie on the cone*

$$(b-c)\,l/x+(c-a)\,m/y+(a-b)\,n/z=0.$$

Solution. Let λ, μ, ν be the d.r.'s of the axes of the section, then proceeding as in § 3, we have [See equation (8)]

$$\lambda\,(ar^2-1)/l=\mu\,(br^2-1)/m=\nu\,(cr^2-1)/n=k \text{ (say)}.$$

$$\therefore\quad lk/\lambda=(ar^2-1),\ mk/\mu=(br^2-1),\ nk/\nu=cr^2-1.$$

Multiplying the above relations by $(b-c)$, $(c-a)$ and $(a-b)$ respectively and adding, we get

$$l\,(b-c)/\lambda+m\,(c-a)/\mu+n\,(a-b)/\nu=0.$$

$\therefore$ the axes $x/\lambda=y/\mu=z/\nu$ lie on the cone

$$l\,(b-c)/x+m\,(c-a)/y+n\,(a-b)/z=0.$$

Ex. 2. *Prove that the cone of Ex.* 1 *above passes through the normal to the plane of section and the diameter to which the plane of section is diametral plane.*

Solution. Consider the section of the cónicoid

$$ax^2+by^2+cz^2=1 \quad ...(1)$$

by the plane $\quad lx+my+nz=0. \quad ...(2)$

The equations of the normal to the plane of section *i.e.*, to the plane (2) are $x/l=y/m=z/n$. ...(3)

The equation of the cone whose generators are the axes of the section is $(b-c)\,l/x+(c-a)\,m/y+(a-b)\,n/z=0$. ...(4)

The cone (4) will pass through the line (3) if we have

$$(b-c)+(c-a)+(a-b)=0, \text{ which is true.}$$

This proves the first part.

Now the equations of the diameter to which the plare (2) is the diametral plane, are given by

$$\frac{x}{l/a}=\frac{y}{m/b}=\frac{z}{n/c}. \quad ...(5)$$

If the cone (4) passes through the line (5), then we should have

$$\frac{(b-c)\,l}{l/a}+\frac{(c-a)\,m}{m/b}+\frac{(a-b)\,n}{n/c}=0$$

or $\qquad a\,(b-c)+b\,(c-a)+c\,(a-b)=0$

which is true. This proves the second part.

Ex. 3. *Prove that the section of the conicoid $ax^2+by^2+cz^2=1$ by the plane whose normal lies on the cone $x^2/a+y^2/b+z^2/c=0$ is a parabola.*

Solution. Let the equation of the plane be $lx+my+nz=0$. The normal to this plane is $x/l=y/m=z/n$. This normal will lie on the given cone if

$$l^2/a+m^2/b+n^2/c=0 \text{ i.e. if } bcl^2+cam^2+abn^2=0$$

which is the condition for the section to be a parabola. [See § 2]

Ex. 4. *Show that the section of the ellipsoid $9x^2+6y^2+14z^2=3$ by the plane $x+y+z=0$ is an ellipse with semi-axes $\frac{1}{2}$ and $3/\sqrt{(22)}$. Also determine their equations.*

Solution. The ellipsoid is $9x^2+6y^2+14z^2=3$ ...(1)

and the plane is $x+y+z=0$. ...(2)

Let λ, μ, ν be the d.c.'s of a semi-diameter of the ellipsoid (1) of length r. Then its equations are

$$x/\lambda+y/\mu=z/\nu=r \text{ (say)}. \quad ...(3)$$

The point $(\lambda r, \mu r, \nu r)$ on (3) lies on (1), therefore we have

$$(9\lambda^2+6\mu^2+14\nu^2)\,r^2=3=3\,(\lambda^2+\mu^2+\nu^2)$$

or $\qquad 3\,(3r^2-1)\,\lambda^2+3\,(2r^2-1)\,\mu^2+(14r^2-3)\,\nu^2=0.$

$\therefore$ the semi-diameters (3) are generators of the cone

$$3\,(3r^2-1)\,x^2+3\,(2r^2-1)\,y^2+(14r^2-3)\,z^2=0. \quad ...(4)$$

Let r become the length of either of the semi-axes of the

conic, then the plane (2) will touch the cone (4) and hence we have

$$\frac{1}{3(3r^2-1)}+\frac{1}{3(2r^2-1)}+\frac{1}{14r^2-3}=0 \text{ or } 88r^4-58r^2+9=0$$

or $88r^4-22r^2-36r^2+9=0$ or $(22r^2-9)(4r^2-1)=0$.

$\therefore$ $r_1^2=\frac{1}{4}$, $r_2^2=9/22$, giving $r_1=\frac{1}{2}$, $r_2=3/\sqrt{(22)}$.

Since r_1^2 and r_2^2 are both positive, therefore the section (*i.e.* the conic) is an ellipse with semi-axes $\frac{1}{2}$, $3/\sqrt{(22)}$.

Now if $2r$ is the length and λ, μ, ν the d.c.'s of an axis, then the section is also given by

$$3(3r^2-1)\lambda x+3(2r^2-1)\mu y+(14r^2-3)\nu z=0.$$

This equation should be identical with the equation of the plane (2). Hence comparing the two equations, we have

$$\frac{3(3r^2-1)\lambda}{1}=\frac{3(2r^2-1)\mu}{1}=\frac{(14r^2-3)\nu}{1}. \quad ...(5)$$

For $r_1^2=\frac{1}{4}$, from (5) we have $3(\frac{3}{4}-1)\lambda=3(\frac{1}{2}-1)\mu=(\frac{7}{2}-3)\nu$

or $-3\lambda=-6\mu=2\nu$ or $\lambda/2=\mu/1=\nu/(-3)$.

$\therefore$ the equations of the semi-axis of length $\frac{1}{2}$ are given by

$$x/2=y/1=z/(-3).$$

Again for $r_2^2=9/22$, from (5) we have $\lambda/(4)=\mu/(-5)=\nu/(1)$.

$\therefore$ the equations of the semi-axis of length $3/\sqrt{(22)}$ are

$$x/4=y/(-5)=z/1.$$

Ex. 5. *Prove that the section of the conicoid* $x^2+7y^2-10z^2+9=0$ *by the plane* $x+2y+3z=0$ *is a hyperbola whose transverse axis is* 6 *and d.c.'s of whose axes are proportional to* 6, 3, -4 *and* 17, -22, 9.

Solution. Proceed as in Ex. 4 above.

Ex. 6. *Prove that the central section of an ellipsoid whose area is constant envelopes a cone of second degree.*

Solution Let the area of the section of the ellipsoid

$$x^2/a^2+y^2/b^2+z^2/c^2=1$$

by the plane $lx+my+nz=0$ be constant, say equal to $\pi abc/d$.

By equation (13) of § 3, we have

$$\pi abc\left\{\frac{l^2+m^2+n^2}{a^2l^2+b^2m^2+c^2n^2}\right\}^{1/2}=\frac{\pi\, abc}{d}.$$

Squaring, $a^2l^2+b^2m^2+c^2n^2=d^2(l^2+m^2+n^2)$

or $l^2(a^2-d^2)+m^2(b^2-d^2)+n^2(c^2-d^2)=0.$

Hence the plane $lx+my+nz=0$ envelopes the cone

$$x^2/(a^2-d^2)+y^2/(b^2-d^2)+z^2/(c^2-d^2)=0.$$

Ex. 7. *If A_1, A_2, A_3 are the areas of three mutually perpendicular central sections of an ellipsoid then show that*

$$A_1^{-2}+A_2^{-2}+A_3^{-2}=\text{constant}.$$

Solution. Let the ellipsoid be $x^2/a^2+y^2/b^2+z^2/c^2=1$ and $l_r x+m_r y+n_r z=0$ $(r=1, 2, 3)$ be the equations of three mutually perpendicular central planes, where l_r, m_r, n_r are the actual d.c.'s of the normals to these planes, so that

$$l_1^2+l_2^2+l_3^2=m_1^2+m_2^2+m_3^2=n_1^2+n_2^2+n_3^2=1. \qquad ...(1)$$

$$\therefore \quad A_1=\frac{\pi abc\,(l_1^2+m_1^2+n_1^2)^{1/2}}{(a^2l_1^2+b^2m_1^2+c^2n_1^2)^{1/2}} \qquad \text{[See equation (13), § 3]}$$

or $$\frac{1}{A_1^2}=\frac{a^2l_1^2+b^2m_1^2+c^2n_1^2}{\pi^2a^2b^2c^2}, \text{ using (1).}$$

Similarly $$\frac{1}{A_2^2}=\frac{a^2l_2^2+b^2m_2^2+c^2n_2^2}{\pi^2a^2b^2c^2}, \quad \frac{1}{A_3^2}=\frac{a^2l_3^2+b^2m_3^2+c^2n_3^2}{\pi^2a^2b^2c^2}.$$

Adding, $$\frac{1}{A_1^2}+\frac{1}{A_2^2}+\frac{1}{A_3^2}=\frac{1}{\pi^2a^2b^2c^2}\,[a^2(l_1^2+l_2^2+l_3^2)+b^2(m_1^2+m_2^2+m_3^2)+c^2(n_1^2+n_2^2+n_3^2)]$$

$$=(a^2+b^2+c^2)/(\pi^2a^2b^2c^2), \text{ using (1)}$$

$$=\text{constant}.$$

Ex. 8. *If A_1, A_2, A_3 are the areas of the sections of the ellipsoid $x^2/a^2+y^2/b^2+z^2/c^2=1$ by the diametral planes of three mutually perpendicular semi-diameters of lengths r_1, r_2, r_3, then show that*

$$\frac{A_1^2}{r_1^2}+\frac{A_2^2}{r_2^2}+\frac{A_3^2}{r_3^2}=\pi^2\left(\frac{b^2c^2}{a^2}+\frac{c^2a^2}{b^2}+\frac{a^2b^2}{c^2}\right)$$

Solution. The given ellipsoid is

$$x^2/a^2+y^2/b^2+z^2/c^2=1. \qquad ...(1)$$

Let $x/l_k=y/m_k=z/n_k$ $(k=1, 2, 3)$ be the equations and r_k, $k=1, 2, 3$ be the lengths of three mutually perpendicular semi-diameters of (1) so that

$$l_1^2+l_2^2+l_3^2=m_1^2+m_2^2+m_3^2=n_1^2+n_2^2+n_3^2=1. \qquad ...(2)$$

The extremity (l_1r_1, m_1r_1, n_1r_1) of the first semi-diameter will lie on (1) if

$$(l_1^2/a^2+m_1^2/b^2+n_1^2/c^2)\,r_1^2=1. \qquad ...(3)$$

The diametral plane of the semi-diameter $x/l_1=y/m_1=z/n_1$ is

$$xl_1/a^2+ym_1/b^2+zn_1/c^2=0. \qquad ...(4)$$

$\therefore \quad A_1=$ the area of the section of (1) by the plane (4)

$$=\pi abc\,\frac{\sqrt{(l_1^2/a^4+m_1^2/b^4+n_1^2/c^4)}}{\sqrt{(l_1^2/a^2+m_1^2/b^2+n_1^2/c^2)}}.$$

$$\therefore \quad \frac{A_1^2}{r_1^2}=\pi^2a^2b^2c^2\left\{\frac{l_1^2}{a^4}+\frac{m_1^2}{b^4}+\frac{n_1^2}{c^4}\right\}, \text{ using (3)}$$

with similar expressions for A_2^2/r_2^2 and A_3^2/r_3^2.

$$\therefore \quad \frac{A_1^2}{r_1^2}+\frac{A_2^2}{r_2^2}+\frac{A_3^2}{r_3^2}=\pi^2a^2b^2c^2\left\{\frac{1}{a^4}\Sigma l_1^2+\frac{1}{b^4}\Sigma m_1^2+\frac{1}{c^4}\Sigma n_1^2\right\}$$

$$=\pi^2a^2b^2c^2\left\{\frac{1}{a^4}+\frac{1}{b^4}+\frac{1}{c^4}\right\}$$

$$=\pi^2\left(\frac{b^2c^2}{a^2}+\frac{c^2a^2}{b^2}+\frac{a^2b^2}{c^2}\right).$$

Ex. 9. *If A_1, A_2, A_3; B_1, B_2, B_3 are the areas of the sections of the ellipsoids $x^2/a^2+y^2/b^2+z^2/c^2=1$, $x^2/\alpha^2+y^2/\beta^2+z^2/\gamma^2=1$ by three conjugate diametral planes of the former, then*

$$\frac{A_1^2}{B_1^2}+\frac{A_2^2}{B_2^2}+\frac{A_3^2}{B_3^2}=\frac{a^2b^2c^2}{\alpha^2\beta^2\gamma^2}\left(\frac{\alpha^2}{a^2}+\frac{\beta^2}{b^2}+\frac{\gamma^2}{c^2}\right).$$

Solution. Let the equations of any three conjugate diametral planes of the ellipsoid $x^2/a^2+y^2/b^2+z^2/c^2=1$ be

$$xx_r/a^2+yy_r/b^2+zz_r/c^2=0$$

or $$l_rx+m_ry+n_rz=0, \ (r=1, 2, 3).$$

Then $$A_1^2=\pi^2a^2b^2c^2\frac{(l_1^2+m_1^2+n_1^2)}{(a^2l_1^2+b^2m_1^2+c^2n_1^2)},$$

$$B_1^2=\pi^2\alpha^2\beta^2\gamma^2\frac{(l_1^2+m_1^2+n_1^2)}{\alpha^2l_1^2+\beta^2m_1^2+\gamma^2n_1^2},$$

with similar expressions for A_2^2, A_3^2, B_2^2, B_3^2.

$$\therefore \quad \frac{A_1^2}{B_1^2}=\frac{a^2b^2c^2}{\alpha^2\beta^2\gamma^2}\cdot\frac{\alpha_1^2l_1^2+\beta^2m_1^2+\gamma^2n_1^2}{a^2l_1^2+b^2m_1^2+c^2n_1^2}$$

$$=\frac{a^2b^2c^2\{\alpha^2(x_1/a^2)^2+\beta^2(y_1/b^2)^2+\gamma^2(z_1/c^2)^2\}}{\alpha^2\beta^2+\gamma^2\{a^2(x_1/a^2)^2+b^2(y_1/b^2)^2+c^2(z_1/c^2)^2\}}$$

$$[\because \ l_1=x_1/a^2, \ m_1=y_1/b^2, \ n_1=z_1/c^2]$$

$$=\frac{a^2b^2c^2\left\{\frac{\alpha^2}{a^2}\cdot\frac{x_1^2}{a^2}+\frac{\beta^2}{b^2}\cdot\frac{y_1^2}{b^2}+\frac{\gamma^2}{c^2}\cdot\frac{z_1^2}{c^2}\right\}}{\alpha^2\beta^2\gamma^2(x_1^2/a^2+y_1^2/b^2+z_1^2/c^2)}$$

$$=\frac{a^2b^2c^2}{\alpha^2\beta^2\gamma^2}\left\{\frac{\alpha^2}{a^4}x_1^2+\frac{\beta^2}{b^4}y_1^2+\frac{\gamma^2}{c^4}z_1^2\right\}, \text{ since } \Sigma(x_1^2/a^2)=1.$$

$$\therefore \quad \Sigma\frac{A_1^2}{B_1^2}=\frac{a^2b^2c^2}{\alpha^2\beta^2\gamma^2}\left\{\frac{\alpha^2}{a^4}\Sigma x_1^2+\frac{\beta^2}{b^4}\Sigma y_1^2+\frac{\gamma^2}{c^4}\Sigma z_1^2\right\}$$

$$=\frac{a^2b^2c^2}{\alpha^2\beta^2\gamma^2}\left\{\frac{\alpha^2}{a^2}+\frac{\beta^2}{b^2}+\frac{\gamma^2}{c^2}\right\},$$

since $\Sigma x_1^2=a^2$, $\Sigma y_1^2=b^2$, $\Sigma z_1^2=c^2$.

Ex. 10. *Find the conditions that any two lines*

$$x/l_1=y/m_1=z/n_1,\; x/l_2=y/m_2=z/n_2$$

be the axes of the section of the conicoid $ax^2+by^2+cz^2=1$ *by a plane through them.*

Solution. Since both the given lines are the axes of the central section, each of them must bisect the chords which are parallel to the other. Therefore each of them must lie in the diametral plane conjugate to the other.

Now the equation of the diametral plane conjugate to

$$x/l_1=y/m_1=z/n_1 \text{ is } al_1x+bm_1y+cn_1z=0.$$

This diametral plane will contain the other line, if

$$al_1l_2+bm_1m_2+cn_1n_2=0. \quad \ldots(1)$$

Since the axes are at right angles so the two given lines must be perpendicular to each other, hence

$$l_1l_2+m_1m_2+n_1n_2=0. \quad \ldots(2)$$

Therefore the required conditions are given by (1) and (2).

Ex. 11. *Prove that the axes of the sections of the conicoid* $ax^2+by^2+cz^2=1$ *which pass through the line* $x/l=y/m=z/n$ *lie on the cone*

$$\left(\frac{b-c}{x}\right)(mz-ny)+\left(\frac{c-a}{y}\right)(nx-lz)+\left(\frac{a-b}{z}\right)(ly-mx)=0.$$

Solution. Let $x/l_1=y/m_1=z/n_1$ ..(1)

and $x/l_2=y/m_2=z/n_2$ ...(2)

be the equations of the principal axes of the section through the given line

$$x/l=y/m=z/n. \quad \ldots(3)$$

Now proceeding as in Ex. 10 above, we have

$$al_1l_2+bm_1m_2+cn_1n_2=0, \quad \ldots(4)$$

and $$l_1l_2+m_1m_2+n_1n_2=0. \quad \ldots(5)$$

Since the lines (1), (2) and (3) are coplanar, we have

$$\begin{vmatrix} l_1 & m_1 & n_1 \\ l_2 & m_2 & n_2 \\ l & m & n \end{vmatrix}=0$$

or $$l_1(m_2n-n_2m)+m_1(n_2l-l_2n)+n_1(l_2m-lm_2)=0. \quad \ldots(6)$$

Eliminating l_1, m_1, n_1 from (5), (4) and (6), we have

$$\begin{vmatrix} l_2 & m_2 & n_2 \\ al_2 & bm_2 & cn_2 \\ m_2n-n_2m & n_2l-l_2n & l_2m-m_2l \end{vmatrix}=0. \quad \ldots(7)$$

Again eliminating l_2, m_2, n_2 from (2) and (7), the equation of the required cone is

$$\begin{vmatrix} x & y & z \\ ax & by & cz \\ yn-zm & zl-xn & xm-yl \end{vmatrix}=0$$

or $\left(\frac{b-c}{x}\right)(mz-ny)+\left(\frac{c-a}{y}\right)(nx-lz)+\left(\frac{a-b}{z}\right)(ly-mx)=0,$

expanding the determinant along the third row.

Ex. 12. *Prove that if l_1, m_1, n_1 ; l_2, m_2, n_2 are the direction ratios of the principal axes of any plane section of the conicoid*

$$ax^2+by^2+cz^2=1, \text{ then } \frac{l_1l_2}{b-c}=\frac{m_1m_2}{c-a}=\frac{n_1n_2}{a-b}$$

Solution. The result follows by solving equations (1) and (2) of Ex. 10 above.

Ex. 13. *One axis of a central section of the conicoid*

$$ax^2+by^2+cz^2=1$$

lies in the plane $lx+my+nz=0$. Show that the other line lies on the cone

$$(b-c)\,lyz+(c-a)\,mzx+(a-b)\,nxy=0.$$

Solution. Let the equations of the two axes of a central plane section be

$x/l_1=y/m_1=z/n_1$ ...(1) and $x/l_2=y/m_2=z/n_2$. ...(2)

Now proceeding as in Ex. 10 above, we have

$$l_1l_2+m_1m_2+n_1n_2=0, \qquad \text{...(3)}$$

and $$al_1l_2+bm_1m_2+cn_1n_2=0. \qquad \text{...(4)}$$

As given let the axis (1) lie in the given plane $lx+my+nz=0$, so that

$$ll_1+mm_1+nn_1=0. \qquad \text{...(5)}$$

Eliminating l_1, m_1, n_1 between (5), (3) and (4), we get

$$\begin{vmatrix} l & m & n \\ l_2 & m_2 & n_2 \\ al_2 & bm_2 & cn_2 \end{vmatrix}=0$$

or $$lm_2n_2\,(b-c)+mn_2l_2\,(c-a)+nm_2l_2\,(a-b)=0. \qquad \text{...(6)}$$

∴ The locus of the axis (2) is the cone given by

$$lyz\,(b-c)+mzx\,(c-a)+nxy\,(a-b)=0.$$

Ex. 14. *Prove that all plane sections of $ax^2+by^2+cz^2=1$ which are rectangular hyperbolas and which pass through the point (α, β, γ) touch the cone*

$$\frac{(x-\alpha)^2}{b+c}+\frac{(y-\beta)^2}{c+a}+\frac{(z-\gamma)^2}{a+b}=0.$$

Solution. If the central plane section of $ax^2+by^2+cz^2=1$ by the plane $lx+my+nz=0$ is a rectangular hyperbola then (as proved in Cor. 3, § 3), we have

$$(b+c)\,l^2+(c+a)\,m^2+(a+b)\,n^2=0. \qquad ...(1)$$

Again the equation of the plane parallel to the plane $lx+my+nz=0$ and passing through the point (α, β, γ) is

$$l\,(x-\alpha)+m\,(y-\beta)+n\,(z-\gamma)=0. \qquad ...(2)$$

Since the plane (2) is parallel to the plane $lx+my+nz=0$, therefore (1) is also the condition for the section of the given conicoid by the plane (2) to be a rectangular hyperbola.

Shifting the origin to the point (α, β, γ), the equation (2) becomes

$$lx+my+nz=0. \qquad (3)$$

$\therefore$ (1) shows that the plane (3) envelopes the cone

$$x^2/(b+c)+y^2/(c+a)+z^2/(a+b)=0. \qquad ...(4)$$

Again shifting the origin back to (α, β, γ), the plane (2) envelopes the cone

$$(x-\alpha)^2/(b+c)+(y-\beta)^2/(c+a)+(z-\gamma)^2/(a+b)=0.$$

Ex. 15. *Find the condition that the section of the conicoid*

$$ax^2+by^2+cz^2+2fyz+2gzx+2hxy=1$$

by the plane $lx+my+nz=0$ may be a rectangular hyperbola.

Solution. Let λ, μ, ν be the d. c.'s of the semi-diameter of length r of the given conicoid. The extremity $(\lambda r, \mu r, \nu r)$ of this semi-diameter will lie on the given conicoid, so that we have

$$(a\lambda^2+b\mu^2+c\nu^2+2f\mu\nu+2g\nu\lambda+2h\lambda\mu)\,r^2=1$$

or $$1/r^2=a\lambda^2+b\mu^2+c\nu^2+2f\mu\nu+2g\nu\lambda+2h\lambda\mu. \qquad ...(1)$$

Now consider any three perpendicular semi-diameters of lengths r_1, r_2, r_3 with their corresponding d.c.'s as λ_1, μ_1, ν_1; λ_2, μ_2, ν_2; λ_3, μ_3, ν_3 so that $\lambda_1^2+\lambda_2^2+\lambda_3^2=1$ etc. and $\lambda_1\mu_1+\lambda_2\mu_2+\lambda_3\mu_3=0$, etc.

Writing the relation (1) for these three mutually perpendicular semi-diameters of lengths r_1, r_2, r_3 and then adding the resulting relations, we get

$$1/r_1^2+1/r_2^2+1/r_3^2=a\Sigma\lambda_1^2+b\Sigma\mu_1^2+c\Sigma\nu_1^2+2f\Sigma\mu_1\nu_1$$
$$+2g\Sigma\nu_1\lambda_1+2h\Sigma\lambda_1\mu_1$$

or $$(r_1^2+r_2^2)/r_1^2r_2^2+1/r_3^2=a+b+c. \quad ...(2)$$

Now if the section of the conicoid by the plane $lx+my+nz=0$ is a rectangular hyperbola having as its principal semi-axes the two perpendicular semi-diameters of lengths r_1 and r_2 then $r_1^2+r_2^2=0$. Hence (2) gives

$$1/r_3^2=a+b+c. \quad ...(3)$$

Hence for any semi-diameter of length r of the conicoid which is perpendicular to the plane of the section which is a rectangular hyperbola, we have

$$1/r^2=a+b+c. \quad ...(4)$$

Also the d.c.'s λ, μ, ν of this semi-diameter become the same as the d.c.'s l, m, n of the normal to the plane $lx+my+nz=0$.

Hence from (1) and (4), the required condition is given by

$$al^2+bm^2+cn^2+2fmn+2gnl+2hlm=a+b+c$$
$$=(a+b+c)\ (l^2+m^2+n^2)$$

or $$(b+c)\ l^2+(c+a)\ m^2+(a+b)\ n^2-2fmn-2gnl\ \ 2hlm=0.$$

Ex 16. *Prove that the normals to the central sections of the ellipsoid* $x^2/a^2+y^2/b^2+z^2/c^2=1$ *which are of given eccentricity lie on the cone*

$$a^2b^2c^2\ (e^2-2)^2\ (x^2+y^2+z^2)\ (a^2x^2+b^2y^2+c^2z^2)$$
$$=(1-e^2)\ [a^2\ (b^2+c^2)\ x^2+b^2\ (c^2+a^2)\ y^2+c^2\ (a^2+b^2)\ z^2]^2$$

Solution. Consider the section of $x^2/a^2+y^2/b^2+z^2/c^2=1$ by the plane $lx+my+nz=0$. Proceeding as in § 3, Cor. 2, the squares of the semi-axes are given by

$$r^4\ (a^2l^2+b^2m^2+c^2n^2)-r^2\ \{a^2\ (b^2+c^2)\ l^2+b^2\ (c^2+a^2)\ m^2$$
$$+c^2\ (a^2+b^2)\ n^2\}+a^2b^2c^2\ (l^2+m^2+n^2)=0. \quad ...(1)$$

If r_1 and r_2 be the lengths of the semi-axes of the section, then r_1^2 and r_2^2 are the roots of (1) and so we have

$$r_1^2+r_2^2=\frac{\Sigma a^2\ (b^2+c^2)\ l^2}{\Sigma\ (a^2l^2)}, \quad ...(2)$$

and $$r_1^2\ r_2^2=\frac{a^2b^2c^2\ (l^2+m^2+n^2)}{\Sigma\ (a^2l^2)}. \quad ...(3)$$

Now in the two dimensional geometry, the eccentricity e of an ellipse is given by the relation $b^2=a^2\ (1-e^2)$. Therefore if e is the eccentricity of the section, then

$$r_2^2/r_1^2=1-e^2$$

or $$\frac{r_2^2}{r_1^2}=\frac{1-e^2}{1} \quad \text{or} \quad \frac{r_1^2+r_2^2}{r_2^2-r_1^2}=\frac{2-e^2}{-e^2}$$

Squaring, $e^4 (r_1^2+r_2^2)^2=(2-e^2)^2 \{(r_1^2+r_2^2)^2-4r_1^2r_2^2\}$

or $$(r_1^2+r_2^2)^2 \{(2-e^2)^2-e^4\}=4r_1^2r_2^2 (2-e^2)^2$$

or $$(r_1^2+r_2^2)^2 (1-e^2)=r_1^2r_2^2 (2-e^2)^2. \quad ...(4)$$

Putting the values from (2) and (3) in (4), we get

$$(e^2-2)^2 \cdot \frac{a^2b^2c^2 (l^2+m^2+n^2)}{\Sigma (a^2l^2)}=(1-e^2) \left\{\frac{\Sigma a^2 (b^2+c^2) l^2}{\Sigma a^2l^2}\right\}^2$$

or $(e^2-2)^2 a^2b^2c^2 (l^2+m^2+n^2) \Sigma (a^2l^2)=(1-e^2) [\Sigma a^2 (b^2+c^2) l^2]^2.$

Hence the locus of the normal $x/l=y/m=z/n$ to the central section $lx+my+nz=0$ is given by

$$(e^2-2)^2 a^2b^2c^2 (x^2+y^2+z^2) \Sigma a^2x^2=(1-e^2) [\Sigma a^2 (b^2+c^2) x^2]^2.$$

Ex. 17. *If through the centre of the ellipsoid $x^2/a^2+y^2/b^2+z^2/c^2=1$ a perpendicular is drawn to any central section and lengths equal to the axes of the section are marked off along the perpendicular, the locus of their extremities is given by*

$$\frac{a^2x^2}{r^2-a^2}+\frac{b^2y^2}{r^2-b^2}+\frac{c^2z^2}{r^2-c^2}=0$$

where $$r^2=x^2+y^2+z^2.$$

Solution. Let the central section of the given ellipsoid be made by the plane

$$lx+my+nz=0 \quad ...(1)$$

where l, m, n are the actual d.c.'s of the normal to the plane. Also the equations of the perpendicular from the centre (0, 0, 0) of the ellipsoid to the plane (1) are

$$x/l=y/m=z/n. \quad ...(2)$$

Let r_1 and r_2 be the lengths of the semi-axes of the section so that the co-ordinates of the points marked off on (2) are

$$(lr_1, mr_1, nr_1) \text{ and } (lr_2, mr_2, nr_2).$$

Therefore if (x, y, z) are the co-ordinates of the extremity in any position whose locus is to be determined, then

$$x^2+y^2+z^2=l^2r_1^2+m^2r_1^2+n^2r_1^2$$

or $$x^2+y^2+z^2=r_1^2. \quad [\because \; l^2+m^2+n^2=1]$$

Similarly $$x^2+y^2+z^2=r_2^2.$$

Thus in either case

$$x^2+y^2+z^2=r^2. \quad ...(3)$$

Now we know [See § 3, Cor. 2] that r_1^2 and r_2^2 are the roots of the equation

$$r^4 (a^2l^2+b^2m^2+c^2n^2)-r^2 \Sigma \{a^2 (b^2+c^2) l^2\}+a^2b^2c^2=0.$$

Multiplying it by r^2, we have

$$r^4 (a^2l^2r^2+b^2m^2r^2+c^2n^2r^2)-r^2 \Sigma \{a^2 (b^2+c^2) \ l^2r^2\}+a^2b^2c^2r^2=0$$

or $$r^4 (a^2x^2+b^2y^2+c^2z^2)-r^2 \Sigma \{a^2 (b^2+c^2) \ x^2\} +a^2b^2c^2 (x^2+y^2+z^2)=0$$

or $$\Sigma [a^2x^2 \{r^4-(b^2+c^2) \ r^2+b^2c^2\}]=0$$

or $$a^2x^2 (r^2-b^2) (r^2-c^2)+b^2y^2 (r^2-c^2) (r^2-a^2) +c^2z^2 (r^2-a^2) (r^2-b^2)=0.$$

Dividing by $(r^2-a^2) (r^2-b^2) (r^2-c^2)$, we get the required locus.

Ex. 18. *Find the angle between the asymptotes of any plane section of a conicoid and hence prove that if* θ *be the angle between the asymptotes of the section of* $ax^2+by^2+cz^2=1$ *by the plane* $lx+my+nz=0$ *then*

$$\tan^2 \theta \ [l^2 (b+c)+m^2 (c+a)+n^2 (a+b)]^2 +4 (bcl^2+cam^2+abn^2)=0.$$

Solution. We know that the section of a conicoid by any plane is a conic. Let the lengths of the semi-axes of this conic section be α and β. Then by a suitable transformation of co-ordinate axes the equation of this conic section can be expressed in the form

$$x^2/\alpha^2+y^2/\beta^2=1. \quad ..(1)$$

Again we know that the equation of the asymptotes differs from the equation of the conic by a constant and so the equation of the asymptotes can be given by

$$x^2/\alpha^2+y^2/\beta^2=k,$$

where k is a constant.

The angle θ between the asymptotes is given by

$$\tan \theta=\frac{2\sqrt{\{0-(1/\alpha^2).(1/\beta^2)\}}}{1/\alpha^2+1/\beta^2}$$

$$\left[\because \ \tan \theta=\frac{2\sqrt{(h^2-ab)}}{a+b} \text{ by plane geometry}\right]$$

or $$\frac{2 \tan \frac{1}{2}\theta}{1-\tan^2 \frac{1}{2}\theta}=\frac{2i\alpha\beta}{\alpha^2+\beta^2}=\frac{2i \ (\beta/\alpha)}{1-(i\beta/\alpha)^2}.$$

$$\therefore \ \tan \tfrac{1}{2}\theta=i\beta/\alpha, \quad \text{or} \quad \theta=2 \tan^{-1} (i\beta/\alpha)$$

Also from above,

$$\tan^2 \theta=-4\alpha^2\beta^2/(\alpha^2+\beta^2)^2. \quad ..(2)$$

Second part : If r_1 and r_2 are the lengths of the semi-axes of the plane section of the conicoid $ax^2+by^2+cz^2=1$ by the plane $lx+my+nz=0$, then from (2), we have

$$\tan^2\theta=\frac{-4r_1^2r_2^2}{(r_1^2+r_2^2)^2}=\frac{-4\{\Sigma(bcl^2)\}\{\Sigma l^2\}}{[\Sigma(b+c)l^2]^2}$$

[From equation (6) of § 3]

or $\tan^2\theta\,[\Sigma(b+c)l^2]^2+4(bcl^2+cam^2+abn^2)=0,$

if $l^2+m^2+n^2=1.$

§ 4. Non-central Plane Section.

To find the lengths and direction cosines of the axes of a non-central plane section of a central conicoid.

Let the conicoid be

$$ax^2+by^2+cz^2=1 \qquad ...(1)$$

and the equation of the plane not passing through the centre of (1) [*i.e.* non-central plane] be

$$lx+my+nz=p. \qquad ...(2)$$

Now the section of (1) by the plane (2) is the non-central plane section. Let $C(\alpha,\beta,\gamma)$ be the centre of this section so that the equation (2) of the plane can be given by

$$a\alpha(x-\alpha)+b\beta(y-\beta)+c\gamma(z-\gamma)=0$$

or $$a\alpha x+b\beta y+c\gamma z=a\alpha^2+b\beta^2+c\gamma^2. \qquad ...(3)$$

Comparing the equations (2) and (3), we have

$$\frac{a\alpha}{l}=\frac{b\beta}{m}=\frac{c\gamma}{n}=\frac{a\alpha^2+b\beta^2+c\gamma^2}{p}=k \text{ (say)}. \qquad ...(4)$$

$$\therefore\quad \alpha=lk/a,\ \beta=mk/b,\ \gamma=nk/c. \qquad ...(5)$$

Putting the values of α,β,γ in the last ratio of (4), we have

$$kp=l^2k^2/a+m^2k^2/b+n^2k^2/c \quad\text{or}\quad k=p/p_0^2$$

where $$p_0^2=l^2/a+m^2/b+n^2/c.$$

Putting the value of k in (5), centre of the section is given by

$$C(lp/ap_0^2,\ mp/bp_0^2,\ np/cp_0^2). \qquad ...(6)$$

Now shifting the origin to the centre C, the equation (1) of the conicoid becomes

$$a\left(x+\frac{lp}{ap_0^2}\right)^2+b\left(y+\frac{mp}{bp_0^2}\right)^2+c\left(z+\frac{np}{cp_0^2}\right)^2=1$$

or $$ax^2+by^2+cz^2+(2p/p_0^2)(lx+my+nz)+(p^2/p_0^2)=1 \qquad ...(7)$$

and the equation (2) of the plane becomes

$$lx+my+nz=0. \qquad ...(8)$$

But the conic which is given by (7) and (8) is the same as the conic given by the equations

$$ax^2+by^2+cz^2=1-(p^2/p_0^2),\ lx+my+nz=0 \qquad ...(9)$$

since all the points which lie on (7) and (8) also lie on (9).

Putting $1-(p^2/p_0^2)=d^2$, the equations (9) of the conic become

$$(a/d^2)\, x^2+(b/d^2)\, y^2+(c/d^2)\, z^2=1,\ lx+my+nz=0. \qquad ...(10)$$

Now proceeding exactly as in § 3, the lengths of the semi-axes of the section are given by

$$\frac{l^2}{\dfrac{ar^2}{d^2}-1}+\frac{m^2}{\dfrac{br^2}{d^2}-1}+\frac{n^2}{\dfrac{cr^2}{d^2}-1}=0 \qquad ...(11)$$

and their direction cosines λ, μ, ν are given by

$$\frac{\lambda\left(\dfrac{ar^2}{d^2}-1\right)}{l}=\frac{\mu\left(\dfrac{br^2}{d^2}-1\right)}{m}=\frac{\nu\left(\dfrac{cr^2}{d^2}-1\right)}{n} \qquad ...(12)$$

Note that the equations (11) and (12) are obtained by replacing a, b, c by a/d^2, b/d^2, c/d^2 respectively in equations (5′) and (8) of § 3.

Corollary 1. The area of any plane section. From equation (9), § 3, the area A_0 of the central plane section (ellipse) of the conicoid $ax^2+by^2+cz^2=1$ by the plane $lx+my+nz=0$ is given by

$$A_0=\pi\left\{\frac{l^2+m^2+n^2}{bcl^2+cam^2+abn^2}\right\}^{1/2}. \qquad ...(13)$$

If the non-central plane section is also an ellipse, the lengths of whose semi-axes are r_1 and r_2, then its area A is obtained by replacing a, b, c by a/d^2, b/d^2, c/d^2 respectively in the expression for A_0 and hence is given by

$$A=\pi d^2\left\{\frac{l^2+m^2+n^2}{bcl^2+cam^2+abn^2}\right\}^{1/2},$$

where $d^2=1-p^2/p_0^2$. ...(14)

Form (14) and (13), we have

$$A=A_0 d^2 \quad \text{or} \quad A=A_0\,(1-p^2/p_0^2). \qquad ...(15)$$

Corollary 2 *To compare the lengths of the semi-axes of any plane section and those of parallel central plane section.*

From § 3, we know that the lengths of the semi-axes of the conic $ax^2+by^2+cz^2=1$, $lx+my+nz=0$ (*i.e.* central plane section) are given by

$$\frac{l^2}{ar^2-1}+\frac{m^2}{br^2-1}+\frac{n^2}{cr^2-1}=0. \qquad ...(16)$$

Also the lengths of the semi-axes of the conic $ax^2+by^2+cz^2=1$, $lx+my+nz=p$ (*i.e.* any plane section) are given by

$$\frac{l^2}{\frac{ar^2}{d^2}-1}+\frac{m^2}{\frac{br^2}{d^2}-1}+\frac{n^2}{\frac{cr^2}{d^2}-1}=0. \quad ...(17)$$

Therefore, if r_1^2 and r_2^2 are the roots of (16) and R_1^2 and R_2^2 those of (17), then comparing (16) and (17), we get

$R_1^2/d^2=r_1^2$ and $R_2^2/d^2=r_2^2$ or $R_1=dr_1$ and $R_2=dr_2$.

Thus we have, the area $A_0=\pi r_1 r_2$,

and the area $A=\pi R_1 R_2=\pi dr_1 . dr_2=\pi d^2 r_1 r_2$.

$\therefore \quad A=d^2 A_0=(1-p^2/p_0^2)\, A_0$, as in corollary (1) above.

SOLVED EXAMPLES (B)

Ex. 1. *Prove that tangent planes to* $x^2/a^2+y^2/b^2-z^2/c^2+1=0$ *which cut* $x^2/a^2+y^2/b^2-z^2/c^2=1$ *in ellipses of constant area* πk^2 *have their points of contact on the surface*

$$x^2/a^4+y^2/b^4+z^2/c^4=k^4/(4a^2b^2c^2).$$

Solution. The equation of the first conicoid is

$$x^2/a^2+y^2/b^2-z^2/c^2+1=0. \quad ...(1)$$

Let (α, β, γ) be the point of contact. The equation of the tangent plane at (α, β, γ) to (1) is

$$\frac{\alpha x}{a^2}+\frac{\beta y}{b^2}-\frac{\gamma z}{c^2}+1=0 \quad ...(2)$$

where $\qquad \alpha^2/a^2+\beta^2/b^2-\gamma^2/c^2=-1. \quad ...(3)$

The equation of the second conicoid is

$$x^2/a^2+y^2/b^2-z^2/c^2=1. \quad ...(4)$$

Let A be the area of the section (ellipse) of (4) by the plane (2) and A_0 the area of the central parallel section (ellipse) of (4) by the parallel plane $\alpha x/a^2+\beta y/b^2-\gamma z/c^2=0$.

Then we know that

$$A=(1-p^2/p_0^2)\, A_0 \quad ...(5)$$

where $\qquad p_0^2=a^2.\frac{\alpha^2}{a^4}+b^2.\frac{\beta^2}{b^4}-c^2.\frac{\gamma^2}{c^4} \left[\because\ p_0^2=\frac{l^2}{a}+\frac{m^2}{b}+\frac{n^2}{c}\right]$

or $\qquad p_0^2=\alpha^2/a^2+\beta^2/b^2-\gamma^2/c^2=-1$, using (3)

and $p=$the length of the perpendicular from (0, 0, 0) to (2)$=-1$, so that $p^2=1$.

Now $\quad A=\pi k^2$, (given).

Also $\quad A_0=\dfrac{\pi ab\sqrt{(-c^2)}.\sqrt{(l^2+m^2+n^2)}}{\sqrt{(a^2l^2+b^2m^2-c^2n^2)}}$ [using formula for A_0]

or $\quad A_0=\dfrac{\pi ab\sqrt{(-c^2)}\sqrt{\{\alpha^2/a^4+\beta^2/b^4+\gamma^2/c^4\}}}{\sqrt{\{a^2\,(\alpha^2/a^4)+b^2\,(\beta^2/b^4)-c^2\,(\gamma^2/c^4)\}}}$

or $A_0=\dfrac{\pi ab\sqrt{(-c^2)}\sqrt{\{\alpha^2/a^4+\beta^2/b^4+\gamma^2/c^4\}}}{\sqrt{(-1)}}$, using (3).

Putting the above values in (5) and squaring, we have

$$\pi^2k^4=\left(1-\frac{1}{-1}\right)^2\cdot\frac{\pi^2a^2b^2(c^2)}{-1}\left(\frac{\alpha^2}{a^4}+\frac{\beta^2}{b^4}+\frac{\gamma^2}{c^4}\right).$$

$\therefore$ the required locus of the point of contact (α, β, γ) is

$$x^2/a^4+y^2/b^4+z^2/c^4=k^4/(4a^2b^2c^2).$$

Ex. 2. *If OP, OQ, OR are conjugate semi-diameters of an ellipsoid, prove that the area of the section of the ellipsoid by the plane PQR is two thirds the area of the parallel central section.*

Or

Show that the area of the section of an ellipsoid by a plane which passes through the extremities of three conjugate semi-diameters is in a constant ratio to the area of the parallel central section.

Solution. Let the equation of the ellipsoid be

$$x^2/a^2+y^2/b^2+z^2/c^2=1. \quad ...(1)$$

Let the co-ordinates of the extremities P, Q, R of conjugate semi-diameters be (x_r, y_r, z_r), $r=1, 2, 3$. The equation of the plane PQR is [See Ex. 3 page 65]

$$\frac{x}{a^2}(x_1+x_2+x_3)+\frac{y}{b^2}(y_1+y_2+y_3)+\frac{z}{c^2}(z_1+z_2+z_3)=1 \quad ...(2)$$

or $lx+my+nz=1$, where $l=(x_1+x_2+x_3)/a^2$, etc.

Let A and A_0 be the areas of the sections of (1) by the plane (2) and the central plane parallel to the plane (2). We have

$$A=A_0(1-p^2/p_0^2) \quad ...(3)$$

where $p=1$ or $p^2=1$

and $p_0^2=a^2l^2+b^2m^2+c^2n^2$ in case of ellipsoid

$$=\frac{a^2}{a^4}(\Sigma x_1)^2+\frac{b^2}{b^4}(\Sigma y_1)^2+\frac{c^2}{c^4}(\Sigma z_1)^2$$

$$=\frac{\Sigma x_1^2}{a^2}+\frac{\Sigma y_1^2}{b^2}+\frac{\Sigma z_1^2}{c^2}+\frac{2\Sigma_3 x_1x_2}{a^2}+\frac{2\Sigma x_2x_3}{a^2}+\frac{2\Sigma x_3x_1}{a^2}$$

$=1+1+1+0+0+0=3$ [See § 17, page 60].

Putting the above values in (3), we get $A=\frac{2}{3}A_0$.

Ex. 3. *Show that the area of the section of the ellipsoid* $x^2/a^2+y^2/b^2+z^2c^2=1$ *by the plane* $x/a+y/b+z/c=1$ *is*

$$2\pi(b^2c^2+c^2a^2+a^2b^2)^{1/2}/(3\sqrt{3}).$$

Solution. Here $p=1$, $p_0^2=a^2l^2+b^2m^2+c^2n^2=\dfrac{a^2}{a^2}+\dfrac{b^2}{b^2}+\dfrac{c^2}{c^2}=3.$

$$A_0=\pi abc\,\frac{(l^2+m^2+n^2)^{1/2}}{\sqrt{(a^2l^2+b^2m^2+c^2n^2)}}=\frac{\pi abc\sqrt{\{1/a^2+1/b^2+1/c^2\}}}{\sqrt{3}}$$
$$=\pi\sqrt{(b^2c^2+c^2a^2+a^2b^2)}/\sqrt{3}.$$
$$\therefore\quad A=A_0\left(1-\frac{p^2}{p_0^2}\right)=\frac{\pi\sqrt{(b^2c^2+c^2a^2+a^2b^2)}}{\sqrt{3}}\left(1-\frac{1}{3}\right)$$
$$=\frac{2\pi\sqrt{(b^2c^2+c^2a^2+a^2b^2)}}{3\sqrt{3}}.$$

Ex. 4. *Find the locus of the centres of the sections of the ellipsoid* $x^2/a^2+y^2/b^2+z^2/c^2=1$ *whose area is constant* $=\pi k^2$.

Solution. The ellipsoid is $x^2/a^2+y^2/b^2+z^2/c^2=1$. .. (1)

Let (x_1, y_1, z_1) be the centre of the section of (1). By the formula '$T=S_1$' the equation of the plane giving this section is

$$\frac{xx_1}{a^2}+\frac{yy_1}{b^2}+\frac{zz_1}{c^2}=\frac{x_1^2}{a^2}+\frac{y_1^2}{b^2}+\frac{z_1^2}{c^2}. \quad \text{...(2)}$$

Let A and A_0 be the areas of the sections of (1) by the plane (2) and the central plane parallel to (2) respectively.

We have $$A=A_0\,(1-p^2/p_0^2) \quad \text{...(3)}$$
where $$p^2=(x_1^2/a^2+y_1^2/b^2+z_1^2/c^2)^2,$$
$$p_0^2=a^2l^2+b^2m^2+c^2n^2=x_1^2/a^2+y_1^2/b^2+z_1^2/c^2.$$
$$\therefore\quad p^2/p_0^2=x_1^2/a^2+y_1^2/b^2+z_1^2/c^2.$$

Now $$A_0=\frac{\pi abc\sqrt{(l^2+m^2+n^2)}}{\sqrt{(a^2l^2+b^2m^2+c^2n^2)}}=\frac{\pi abc\sqrt{\{x_1^2/a^4+y_1^2/b^4+z_1^2/c^4\}}}{\sqrt{(x_1^2/a^2+y_1^2/b^2+z_1^2/c^2)}}.$$

Also $A=\pi k^2$, (given).

Putting the above values in (3) and squaring, we get

$$\pi^2k^4=\frac{\pi^2a^2b^2c^2\,\{x_1^2/a^4+y_1^2/b^4+z_1^2/c^4\}}{(x_1^2/a^2+y_1^2/b^2+z_1^2/c^2)}\cdot\left\{1-\frac{x_1^2}{a^2}-\frac{y_1^2}{b^2}-\frac{z_1^2}{c^2}\right\}^2.$$

$\therefore$ The required locus of (x_1, y_1, z_1) is

$$a^2b^2c^2\left(\frac{x^2}{a^4}+\frac{y^2}{b^4}+\frac{z^2}{c^4}\right)\left\{1-\frac{x^2}{a^2}-\frac{y^2}{b^2}-\frac{z^2}{c^2}\right\}^2=k^4\left(\frac{x^2}{a^2}+\frac{y^2}{b^2}+\frac{z^2}{c^2}\right)$$

Ex. 5. *Prove that the section of the ellipsoid* $x^2/a^2+y^2/b^2+z^2/c^2=1$ *whose centre is the point* $(\frac{1}{3}a, \frac{1}{3}b, \frac{1}{3}c)$ *passes through the three of the extremities of its principal axes.*

Solution By the formula '$T=S_1$' the equation of the plane section with $(\frac{1}{3}a, \frac{1}{3}b, \frac{1}{3}c)$ as its centre is

$$\frac{\frac{1}{3}a\,x}{a^2}+\frac{\frac{1}{3}bx}{b^2}+\frac{\frac{1}{3}cx}{c^2}=\frac{a^2}{9a^2}+\frac{b^2}{9b^2}+\frac{c^2}{9c^2}$$

or $$x/a+y/b+z/c=1$$

which clearly passes through $(a, 0, 0)$, $(0, b, 0)$, $(0, 0, c)$, the three of the extremities of the principal axes of the given ellipsoid.

Ex. 6. *Through a given point (α, β, γ) planes are drawn parallel to three conjugate diametral planes of the ellipsoid*

$$x^2/a^2+y^2/b^2+z^2/c^2=1.$$

Show that the sum of the ratios of the areas of the sections by these planes to the areas of the parallel diametral planes is

$$3-\alpha^2/a^2-\beta^2/b^2-\gamma^2/c^2.$$

Solution. The given ellipsoid is

$$x^2/a^2+y^2/b^2+z^2/c^2=1. \quad \ldots(1)$$

Let (x_r, y_r, z_r), $r=1, 2, 3$ be the co-ordinates of the three extremities of the three conjugate semi-diameters of (1). The equation of the diametral plane of the diameter through (x_1, y_1, z_1) is

$$xx_1/a^2+yy_1/b^2+zz_1/c^2=0. \quad \ldots(2)$$

The equation of the plane through the given point (α, β, γ) and parallel to the plane (2) is

$$(x-\alpha)\,(x_1/a^2)+(y-\beta)\,(y_1/b^2)+(z-\gamma)\,(z_1/c^2)=0$$

or $xx_1/a^2+yy_1/b^2+zz_1/c^2=\alpha x_1/a^2+\beta y_1/b^2+\gamma z_1/c^2=p_1$ (say). ...(3)

Let A_1 and $A_1{}^0$ be the areas of the sections of (1) by the plane (3) and the central plane (2) respectively. We have

$$A_1=A_1{}^0\left(1-\frac{p_1{}^2}{p_0{}^2}\right) \text{ or } \frac{A_1}{A_1{}^0}=1-\frac{p_1{}^2}{p_0{}^2} \quad \ldots(4)$$

where $p_0{}^2=a^2l^2+b^2m^2+c^2n^2$ for the ellipsoid

or $p_0{}^2=x_1{}^2/a^2+y_1{}^2/b^2+z_1{}^2/c^2=1$. [$\because$ (x_1, y_1, z_1) lies on (1)]

Putting the value of $p_0{}^2$ from above and that of p_1 from (3) in (4),

we get $\dfrac{A_1}{A_1{}^0}=1-p_1{}^2=1-\left(\dfrac{\alpha x_1}{a^2}+\dfrac{\beta y_1}{b^2}+\dfrac{\gamma z_1}{c^2}\right)^2$

with similar expressions for other two ratios of the areas.

$$\therefore \sum\frac{A_1}{A_1{}^0}=3-\sum\left(\frac{\alpha x_1}{a^2}+\frac{\beta y_1}{b^2}+\frac{\gamma z_1}{c^2}\right)^2$$

$$=3-\left[\frac{\alpha^2}{a^4}\Sigma x_1{}^2+\frac{\beta^2}{b^4}\Sigma y_1{}^2+\frac{\gamma^2}{c^4}\Sigma z_1{}^2+\frac{2\alpha\beta}{a^2b^2}\Sigma x_1y_1\right.$$

$$\left.+\frac{2\beta\gamma}{b^2c^2}\Sigma y_1z_1+\frac{2\gamma\alpha}{c^2a^2}\Sigma z_1x_1\right]$$

$$=3-[(\alpha^2/a^4).a^2+(\beta^2/b^4).b^2+(\gamma^2/c^4).c^2]$$

[See § 17, page 60]

$$=3-\alpha^2/a^2-\beta^2/b^2-\gamma^2/c^2.$$

Ex. 7 (a). *Prove that the axes of the section of the cone $ax^2+by^2+cz^2=0$ by the plane $lx+my+nz=p$ are given by*

$$\frac{l^2}{ap_0{}^2r^2+p^2}+\frac{m^2}{bp_0{}^2r^2+p^2}+\frac{n^2}{cp_0{}^2r^2+p^2}=0.$$

Solution. Let the centre of the section of $ax^2+by^2+cz^2=0$ by the plane $lx+my+nz=p$ be (α, β, γ) so that the equation of this plane can also be given by $T=S_1$ *i.e.* by

$$a\alpha x+b\beta y+c\gamma z=a\alpha^2+b\beta^2+c\gamma^2.$$

Now proceeding exactly as in § 4 above, we shall get $d^2=-p^2/p_0^2$ and putting this value of d^2 in equation (11) of § 4, we at once get the result.

Ex. 7 (b). *Prove that the area of the section of the cone $x^2/a+y^2/b+z^2/c=0$ by the plane $lx+my+nz=p$ is*

$$\pi p^2\sqrt{(abc)}/(al^2+bm^2+cn^2)^{3/2}.$$

Solution. Proceed as in § 4 above.

Ex. 7 (c). *The locus of the centres of the sections of the cone $ax^2+by^2+cz^2=0$ such that the sum of the squares of their axes is constant $(=k^2)$ is the conicoid*

$$a^2(b+c)x^2+b^2(c+a)y^2+c^2(a+b)z^2+abck^2=0.$$

Solution. Let (α, β, γ) be the centre of the section. Proceeding exactly as in § 4, the axes are given by

$$\frac{l^2}{ap_0^2r^2+p^2}+\frac{m^2}{bp_0^2r^2+p^2}+\frac{n^2}{cp_0^2r^2+p^2}=0.$$

This is a quadratic equation in r^2. Let its roots be r_1^2, r_2^2. Then $r_1^2+r_2^2=k^2$, etc.

Ex. 8. *Prove that the areas of the sections of the greatest and least areas of the ellipsoid $x^2/a^2+y^2/b^2+z^2/c^2=1$ which pass through the fixed line $x/l=y/m=z/n$ are $\pi abc/r_1$, $\pi abc/r_2$ where r_1 and r_2 are the axes of the section by the plane $lx/a+my/b+nz/c=0$.*

Solution. The equation of any plane through $x/l=y/m=z/n$ is

$$Lx+My+Nz=0, \quad \text{...(1)}$$

where

$$Ll+Mm+Nn=0. \quad \text{...(2)}$$

We know that the area of the section of

$$x^2/a^2+y^2/b^2+z^2/c^2=1$$

by the plane (1) is $\pi abc/p$,
where $p^2=a^2L^2+b^2M^2+c^2N^2$, [L, M, N being the d.c.'s].

The area $\pi abc/p$ will be maximum or minimum according as p is minimum or maximum. We shall discuss the maximum and minimum of p (or of p^2) by Lagrange's method of undetermined multipliers. We have

$$p^2=a^2L^2+b^2M^2+c^2N^2 \quad \text{...(3)}$$

subject to the conditions

$$Ll+Mm+Nn=0, \quad \text{...(4)}$$

and

$$L^2+M^2+N^2=1. \quad \text{...(5)}$$

Differentiating the above relations (3), (4), (5), we get

$$\left.\begin{aligned} a^2LdL+b^2MdM+c^2NdN=0,\\ ldL+mdM+ndN=0,\\ \text{and}\qquad LdL+MdM+NdN=0.\end{aligned}\right\}$$

Multiplying the above relations by 1, λ_1, λ_2 respectively and adding and then equating to zero the coefficients of dL, dM and dN, we get

$$a^2L+\lambda_1 l+\lambda_2 L=0,\ b^2M+\lambda_1 m+\lambda_2 M=0,\ c^2N+\lambda_1 n+\lambda_2 N=0. \quad ...(6)$$

Multiplying the relations (6) by L, M, N in that order and adding, we get

$$(a^2L^2+b^2M^2+c^2N^2)+\lambda_1\ (lL+mM+nN)+\lambda_2\ (L^2+M^2+N^2)=0$$

or $p^2+\lambda_1\ (0)+\lambda_2\ (1)=0$, using (3), (4) and (5)

or $$\lambda_2=-p^2.$$

Putting $\lambda_2=-p^2$ in (6), we get

$L=l\lambda_1/(p^2-a^2)$, $M=m\lambda_1/(p^2-b^2)$, $N=n\lambda_1/(p^2-c^2)$.

Putting these values of L, M, N in (2), we get

$$l^2\lambda_1/(p^2-a^2)+m^2\lambda_1/(p^2-b^2)+n^2\lambda_1/(p^2-c^2)=0$$

or $l^2/(p^2-a^2)+m^2/(p^2-b^2)+n^2/(p^2-c^2)=0$ [as $\lambda_1\neq 0$]. ...(7)

The equation (7) gives maximum and minimum values of p^2. Let p_1^2 and p_2^2 be these values of p^2.

Now the axes of the section of the conicoid $ax^2+by^2+cz^2=1$ by the plane $lx+my+nz=0$ are given by [§ 3]

$$l^2/(ar^2-1)+m^2/(br^2-1)+n^2/(cr^2-1)=0.$$

$\therefore$ the axes of the section of the ellipsoid $x^2/a^2+y^2/b^2+z^2/c^2=1$ by the plane $x\ (l/a)+y\ (m/b)+z\ (n/c)=0$ are given by

$$\frac{(l/a)^2}{r^2/a^2-1}+\frac{(m/b)^2}{r^2/b^2-1}+\frac{(n/c)^2}{r^2/c^2-1}=0$$

or $$l^2/(r^2-a^2)+m^2/(r^2-b^2)+n^2/(r^2-c^2)=0. \quad ...(8)$$

Let its roots be r_1^2 and r_2^2. Comparing (7) and (8) we see that the values of p^2 and r^2 are the same. Hence $p_1^2=r_1^2$ and $p_2^2=r_2^2$. Therefore the maximum and minimum areas are $\pi abc/r_1$ and $\pi abc/r_2$.

Ex. 9. *Prove that if* l_1, m_1, n_1 ; l_2, m_2, n_2 *are direction cosines of the axes of any plane section of the ellipsoid* $x^2/a^2+y^2/b^2+z^2/c^2=1$, *then*

$$\frac{l_1 l_2}{a^2\ (b^2-c^2)}=\frac{m_1 m_2}{b^2\ (c^2-a^2)}=\frac{n_1 n_2}{c^2\ (a^2-b^2)}.$$

Solution. Consider the section of

$$x^2/a^2+y^2/b^2+z^2/c^2=1, \quad ...(1)$$

by the plane $\quad Lx+My+Nz=p. \quad ...(2)$

If l, m, n be the d.c.'s of either axis of the section, then we have [In equation (12) of § 4, replace l, m, n by L, M, N ; a, b, c by $1/a^2, 1/b^2, 1/c^2$; and λ, μ, ν by l, m, n]

$$\frac{l\left(\dfrac{r^2}{a^2d^2}-1\right)}{L}=\frac{m\left(\dfrac{r^2}{b^2d^2}-1\right)}{M}=\frac{n\left(\dfrac{r^2}{c^2d^2}-1\right)}{N}=(k) \text{ say.}$$

From these, we have

$$\frac{r^2-a^2d^2}{kd^2}=\frac{La^2}{l}, \quad \frac{r^2-b^2d^2}{kd^2}=\frac{Mb^2}{m}, \quad \frac{r^2-c^2d^2}{kd^2}=\frac{Nc^2}{n}.$$

Multiplying these relations by $b^2-c^2, c^2-a^2, a^2-b^2$ in that order and then adding, we get

$$La^2(b^2-c^2)/l+Mb^2(c^2-a^2)/m+Nc^2(a^2-b^2)/n=0. \quad ...(3)$$

Again since the axis lies in the plane (2), we have

$$Ll+Mm+Nn=0. \quad ...(4)$$

Now eliminating n between (3) and (4), we have

$$\frac{La^2(b^2-c^2)}{l}+\frac{Mb^2(c^2-a^2)}{m}-\frac{Nc^2(a^2-b^2)N}{Ll+Mm}=0$$

or
$$LMb^2(c^2-a^2)(l/m)^2+\{L^2a^2(b^2-c^2)+M^2b^2(c^2-a^2)$$
$$-N^2c^2(a^2-b^2)\}(l/m)+LMa^2(b^2-c^2)=0. \quad ...(5)$$

The equation (5) is a quadratic in l/m and hence gives two values of l/m. Let l_1, m_1, n_1 and l_2, m_2, n_2 be the d.c.'s of the axes. Then l_1/m_1 and l_2/m_2 are the roots of (5) and so from (5), we have

$$\frac{l_1}{m_1}\cdot\frac{l_2}{m_2}=\frac{LMa^2(b^2-c^2)}{LMb^2(c^2-a^2)}$$

or
$$\frac{l_1l_2}{a^2(b^2-c^2)}=\frac{m_1m_2}{b^2(c^2-a^2)}=\frac{n_1n_2}{c^2(a^2-b^2)} \text{ [by symmetry].}$$

Ex. 10. *The normal section of an enveloping cylinder of the ellipsoid* $x^2/a^2+y^2/b^2+z^2/c^2=1$ *has a given area* πk^2. *Prove that the planes of contact of the cylinder and ellipsoid touch the cone*

$$\frac{x^2}{a^4(b^2c^2-k^4)}+\frac{y^2}{b^4(c^2a^2-k^4)}+\frac{z^2}{c^4(a^2b^2-k^4)}=0.$$

Solution. The equation of the enveloping cylinder of $x^2/a^2+y^2/b^2+z^2/c^2=1$ is

$$\left(\frac{x^2}{a^2}+\frac{y^2}{b^2}+\frac{z^2}{c^2}-1\right)\left(\frac{l^2}{a^2}+\frac{m^2}{b^2}+\frac{n^2}{c^2}\right)=\left(\frac{lx}{a^2}+\frac{my}{b^2}+\frac{nz}{c^2}\right)^2, \quad ...(1)$$

its generating lines being parallel to

$$x/l=y/m=z/n. \quad ...(2)$$

The plane of contact is the diametral plane of (2) and is given by

$$lx/a^2+my/b^2+nz/c^2=0. \quad ...(3)$$

The area A of the section of $x^2/a^2+y^2/b^2+z^2/c^2=1$ by the plane (3) is given by

$$A=\frac{\pi abc\sqrt{\{(l^2/a^4)+(m^2/b^4)+(n^2/c^4)\}}}{\sqrt{(l^2/a^2+m^2/b^2+n^2/c^2)}}. \quad ...(4)$$

Now all the normal sections of a cylinder are equal and the central normal section being perpendicular to the generating line (2) is given by

$$lx+my+nz=0. \quad ...(5)$$

If θ be the angle between (3) and (5), we have

$$\cos\theta=\left[\frac{l^2/a^2+m^2/b^2+n^2/c^2}{\sqrt{\{(l^2/a^4+m^2/b^4+n^2/c^4)(l^2+m^2+n^2)\}}}\right]. \quad ...(6)$$

Hence the area πk^2 of the normal section $=A\cos\theta$

or $$\pi k^2=\frac{\pi abc\sqrt{(l^2/a^2+m^2/b^2+n^2/c^2)}}{\sqrt{(l^2+m^2+n^2)}}$$

[Putting for A and $\cos\theta$ from (4) and (6)].

Squaring, $k^4(l^2+m^2+n^2)=a^2b^2c^2\left(\frac{l^2}{a^2}+\frac{m^2}{b^2}+\frac{n^2}{c^2}\right)$

or $$(b^2c^2-k^4)\,l^2+(c^2a^2-k^4)\,m^2+(a^2b^2-k^4)\,n^2=0.$$

$\therefore$ The normal namely $\frac{x}{l/a^2}=\frac{y}{m/b^2}=\frac{z}{n/c^2}$ to the plane of contact (3) generates the cone

$$a^4(b^2c^2-k^4)\,x^2+b^4(c^2a^2-k^4)\,y^2+c^4(a^2b^2-k^4)\,z^2=0. \quad ...(7)$$

$\therefore$ The plane of contact (3) will touch the reciprocal cone of (7) *i.e.* the cone

$$\frac{x^2}{a^4(b^2c^2-k^4)}+\frac{y^2}{b^4(c^2a^2-k^4)}+\frac{z^2}{c^4(a^2b^2-k^4)}=0.$$

PLANE SECTIONS OF A PARABOLOID

§ 5. *To determine the nature of a given section of a paraboloid.*

Let the equation of the paraboloid be

$$ax^2+by^2=2cz, \quad ...(1)$$

and the equation of the plane be

$$lx+my+nz=p. \quad ...(2)$$

The equation of the cylinder passing through the section of the paraboloid (1) by the plane (2) and having its generators parallel to x-axis is obtained by eliminating x between (1) and (2) and is therefore given by

$$(a/l^2)\{p-(my+nz)\}^2+by^2-2cz=0$$

or $\quad (am^2+bl^2)y^2+2amnyz+an^2z^2-2apmy-2(apn+cl^2)z+ap^2=0. \quad ...(3)$

The plane $x=0$ being perpendicular to the generators of the cylinder (3) cuts it in the conic given by

$$x=0,\ (am^2+bl^2)y^2+2amnyz+an^2z^2-2apmy-2(apn+cl^2)z+ap^2=0. \quad ...(4)$$

The conic given by (4) represents the projection of the given section on the plane $x=0$. It will represent a hyperbola, a parabola or an ellipse according as [See § 2 above]

$$a^2m^2n^2-(am^2+bl^2)an^2 >, =, \text{ or } <0 \ [h^2-ab >, =, \text{ or } < 0]$$

or $\quad abn^2l^2 <, =, \text{ or } > 0.$

Here $l\neq 0$ since if $l=0$ the plane (2) will be at right angles to $x=0$ and then there will exist no projection.

Hence for the section to be a parabola $n=0$.

Again if $n\neq 0$, the section will be a hyperbola if ab is $-$ve and an ellipse if ab is $+$ve.

§ 6. ***To find the lengths and direction ratios of the axes of the section of the paraboloid.***

Let the equation of the paraboloid be

$$ax^2+by^2=2cz, \quad ...(1)$$

and the equation of the plane be

$$lx+my+nz=p. \quad ...(2)$$

Let $C(\alpha, \beta, \gamma)$ be the centre of the section of (1) by (2). Then the equation of the plane (2) is also given by '$T=S_1$' *i.e.* by

$$a\alpha x+b\beta y-cz=a\alpha^2+b\beta^2-c\gamma. \quad ...(3)$$

Now comparing (2) and (3), we obtain

$$\frac{a\alpha}{l}=\frac{b\beta}{m}=\frac{-c}{n}=\frac{a\alpha^2+b\beta^2-c\gamma}{p}.$$

$\therefore \quad \alpha=-(lc)/(an),\ \beta=-(mc)/(bn)$

and from the last two relations, $c\gamma=a\alpha^2+b\beta^2+cp/n$

or $$c\gamma=\frac{c^2}{n^2}\left(\frac{l^2}{a}+\frac{m^2}{b}+\frac{np}{c}\right)=\frac{c^2k}{n^2}$$

where $$k=\frac{l^2}{a}+\frac{m^2}{b}+\frac{np}{c}. \quad ...(4)$$

$\therefore$ The centre C of the section is

$$\left(\frac{-lc}{an}, \frac{-mc}{bn}, \frac{ck}{n^2}\right). \quad ...(5)$$

Shifting the origin to the centre C, the equation (1) becomes

$$a\left(x-\frac{lc}{an}\right)^2+b\left(y-\frac{mc}{bn}\right)^2-2c\left(z+\frac{ck}{n^2}\right)=0$$

or
$$ax^2+by^2-\frac{2c}{n}(lx+my+nz)-\frac{c}{n^2}(kc+np)=0. \quad ..(6)$$

And the equation (2) of the plane becomes

$$lx+my+nz=0. \quad ...(7)$$

But the conic which is given by (6) and (7) is the same as the conic given by the equations

$$ax^2+by^2-(c/n^2)(kc+np)=0,\ lx+my+nz=0. \quad ...(8)$$

Let us put $\quad p_0^2=c(kc+np)$.

Then using (4), we have

$$p_0^2=c(cl^2/a+cm^2/b+2np). \quad ...(9$$

Putting $c(kc+np)=p_0^2$ in (8), the equation of the conic becomes

$$ax^2+by^2=p_0^2/n^2,\ lx+my+nz=0. \quad ...(10)$$

If λ, μ, ν are the d.c.'s of a semi-diameter of length r then its equations are

$$x/\lambda=y/\mu=z/\nu=r. \quad ..(11)$$

The point $(\lambda r, \mu r, \nu r)$ which is the extremity of the semi-diameter (11), will lie on $ax^2+by^2=p_0^2/n^2$.

Hence $a\lambda^2r^2+b\mu^2r^2=p_0^2/n^2=(p_0^2/n^2)(\lambda^2+\mu^2+\nu^2)$

or
$$\lambda^2(ar^2n^2-p_0^2)+\mu^2(br^2n^2-p_0^2)-p_0^2\nu^2=0. \quad ..(12)$$

$\therefore$ the semi-diaemters (11) are the generators of the cone

$$x^2(ar^2n^2-p_0^2)+y^2(br^2n^2-p_0^2)-p_0^2z^2=0. \quad ..(13)$$

The plane (7) should touch the cone (13) along the generator of contact, the condition for which is

$$\frac{l^2}{ar^2n^2-p_0^2}+\frac{m^2}{br^2n^2-p_0^2}-\frac{n^2}{p_0^2}=0 \quad ...(14)$$

or
$$abn^6r^4-n^2r^2p_0^2[(a+b)n^2+am^2+bl^2]+p_0^4(l^2+m^2+n^2)=0. \quad ...(15)$$

The roots of this quadratic equation in r^2 give the squares of the semi-axes of the conic. Let r_1^2 and r_2^2 be its roots so that r_1 and r_2 are the lengths of the semi-axes of the conic.

Also
$$r_1^2r_2^2=p_0^4(l^2+m^2+n^2)/(abn^6). \quad ...(16)$$

Again if $2r$ is the length, λ, μ, ν are the d.c.'s of an axis, the plane (7) touches the cone (13) along that axis namely the line $x/\lambda=y/\mu=z/\nu$. Hence the plane (7) is identical with the tangent plane to the cone (13) namely

$$\lambda x\,(ar^2n^2-p_0^2)+\mu y\,(br^2n^2-p_0^2)-\nu zp_0^2=0 \quad ...(17)$$

at any point $(\lambda r, \mu r, \nu r)$ on $x/\lambda=y/\mu=z/\nu$. Comparing (7) and (17), we have

$$\lambda\,(ar^2n^2-p_0^2)/l=\mu\,(br^2n^2-p_0^2)/m=-\nu p_0^2/n \quad ...(18)$$

which give the direction ratios of the two axes for the two values of r^2 given by (15).

Corollary 1. The area of the section. If the section is an ellipse the lengths of whose semi-axes are r_1 and r_2, then its area is given by

$$\pi r_1 r_2=\frac{\pi p_0^2}{n^3}\left\{\frac{l^2+m^2+n^2}{ab}\right\}^{1/2}, \text{ using (16)}$$

$$=\frac{\pi c}{n^3}\left(\frac{cl^2}{a}+\frac{cm^2}{b}+2np\right)\Big/\sqrt{\left(\frac{l^2+m^2+n^2}{ab}\right)}, \text{ using (9).}$$

Corollary 2. The angle between the asymptotes. Let θ be the angle between the asymptotes of the conic $ax^2+by^2=2cz$, $lx+my+nz=p$. Proceeding as in Ex. 18 of the set of solved examples (A), we have

$$\tan^2\theta=\frac{-4r_1^2r_2^2}{(r_1^2+r_2^2)^2}=\frac{-4abn^2\,(l^2+m^2+n^2)}{\{(a+b)\,n^2+am^2+bl^2\}^2}$$

This result being independent of p shows that θ is same for all parallel plane sections of a paraboloid.

Corollary 3. The condition for the section to be a rectangular hyperbola. If the section (*i.e.* conic) be a rectangular hyperbola then r_1^2 and r_2^2 are equal in magnitude but opposite in sign *i.e.* $r_1^2+r_2^2=0$.

$\therefore\quad (a+b)\,n^2+am^2+bl^2=0$, from (15).

SOLVED EXAMPLES (C)

Ex. 1. *Find the lengths of the semi-axes of the section of the paraboloid* $2x^2+y^2=z$ *by the plane* $x+2y+z=4$.

Solution. The paraboloid is

$$2x^2+y^2=z, \quad ...(1)$$

and the plane is $\quad x+2y+z=4. \quad ...(2)$

Let the co-ordinates of the centre of the section be (α, β, γ), then the plane (2) is also given by $T=S_1$

i.e. $\quad 2\alpha x+\beta y-\frac{1}{2}(z+\gamma)=2\alpha^2+\beta^2-\gamma$

or $\quad 4\alpha x+2\beta y-z=4\alpha^2+2\beta^2-\gamma. \quad ...(3)$

Comparing (2) and (3), $\dfrac{4\alpha}{1}=\dfrac{2\beta}{2}=\dfrac{-1}{1}=\dfrac{4\alpha^2+2\beta^2-\gamma}{4}=\dfrac{p_0^2}{4}$ (say).

$\therefore\quad \alpha=-\frac{1}{4}, \beta=-1, \gamma=4\alpha^2+2\beta^2+4=25/4.$

Shifting the origin to the centre $(-\frac{1}{4}, -1, 25/4)$, the equations (1) and (2) become

$$2\,(x-\tfrac{1}{4})^2+(y-1)^2=(z+25/4)$$

or $$2x^2+y^2-(x+2y+z)=41/8 \quad \ldots(4)$$

and $$x+2y+z=0. \quad \ldots(5)$$

The section given by (3) and (4) is the same as given by

$$2x^2+y^2=41/8, \text{ and } x+2y+z=0. \quad \ldots(6)$$

Comparing the equations (5) with the equations (10) of § 6, we get

$$l=1, m=2, n=1, p_0^2=41/8. \quad \text{Also } a=2, b=1.$$

$\therefore$ The lengths r of the semi-axes are given by the roots of r^2 in the equation [See equation (15) of § 6]

$$2.1.(1)^6\, r^4-(1)^2\, r^2\, (41/8)\, [(2+1)\,(1)^2+2(2)^2+1.(1)^2] +(41/8)\,(1+4+1)=0$$

or $$8r^4-246r^2+123=0.$$

If its roots are r_1^2 and r_2^2, then solving we get

$$r_1=5.28,\ r_2=1.68.$$

Ex. 2. *Planes are drawn through a fixed point (α, β, γ) so that their sections of the paraboloid $ax^2+by^2=2z$ are rectangular hyperbolas. Prove that they touch the cone*

$$\frac{(x-\alpha)^2}{b}+\frac{(y-\beta)^2}{a}+\frac{(z-\gamma)^2}{a+b}=0.$$

Solution. The equation of any plane through (α, β, γ) is

$$l\,(x-\alpha)+m\,(y-\beta)+n\,(z-\gamma)=0 \quad \ldots(1)$$

or $$lx+my+nz=l\alpha+m\beta+n\gamma=p \text{ (say)}.$$

The lengths of the axes of the section of $ax^2+by^2=2z$ by the plane (1) are given by [See equation (15) § 6]

$$abn^6r^4-n^2r^2p_0^2\,[(a+b)\,n^2+am^2+bl^2]+p_0^4\,(l^2+m^2+n^2)=0$$

where $$p_0^2=\frac{l^2}{a}+\frac{m^2}{b}+2np, \text{ (since } c=1)$$

$$=\frac{l^2}{a}+\frac{m^2}{b}+2n\,(l\alpha+m\beta+n\gamma).$$

The section will be a rectangular hyperbola if

$$r_1^2+r_2^2=0 \text{ i.e. if } (a+b)\,n^2+am^2+bl^2=0. \quad \ldots(2)$$

The equations of the normal to the plane (1) through (α, β, γ)

are $$\frac{x-\alpha}{l}=\frac{y-\beta}{m}=\frac{z-\gamma}{n}. \quad \ldots(3)$$

Eliminating l, m, n between (2) and (3), the normal (3) is a generator of the cone

$$(a+b)(z-\gamma)^2+a(y-\beta)^2+b(x-\alpha)^2=0. \quad ...(4)$$

Hence the plane (1) will touch the cone reciprocal to (4) *i.e.* the cone $(x-\alpha)^2/b+(y-\beta)^2/a+(z-\gamma)^2/(a+b)=0.$

Ex. 3. *Show that the section of the paraboloid* $ax^2+by^2=2z$ *by a tangent plane to the cone* $\dfrac{x^2}{b}+\dfrac{y^2}{a}+\dfrac{z^2}{a+b}=0$ *is a rectangular hyperbola.*

Solution. Let the equation of the tangent plane to the given cone be $lx+my+nz=0$. Hence its normal namely $x/l=y/m=z/n$ will be the generator of the reciprocal cone

$$bx^2+ay^2+(a+b)z^2=0. \quad ...(1)$$

Since $x/l=y/m=z/n$ is a generator of the cone (1), therefore

$$(a+b)n^2+am^2+bl^2=0$$

which is the condition for the section of $ax^2+by^2=2z$ to be a rectangular hyperbola. [See Cor. 3, § 6]

Ex. 4. *Find the locus of the centres of sections of the paraboloid* $x^2/a^2+y^2/b^2=2z$ *which are of constant area* πk^2.

Solution. Replacing a by $1/a^2$, b by $1/b^2$ and c by 1 in Cor. 1 § 6, the area A of the section of $x^2/a^2+y^2/b^2=2z$ by the plane $lx+my+nz=p$ is given by

$$A=(\pi/n^3)(a^2l^2+b^2m^2+2np)\sqrt{\{a^2b^2(l^2+m^2+n^2)\}}. \quad ...(1)$$

Let (α, β, γ) be the centre of the section, then the plane $lx+my+nz=p$ is also given by '$T=S_1$'

i.e. $$\frac{\alpha x}{a^2}+\frac{\beta y}{b^2}-(z+\gamma)=\frac{\alpha^2}{a^2}+\frac{\beta^2}{b^2}-2\gamma$$

i.e. $$\frac{\alpha x}{a^2}+\frac{\beta y}{b^2}-z=\frac{\alpha^2}{a^2}+\frac{\beta^2}{b^2}-\gamma.$$

$$\therefore \quad \frac{\alpha}{a^2 l}=\frac{\beta}{b^2 m}=-\frac{1}{n}=\left(\frac{\alpha^2}{a^2}+\frac{\beta^2}{b^2}-\gamma\right)\Big/p.$$

$$\therefore \quad \frac{l}{n}=-\frac{\alpha}{a^2},\ \frac{m}{n}=-\frac{\beta}{b^2},\ \frac{p}{n}=-\left(\frac{\alpha^2}{a^2}+\frac{\beta^2}{b^2}-\gamma\right). \quad ...(2)$$

From (1), we have

$$A=\pi ab\left(\frac{a^2l^2}{n^2}+\frac{b^2m^2}{n^2}+\frac{2p}{n}\right)\sqrt{\left(\frac{l^2}{n^2}+\frac{m^2}{n^2}+1\right)}.$$

$$\therefore \quad \pi k^2=\pi ab\left\{a^2\cdot\frac{\alpha^2}{a^4}+b^2\cdot\frac{\beta^2}{b^4}-2\left(\frac{\alpha^2}{a^2}+\frac{\beta^2}{b^2}-\gamma\right)\right\}\sqrt{\left(\frac{\alpha^2}{a^4}+\frac{\beta^2}{b^4}+1\right)}.$$

[Putting the values from (2). Also $A=\pi k^2$, as given]

Squaring, $a^2b^2\left(-\frac{\alpha^2}{a^2}-\frac{\beta^2}{b^2}+2\gamma\right)^2\left(\frac{\alpha^2}{a^4}+\frac{\beta^2}{b^4}+1\right)=k^4$.

Therefore, the required locus of (α, β, γ) is

$$a^2b^2\left(\frac{x^2}{a^2}+\frac{y^2}{b^2}-2\right)^2\left(\frac{x^2}{a^4}+\frac{y^2}{b^4}+1\right)=k^4.$$

Ex. 5. *If the area of the section of $ax^2+by^2=2cz$ be constant $(=\pi k^2)$, show that the locus of the centre is*

$$(ax^2+by^2-2cz)^2\,(a^2x^2+b^2y^2+c^2)=abc^2k^4.$$

Solution. Proceed exactly as in Ex. 4 above.

Ex. 6. *If the area of the section of $y^2/b^2+z^2/c^2=2x$ be constant $(=a^2)$, prove that the locus of the centre is*

$$\pi^2bc\left(2x-\frac{y^2}{b^2}-\frac{z^2}{c^2}\right)\left(1+\frac{y^2}{b^2}+\frac{z^2}{c^2}\right)=a^4.$$

Solution. Proceed as in Ex. 4 above.

Ex. 7. *Find the radius of curvature at the origin of the conic*

$$ax^2+by^2=2z,\ lx+my+nz=0.$$

Solution. Let $C\,(\alpha, \beta, \gamma)$ be the centre of the section (conic), then the plane $lx+my+nz=0$ is also given by $T=S_1$

i.e. $$a\alpha x+b\beta y-(z+\gamma)=a\alpha^2+b\beta^2-2\gamma$$

or $$a\alpha x+b\beta y-z=a\alpha^2+b\beta^2-\gamma.$$

$$\therefore\quad \frac{a\alpha}{l}=\frac{b\beta}{m}=\frac{-1}{n}=\frac{a\alpha^2+b\beta^2-\gamma}{0}.$$

$$\therefore\quad \alpha=-\frac{l}{an},\ \beta=\frac{-m}{bn},\ \gamma=a\alpha^2+b\beta^2=\frac{l^2}{an^2}+\frac{m^2}{bn^2}.$$

$$\therefore\quad CO^2=\alpha^2+\beta^2+\gamma^2=\frac{l^2}{a^2n^2}+\frac{m^2}{b^2n^2}+\left(\frac{l^2}{an^2}+\frac{m^2}{bn^2}\right)^2.$$

The lengths of the semi-axes are given by

$$abn^6r^4-n^2r^2p_0^2\,\{(a+b)\,n^2+am^2+bl^2\}+p_0^4\,(l^2+m^2+n^2)=0. \quad ...(1)$$

$$\therefore\quad r_1^2+r_2^2=n^2p_0^2[(a+b)\,n^2+am^2+bl^2]/(abn^6) \quad ...(2)$$

$$r_1^2r_2^2=p_0^4\,(l^2+m^2+n^2)/(abn^6) \quad ...(3)$$

where $$p_0^2=l^2/a+m^2/b. \quad [\because\ p=0] \quad ...(4)$$

Now let CO and CD be the conjugate semi-diameters of the conic.

Then $$CO^2+CD^2=r_1^2+r_2^2$$

or $$CD^2=r_1^2+r_2^2-CO^2$$

or $$CD^2=\frac{n^2p_0^2\,[(a+b)\,n^2+am^2+bl^2]}{abn^6}-\left[\frac{l^2}{a^2n^2}+\frac{m^2}{b^2n^2}+\left(\frac{l^2}{an^2}+\frac{m^2}{bn^2}\right)^2\right]$$

$$=\frac{n^2p_0^2\,[(a+b)\,n^2+am^2+bl^2]}{abn^6}-\left[\frac{l^2}{a^2n^2}+\frac{m^2}{b^2n^2}+\frac{p_0^4}{n^4}\right], \text{ using (4)}$$

$$=p_0^2.\frac{[(a+b)n^2+am^2+bl^2-bl^2-am^2]}{abn^4}-\frac{1}{n^2}\left(\frac{l^2}{a^2}+\frac{m^2}{b^2}\right)$$

$$=\left(\frac{a+b}{ab}\right)\frac{1}{n^2}\left(\frac{l^2}{a}+\frac{m^2}{b}\right)-\frac{1}{n^2}\left(\frac{l^2}{a^2}+\frac{m^2}{b^2}\right)=\frac{l^2+m^2}{abn^2}. \quad ...(5)$$

We know that the radius of curvature ρ of a central conic at any point P is $CD^3/(\alpha\beta)$, where CP and CD are the conjugate semi-diameters, C is the centre and α, β are the lengths of the semi-axes. Hence if ρ_0 be the radius of curvature at the origin O, then

$$\rho_0=\frac{CD^3}{r_1r_2}=\frac{\left(\dfrac{l^2+m^2}{abn^2}\right)^{3/2}}{\dfrac{p_0^2}{n^3}\left(\dfrac{l^2+m^2+n^2}{ab}\right)^{1/2}}=\frac{(l^2+m^2)^{3/2}}{ab\left(\dfrac{l^2}{a}+\dfrac{m^2}{b}\right)(l^2+m^2+n^2)^{1/2}}$$

Ex. 8. *Show that the semi-axes of the section of the paraboloid $xy=az$ by the plane $lx+my+nz=0$ are given by*

$$n^6r^4-4a^2r^2l^2m^2n^2-4a^4m^2l^2\ (l^2+m^2+n^2)=0.$$

Solution. Proceed exactly as in § 6 above.

CIRCULAR SECTIONS

§ 7. **Introduction.** Let $F(x, y, z)=0$ be the equation of a conicoid. If this equation can be written in the form

$$F(x, y, z)\equiv S+\lambda uv=0,$$

where $S=0$ represents a sphere and $u=0$, $v=0$ are the equations of two planes, then the points common to the conicoid $F(x, y,z)=0$ and the two planes namely $u=0, v=0$ lie on the sphere $S=0$. Hence we conclude that the sections of the conicoid by the planes are circles since every plane must meet a sphere in a circle.

§ 8 (A). **To determine the circular sections of an ellipsoid.**

Let the equation of the ellipsoid be

$$F(x, y, z)\equiv x^2/a^2+y^2/b^2+z^2/c^2-1=0. \quad ...(1)$$

The equation (1) can be rewritten as

$$(x^2+y^2+z^2-a^2)/a^2+y^2\ (1/b^2-1/a^2)+z^2\ (1/c^2-1/a^2)=0. \quad ...(2)$$

The equation (2) is of the form $S+\lambda uv=0$.

We observe that the pair of planes given by

$$y^2\ (1/b^2-1/a^2)+z^2\ (1/c^2-1/a^2)=0 \quad ...(3)$$

meet the ellipsoid (1) where they meet the sphere given by

$$x^2+y^2+z^2=a^2. \quad ...(4)$$

Hence the sections of the ellipsoid (1) by the planes given by (2) are circles each of radius a.

Similarly the equation (1) of the ellipsoid can also be rewritten in the following two forms

$$(x^2+y^2+z^2-b^2)/b^2+x^2(1/a^2-1/b^2)+z^2(1/c^2-1/b^2)=0, \quad ...(5)$$

and $$(x^2+y^2+z^2-c^2)/c^2+x^2(1/a^2-1/c^2)+y^2(1/b^2-1/c^2)=0. \quad ...(6)$$

Discussing as above, the following two pairs of planes also cut the ellipsoid in circles of radii b and c respectively.

One plane is $x^2(1/a^2-1/b^2)+z^2(1/c^2-1/b^2)=0$, ...(7)

and the other is $x^2(1/a^2-1/c^2)+y^2(1/b^2-1/c^2)=0$. ...(8)

Now if $a^2 > b^2 > c^2$ then only the planes given by (7) cut the ellipsoid (1) in real circular sections, and hence the real pair of central circular sections of the ellipsoid (1) are given by

$$x^2(a^2-b^2)/a^2-z^2(b^2-c^2)/c^2=0, \quad \text{from (7)}$$

i.e. $$\frac{x}{a}\sqrt{(a^2-b^2)}\pm\frac{z}{c}\sqrt{(b^2-c^2)}=0. \quad ...(9)$$

Again we know that the parallel plane sections are similar and similarly situated conics, and so any two planes parallel to the planes (9) *i.e.* the planes

$$\frac{x}{a}\sqrt{(a^2-b^2)}+\frac{z}{c}\sqrt{(b^2-c^2)}=\lambda \quad ...(10)$$

and $$\frac{x}{a}\sqrt{(a^2-b^2)}-\frac{z}{c}\sqrt{(b^2-c^2)}=\mu \quad ...(11)$$

will also cut the ellipsoid (1) in circles for all values of λ and μ.

§ 8 (B). *To show that any two circular sections of an ellipsoid which are not parallel lie on a sphere.*

The equation of the ellipsoid is

$$x^2/a^2+y^2/b^2+z^2/c^2=1. \quad ...(1)$$

Let the equations of any two circular sections of the ellipsoid (1) which are not parallel be given by the intersection of

$$\frac{x}{a}\sqrt{(a^2-b^2)}+\frac{z}{c}\sqrt{(b^2-c^2)}=\lambda \quad ...(2)$$

and $$\frac{x}{a}\sqrt{(a^2-b^2)}-\frac{z}{c}\sqrt{(b^2-c^2)}=\mu \quad ...(3)$$

and the ellipsoid (1).

Therefore the conicoid

$$\left(\frac{x^2}{a^2}+\frac{y^2}{b^2}+\frac{z^2}{c^2}-1\right)+k\left\{\frac{x}{a}\sqrt{(a^2-b^2)}+\frac{z}{c}\sqrt{(b^2-c^2)}-\lambda\right\}\times$$
$$\left\{\frac{x}{a}\sqrt{(a^2-b^2)}-\frac{z}{c}\sqrt{(b^2-c^2)}-\mu\right\}=0 \quad ...(4)$$

passing through the two circular sections for all values of k will be a sphere if k be chosen in such a way that the equation (4) satisfies all conditions for a sphere *i.e.* the coefficients of x^2, y^2,

z^2 are equal and the terms of yz, zx and xy are absent. Hence putting the coefficients of x^2, y^2 and z^2 equal, we have

$$\frac{1}{a^2}+\frac{k(a^2-b^2)}{a^2}=\frac{1}{b^2}=\frac{1}{c^2}-\frac{k(b^2-c^2)}{c^2}.$$

If we choose $k=1/b^2$, all the above conditions are clearly satisfied and the equation (4) becomes

$$x^2+y^2+z^2-(\lambda+\mu)\sqrt{(a^2-b^2)}\,(x/a)+(\lambda-\mu)\sqrt{(b^2-c^2)}\,(z/c)$$
$$+\lambda\mu-b^2=0 \quad \ldots(5)$$

which clearly represents a sphere on which lie the two circular sections of the ellipsoid which are not parallel.

§ 9. The circular sections of any central conicoid.

The general equation of any central conicoid is

$$F(x, y, z)\equiv ax^2+by^2+cz^2+2fyz+2gzx+2hxy-1=0. \quad \ldots(1)$$

The equation (1) can be written in the form

$$(ax^2+by^2+cz^2+2fyz+2gzx+2hxy)-\lambda(x^2+y^2+z^2)$$
$$+\lambda\,(x^2+y^2+z^2-1/\lambda)=0. \quad \ldots(2)$$

Clearly if the equation

$$ax^2+by^2+cz^2+2fyz+2gzx+2hxy-\lambda(x^2+y^2+z^2)=0$$

i.e. $(a-\lambda)\,x^2+(b-\lambda)\,y^2+(c-\lambda)\,z^2+2fyz+2gzx+2hxy=0$ ...(3)

represents two planes, then these planes will meet the conicoid (1) in circular sections.

Now the equation (3) will represent two planes if

$$\begin{vmatrix} a-\lambda & h & g \\ h & b-\lambda & f \\ g & f & c-\lambda \end{vmatrix}=0.$$

This is a cubic equation in λ and so gives three values of λ which are all real, but only one value of λ (mean value) will provide the real planes.

§ 10. The circular sections of the paraboloid.

The equation of the paraboloid is

$$F(x, y, z)\equiv ax^2+by^2-2cz=0. \quad \ldots(1)$$

The equation (1) can be written in the forms

$$a(x^2+y^2+z^2-2cz/a)+y^2\,(b-a)-az^2=0, \quad \ldots(2)$$

and $$b\,(x^2+y^2+z^2-2cz/b)+x^2\,(a-b)-bz^2=0. \quad \ldots(3)$$

Hence the pairs of planes given by

$$y^2\,(b-a)-az^2=0 \quad \ldots(4)$$

and $$x^2\,(a-b)-bz^2=0 \quad \ldots(5)$$

determine circular sections through the origin.

Now if $a > b > 0$ then only the pair of planes given by (5) determine the real circular sections through the origin and they are given by

$$x\sqrt{(a-b)} \pm z\sqrt{b}=0. \qquad ...(6)$$

Again we know that the parallel plane sections are similar and similarly situated conics and so any two planes parallel to the planes (6) *i.e.* the planes

$$x\sqrt{(a-b)}+z\sqrt{b}=\lambda \quad \text{and} \quad x\sqrt{(a-b)}-z\sqrt{b}=\mu$$

will also cut the paraboloid (1) in circles for all values of λ and μ.

If a and b are of opposite signs (*i.e.* one is +ve and other −ve) then neither (4) nor (5) gives real planes because in this case the equation $ax^2+by^2=0$ represents the only real planes.

Also we know that when a and b are of opposite signs the paraboloid is a hyperbolic paraboloid. *Hence we conclude that the hyperboloic paraboloid has no real circular sections.*

SOLVED EXAMPLES (D)

Ex. 1. *Find the conditions that the section of the ellipsoid $x^2/a^2+y^2/b^2+z^2/c^2=1$ by the plane $lx+my+nz=0$ may be a circle.*

Solution. We know that the parallel plane sections are similar and similarly situated conics. Hence if the section of the ellipsoid by the plane $lx+my+nz=0$ is a circle, then the section of the ellipsoid by a plane parallel to $lx+my+nz=0$ is also a circle. Now the real circular sections of the given ellipsoid are [See § 8(A) above]

$$(x/a)\sqrt{(a^2-b^2)} \pm (z/c)\sqrt{(b^2-c^2)}=0. \qquad ...(1)$$

∴ Comparing (1) with $lx+my+nz=0$, the required conditions are given by

$$\frac{al}{\sqrt{(a^2-b^2)}}=\frac{m}{0}=\pm\frac{cn}{\sqrt{(b^2-c^2)}}.$$

Ex. 2. *Show that the radius of the circle in which the plane $(x/a)\sqrt{(a^2-b^2)}+(z/c)\sqrt{(b^2-c^2)}=\lambda$ cuts the ellipsoid $x^2/a^2+y^2/b^2+z^2/c^2=1$ is $b\sqrt{\{1-\lambda^2/(a^2-c^2)\}}$.*

Solution. The equation of the sphere through the intersection of the ellipsoid and the given plane is [See § 8(A), equations (5)]

$$b^2\left(\frac{x^2}{a^2}+\frac{y^2}{b^2}+\frac{z^2}{c^2}-1\right)$$
$$+\left\{\frac{x}{a}\sqrt{(a^2-b^2)}-\frac{z}{c}\sqrt{(b^2-c^2)}\right\}\left\{\frac{x}{a}\sqrt{(a^2-b^2)}\right.$$
$$\left.+\frac{z}{c}\sqrt{(b^2-c^2)}-\lambda\right\}=0. \quad \ldots(1)$$

The co-ordinates of the centre C of the sphere (1) are
$$(\lambda\sqrt{(a^2-b^2)}/(2a), 0, -\lambda\sqrt{(b^2-c^2)}/(2c)).$$
If R be the radius of the sphere (1), it is given by
$$R^2=\frac{\lambda^2(a^2-b^2)}{4a^2}+\frac{\lambda^2(b^2-c^2)}{4c^2}+b^2=b^2+\frac{\lambda^2b^2(a^2-c^2)}{4a^2c^2}.$$
Also p=the length of the perpendicular from the centre C of the sphere to the given plane
$$=\frac{\dfrac{\lambda(a^2-b^2)}{2a^2}-\dfrac{\lambda(b^2-c^2)}{2c^2}-\lambda}{\sqrt{\{(a^2-b^2)/a^2+(b^2-c^2)/c^2\}}}=\frac{-b\lambda(a^2+c^2)}{2ca\sqrt{(a^2-c^2)}}.$$
If r is the radius of the circular section, then
$$r^2=R^2-p^2=b^2+\frac{\lambda^2b^2}{4a^2c^2}\left\{\frac{(a^2-c^2)}{1}-\frac{(a^2+c^2)^2}{a^2-c^2}\right\}$$
$$=b^2+\frac{\lambda^2b^2}{4a^2c^2}\left\{\frac{(a^2-c^2)^2-(a^2+c^2)^2}{(a^2-c^2)}\right\}=b^2\left(1-\frac{\lambda^2}{a^2-c^2}\right)$$
$$\therefore \quad r=b\sqrt{\left(1-\frac{\lambda^2}{a^2-c^2}\right)}.$$

Ex. 3. *Prove that the radius of the circular section of the ellipsoid at a distance p from the centre is* $b\sqrt{\{1-p^2b^2/(a^2c^2)\}}$.

Solution. Let r be the radius of the circular section
$$(x/a)\sqrt{(a^2-b^2)}+(z/c)\sqrt{(b^2-c^2)}=\lambda. \quad \ldots(1)$$
From Ex. 2 above, $r=b\sqrt{\left(1-\dfrac{\lambda^2}{a^2-c^2}\right)}$ ...(2)

We are given that p is the length of the perpendicular from the centre (0, 0, 0) of the ellipsoid to the plane (1).
$$\therefore \quad p=\frac{-\lambda}{\sqrt{\{(a^2-b^2)/a^2+(b^2-c^2)/c^2\}}}=\frac{-\lambda ac}{b\sqrt{(a^2-c^2)}}.$$
Squaring, $p^2=\dfrac{\lambda^2a^2c^2}{b^2(a^2-c^2)}$, or $\dfrac{\lambda^2}{a^2-c^2}=\dfrac{b^2p^2}{a^2c^2}$.

$\therefore$ From (2), $r=b\sqrt{\{1-b^2p^2/(a^2c^2)\}}$.

Ex. 4. *Show that the circular sections of the ellipsoid passing through one extremity of x-axis are both of radius r where*
$$\frac{r^2}{b^2}=\frac{b^2-c^2}{a^2-c^2}.$$

Solution. The real circular sections of the ellipsoid are

$$(x/a)\sqrt{(a^2-b^2)}+(z/c)\sqrt{(b^2-c^2)}=\lambda, \quad ...(1)$$

and

$$(x/a)\sqrt{(a^2-b^2)}-(z/c)\sqrt{(b^2-c^2)}=\mu. \quad ...(2)$$

Let r be the radius of the circular section in which the plane (1) cuts the ellipsoid. Then proceeding as in Ex. 2 above, we have

$$r=b\sqrt{\{1-\lambda^2/(a^2-c^2)\}}. \quad ...(3)$$

Similarly the radius of the circular section in which the plane (2) cuts the ellipsoid is $b\sqrt{\{1-\mu^2/(a^2-c^2)\}}$. [Replacing λ by μ and c by $-c$ in (3)].

Now as given if the plane (1) passes through $(a, 0, 0)$, an extremity of the x-axis, then (1) gives $\lambda=\sqrt{(a^2-b^2)}$.

$\therefore$ From (3), we have

$$r^2=b^2\left\{1-\frac{a^2-b^2}{a^2-c^2}\right\} \text{ or } \frac{r^2}{b^2}=\frac{b^2-c^2}{a^2-c^2}.$$

Again if the plane (2) also passes through $(a, 0, 0)$, then (2) gives $\mu=\sqrt{(a^2-b^2)}$.

Hence in this case also $\dfrac{r^2}{b^2}=\dfrac{b^2-c^2}{a^2-c^2}$.

Ex. 5. *Find the locus of the centres of spheres of constant radius k which cut the ellipsoid in a pair of circles.*

Solution. Consider the circular sections of the ellipsoid given by the planes

$$(x/a)\sqrt{(a^2-b^2)}\mp(z/c)\sqrt{(b^2-c^2)}=\lambda, \quad ...(1)$$

and

$$(x/a)\sqrt{(a^2-b^2)}-(z/c)\sqrt{(b^2-c^2)}=\mu. \quad ...(2)$$

The circular sections (1) and (2) lie on the sphere [See § 8(B), equation (5)]

$$x^2+y^2+z^2-(\lambda+\mu)\sqrt{(a^2-b^2)}\,(x/a)+(\lambda-\mu)\sqrt{(b^2-c^2)}\,(z/c)$$
$$+\lambda\mu-b^2=0. \quad ...(3)$$

If the centre of the sphere (3) be (f, g, h), then

$$2f=(\lambda+\mu)\sqrt{(a^2-b^2)}/a,\ g=0,\ 2h=-(\lambda-\mu)\sqrt{(b^2-c^2)}/c. \quad ...(4)$$

Also it is given that the radius of the sphere (3) is k.

$$\therefore\ k^2=\frac{(\lambda+\mu)^2\,(a^2-b^2)}{4a^2}+\frac{(\lambda-\mu)\,(b^2-c^2)}{4c^2}-(\lambda\mu-b^2)$$

[$\because$ in the standard equation of a sphere, $(\text{radius})^2=g^2+f^2+h^2-d$]

or $\quad f^2+h^2+b^2-\lambda\mu=k^2$, using (4)

or $$f^2+h^2-k^2+b^2=\lambda\mu. \quad ...(5)$$

Again from (4), we have

$$\frac{2af}{\sqrt{(a^2-b^2)}}=(\lambda+\mu),\ \frac{2ch}{\sqrt{(b^2-c^2)}}=-(\lambda-\mu),\ g=0.$$

Squaring and subtracting the first two of these three relations, we have

$$4\left\{\frac{a^2f^2}{a^2-b^2}-\frac{c^2h^2}{b^2-c^2}\right\}=(\lambda+\mu)^2-(\lambda-\mu)^2=4\lambda\mu$$

$$=4\,(f^2+h^2-k^2+b^2),\ \text{from (5).}$$

$\therefore$ from the above three relations, we have

$$f^2\left(\frac{a^2}{a^2-b^2}-1\right)-h^2\left(\frac{c^2}{b^2-c^2}+1\right)=b^2-k^2,\ g=0$$

or
$$\frac{f^2}{a^2-b^2}-\frac{h^2}{b^2-c^2}=1-\frac{k^2}{b^2},\ g=0.$$

$\therefore$ the required locus of (f, g, h) is given by

$$x^2/(a^2-b^2)-z^2/(b^2-c^2)=1-k^2/b^2,\ \text{and}\quad y=0.$$

Ex. 6. *Show that the locus of the centres of the spheres which pass through the origin and cut the ellipsoid $x^2/a^2+y^2/b^2+z^2/c^2=1$ in a pair of real circles is the hyperbola*

$$\frac{a^2x^2}{a^2-b^2}-\frac{c^2x^2}{b^2-c^2}=b^2,\ y=0.$$

Solution. Proceed as in Ex. 5, above.

The sphere (3) will pass through (0, 0, 0) if $\lambda\mu=b^2$.

Let (f, g, h) be the centre of the sphere; then from equations (4), we have

$$\frac{4a^2f^2}{a^2-b^2}-\frac{4c^2h^2}{b^2-c^2}=(\lambda+\mu)^2-(\lambda-\mu)^2=4\lambda\mu,\ g=0$$

or
$$\frac{a^2f^2}{a^2-b^2}-\frac{c^2h^2}{b^2-c^2}=b^2,\ g=0. \qquad [\because\ \lambda\mu=b^2]$$

$\therefore$ The required locus of the centres (f, g, h) is

$$a^2x^2/(a^2-b^2)-c^2z^2/(b^2-c^2)=b^2,\ y=0.$$

Ex. 7. *If p_1, p_2, p_3 be the lengths of the perpendiculars from the extremities P_1, P_2, P_3 of conjugate semi-diameters on one of the planes of central circular sections of the ellipsoid $x^2/a^2+y^2/b^2+z^2/c^2=1$, then prove that $p_1^2+p_2^2+p_3^2=a^2c^2/b^2$.*

Solution. We know that one of the real central circular sections of the given ellipsoid is

$$(x/a)\sqrt{(a^2-b^2)}+(z/c)\sqrt{(b^2-c^2)}=0 \qquad ..(1)$$

$$(a>b>c).$$

Let $P_1\ (x_1, y_1, z_1)$, $P_2\ (x_2, y_2, z_2)$ and $P_3\ (x_3, y_3, z_3)$ be the extremities of conjugate semi-diameters.

$\therefore$ p_1=the length of the perpendicular from P_1 (x_1, y_1, z_1) to (1)

$$=\frac{(x_1/a)\sqrt{(a^2-b^2)}+(z_1/c)\sqrt{(b^2-c^2)}}{\sqrt{\{(a^2-b^2)/a^2+(b^2-c^2)/c^2\}}}$$

or $$p_1^2=\frac{(x_1^2/a^2)(a^2-b^2)+(z_1^2/c^2)(b^2-c^2)+(2z_1x_1/ac)\sqrt{\{(a^2-b^2)(b^2-c^2)\}}}{b^2(a^2-c^2)/(a^2c^2)}. \quad \text{..(2)}$$

Replacing x_1, y_1, z_1 by x_2, y_2, z_2 respectively in (2) we get p_2^2 and similarly we get p_3^2.

$$\therefore \quad p_1^2+p_2^2+p_3^2=\frac{a^2c^2}{b^2(a^2-c^2)}\left[\frac{a^2-b^2}{a^2}\,\Sigma x_1^2+\frac{b^2-c^2}{c^2}\,\Sigma z_1^2 + \frac{2}{ac}\sqrt{\{(a^2-b^2)(b^2-c^2)\}}\,\Sigma z_1x_1\right]$$

$$=\frac{a^2c^2}{b^2(a^2-c^2)}\left[\left(\frac{a^2-b^2}{a^2}\right).a^2+\left(\frac{b^2-c^2}{c^2}\right).c^2+0\right]$$

$$[\because \Sigma x_1^2=a^2,\ \Sigma z_1^2=c^2,\ \Sigma z_1x_1=0]$$

$$=a^2c^2/b^2.$$

Ex. 8. *If p_1, p_2, p_3 and π_1, π_2, π_3 be the perpendiculars from the extremities P_1, P_2, P_3 of conjugate semi-diameters on the two central circular sections of the ellipsoid $x^2/a^2+y^2/b^2+z^2/c^2=1$ then prove that*

$$p_1\pi_1+p_2\pi_2+p_3\pi_3=a^2c^2(a^2+c^2-2b^2)/\{(a^2-c^2)\,b^2\}.$$

Solution. We know that the two real central circular sections of the given ellipsoid are

$$(x/a)\sqrt{(a^2-b^2)}+(z/c)\sqrt{(b^2-c^2)}=0, \quad \text{...(1)}$$

and $$(x/a)\sqrt{(a^2-b^2)}-(z/c)\sqrt{(b^2-c^2)}=0. \quad \text{...(2)}$$

Proceeding as in Ex. 7 above, we have

$$p_1=\frac{(x_1/a)\sqrt{(a^2-b^2)}+(z_1/c)\sqrt{(b^2-c^2)}}{\sqrt{\{(a^2-b^2)/a^2+(b^2-c^2)/c^2\}}},$$

π_1=the length of the perpendicular from $P_1(x_1, y_1, z_1)$ on (2)

$$=\frac{(x_1/a)\sqrt{(a^2-b^2)}-(z_1/c)\sqrt{(b^2-c^2)}}{\sqrt{\{(a^2-b^2)/a^2+(b^2-c^2)/c^2\}}}.$$

$$\therefore \quad p_1\pi_1=\frac{(x_1^2/a^2)(a^2-b^2)-(z_1^2/c^2)(b^2-c^2)}{b^2(a^2-c^2)/(a^2c^2)}$$

$$=\frac{a^2c^2}{b^2(a^2-c^2)}\left\{\left(\frac{a^2-b^2}{a^2}\right)x_1^2-\left(\frac{b^2-c^2}{c^2}\right)z_1^2\right\}$$

Similar expressions can be obtained for $p_2\pi_2$ and $p_3\pi_3$.

$$\therefore\quad p_1\pi_1+p_2\pi_2+p_3\pi_3=\frac{a^2c^2}{b^2(a^2-c^2)}\left[\left(\frac{a^2-b^2}{a^2}\right)\Sigma x_1^2-\left(\frac{b^2-c^2}{c^2}\right)\Sigma z_1^2\right]$$

$$=\frac{a^2c^2}{b^2(a^2-c^2)}\left[\left(\frac{a^2-b^2}{a^2}\right).a^2-\left(\frac{b^2-c^2}{c^2}\right).c^2\right]$$

$$=\frac{a^2c^2(a^2-2b^2+c^2)}{b^2(a^2-c^2)}.$$

Ex. 9. *A cone is drawn with its vertex at the centre of the ellipsoid $x^2/a^2+y^2/b^2+z^2/c^2=1$ and its base is a circular section of the ellipsoid. If the cone contains three mutually perpendicular generators, show that the distance from the centre of the ellipsoid to the section is $abc/\sqrt{(b^2c^2+c^2a^2+a^2b^2)}$.*

Solution. The ellipsoid is $x^2/a^2+y^2/b^2+z^2/c^2=1$. ...(1)

Any real circular section of (1) is

$$(x/a)\sqrt{(a^2-b^2)}+(z/c)\sqrt{(b^2-c^2)}=\lambda. \quad ...(2)$$

Making (1) homogeneous with the help of (2), the equation of the cone with its vertex at the centre (0, 0, 0) of (1) and having its base as the above circular section is given by

$$\frac{x^2}{a^2}+\frac{y^2}{b^2}+\frac{z^2}{c^2}=\frac{1}{\lambda^2}\left\{\frac{x}{a}\sqrt{(a^2-b^2)}+\frac{z}{c}\sqrt{(b^2-c^2)}\right\}^2.$$

The above cone has three mutually perpendicular generators.

$\therefore$ the coeff. of x^2 + the coeff. of y^2 + the coeff. of $z^2=0$

or $$\left(\frac{1}{a^2}-\frac{a^2-b^2}{a^2\lambda^2}\right)+\frac{1}{b^2}+\left(\frac{1}{c^2}-\frac{b^2-c^2}{c^2\lambda^2}\right)=0$$

or $$\lambda^2\left(\frac{1}{a^2}+\frac{1}{b^2}+\frac{1}{c^2}\right)=\frac{a^2-b^2}{a^2}+\frac{b^2-c^2}{c^2}. \quad ...(3)$$

Now the length of the perpendicular (*i.e.* distance) from the centre (0, 0, 0) of (1) to the plane (2) is

$$=\frac{\lambda}{\sqrt{\{(a^2-b^2)/a^2+(b^2-c^2)/c^2\}}}=\frac{1}{\sqrt{(1/a^2+1/b^2+1/c^2)}},\text{ from (3)}$$

$=abc/\sqrt{(b^2c^2+c^2a^2+a^2b^2)}$.

Ex. 10. *Find the equations to the real central circular sections of the conicoid*

$$6x^2+13y^2+6z^2-10yz+4zx-10xy-1=0.$$

Solution. The equation of the given conicoid can be re-written as

$$\{6x^2+13y^2+6z^2-10yz+4zx-10xy-\lambda(x^2+y^2+z^2)\}$$
$$+\lambda(x^2+y^2+z^2-1/\lambda)=0. \quad ...(1)$$

Now the equation (1) will represent a surface passing through the intersection of a sphere and a pair of planes if

$$6x^2+13y^2+6z^2-10yz+4zx-10xy-\lambda\,(x^2+y^2+z^2)=0 \quad \ldots(2)$$

represents a pair of planes the condition for which is

$$\begin{vmatrix} 6-\lambda & -5 & 2 \\ -5 & 13-\lambda & -5 \\ 2 & -5 & 6-\lambda \end{vmatrix}=0 \qquad \text{[See § 9 above]}$$

or $\lambda^3-25\lambda^2+138\lambda-216=0$ or $(\lambda-3)(\lambda-4)(\lambda-18)=0$

or $\lambda=3, 4, 18.$

We know that the mean value of λ *i.e.* $\lambda=4$ will give real circular sections. Putting $\lambda=4$ in (2), the real central circular sections are given by $2x^2+9y^2+2z^2-10yz+4zx-10xy=0$

or $2(x+z)^2-10(x+z)\,y+9y^2=0.$

Ex. 11. *Find the central circular sections of the conicoid* $3x^2+5y^2+3z^2+2zx-4=0$. *Also find any circular sections.*

Solution. The equation of the given conicoid can be rewritten as

$$[3x^2+5y^2+3z^2+2zx-\lambda(x^2+y^2+z^2)]+\lambda\,(x^2+y^2+z^2-4/\lambda)=0 \ \ldots(1)$$

The equation (1) will represent a surface passing through the intersection of a sphere and a pair of planes if

$$3x^2+5y^2+3z^2+2zx-\lambda\,(x^2+y^2+z^2)=0 \quad \ldots(2)$$

represents a pair of planes. The condition for this is

$$\begin{vmatrix} 3-\lambda & 0 & 1 \\ 0 & 5-\lambda & 0 \\ 1 & 0 & 3-\lambda \end{vmatrix}=0,$$

or $(3-\lambda)(5-\lambda)(3-\lambda)-(5-\lambda)=0$

or $\lambda^3-11\lambda^2+38\lambda-40=0$

or $(\lambda-2)(\lambda-4)(\lambda-5)=0$

or $\lambda=2, 4, 5.$

The mean value of λ *i.e.* $\lambda=4$ will give real circular sections. Putting $\lambda=4$ in (2), the real circular sections are given by

$$-x^2+y^2-z^2+2zx=0 \quad \text{or} \quad (x-z)^2-y^2=0$$

or $(x+y-z)=0$ and $x-y-z=0.$ ...(3)

Also any circular sections are those which are parallel to (3) and hence they are given by

$$x+y-z=\lambda \quad \text{and} \quad x-y-z=\mu.$$

Ex. 12. *Find the real circular sections of the following :*

(*i*) $5y^2-8z^2+18yz-14zx-10xy+27=0$

(*ii*) $x^2+2y^2+6z^2=8$

(*iii*) $15x^2-y^2-10z^2+4=0.$

Solution. Proceeding as in Ex. 10 or Ex. 11 above, the real circular sections are given by

(i) $3x-4y+z=\lambda,\ x-2y-5z=\mu$

(ii) $x+2z=\lambda,\ x-2z=\mu$

(iii) $4x+3z=\lambda,\ 4x-3z=\mu$.

If we choose $\lambda=\mu=0$ the central circular sections are obtained.

Ex. 13. *Show that the real central sections of the hyperboloids* $x^2/a^2+y^2/b^2-z^2/c^2=1$ *and* $x^2/a^2-y^2/b^2-z^2/c^2=1$ *are given by the planes* $(y/b)\sqrt{(a^2-b^2)}\pm(z/c)\sqrt{(a^2+c^2)}=0$

and $(x/a)\sqrt{(a^2+b^2)}\pm(z/c)\sqrt{(b^2-c^2)}=0$.

Solution. The equation $x^2/a^2+y^2/b^2-z^2/c^2=1$ ...(1)

can be rewritten in the following three forms :

$$\left(\frac{x^2+y^2+z^2-a^2}{a^2}\right)+y^2\left(\frac{1}{b^2}-\frac{1}{a^2}\right)-z^2\left(\frac{1}{c^2}+\frac{1}{a^2}\right)=0, \quad ...(2)$$

$$\left(\frac{x^2+y^2+z^2-b^2}{b^2}\right)+x^2\left(\frac{1}{a^2}-\frac{1}{b^2}\right)-z^2\left(\frac{1}{c^2}+\frac{1}{b^2}\right)=0, \quad ...(3)$$

and $$\left(\frac{x^2+y^2+z^2-c^2}{c^2}\right)+x^2\left(\frac{1}{a^2}+\frac{1}{c^2}\right)+y^2\left(\frac{1}{b^2}+\frac{1}{c^2}\right)=0. \quad ...(4)$$

In case $a>b>c$, we have $1/a<1/b<1/c$. Then the only real central circular sections of (1) are given by the planes

$$y^2\left(\frac{1}{b^2}-\frac{1}{a^2}\right)-z^2\left(\frac{1}{c^2}+\frac{1}{a^2}\right)=0 \text{ or } \frac{y^2}{b^2}(a^2-b^2)-\frac{z^2}{c^2}(a^2+c^2)=0$$

or $$(y/b)\sqrt{(a^2-b^2)}\pm(z/c)\sqrt{(a^2+c^2)}=0.$$

Again the equation of the hyperboloid $x^2/a^2-y^2/b^2-z^2/c^2=1$ may be rewritten as

$$-\left(\frac{x^2+y^2+z^2+b^2}{b^2}\right)+x^2\left(\frac{1}{a^2}+\frac{1}{b^2}\right)-z^2\left(\frac{1}{c^2}-\frac{1}{b^2}\right)=0.$$

Hence discussing as above the real central circular sections are $(x/a)\sqrt{(a^2+b^2)}\pm(z/c)\sqrt{(b^2-c^2)}=0$.

Ex. 14. *Prove that the planes* $2x+3z-5=0,\ 2x-3z+7=0$ *meet the hyperboloid* $-x^2+3y^2+12z^2=75$ *in circles which lie on the sphere* $3(x^2+y^2+z^2)+4x+36z-110=0$.

Solution. The equation of any surface passing through the sections of the given hyperboloid by the two given planes is given by

$$(-x^2+3y^2+12z^2-75)+k(2x+3z-5)(2x-3z+7)=0. \quad ..(1)$$

The equation (1) will be that of a sphere if the coefficients of x^2, y^2 and z^2 are equal *i.e.* if $-1+4k=3=12-9k$ *i.e.* if $k=1$.

Putting $k=1$ in (1), the circular sections lie on the sphere

$$3(x^2+y^2+z^2)+4x+36z-110=0.$$

Ex. 15. *If the section of the cone whose vertex is $P(\alpha, \beta, \gamma)$ and base $z=0$, $ax^2+by^2=1$, by the plane $x=0$ is a circle, then P lies on $y=0$, $ax^2-bz^2=1$ and the section of the cone by the plane $(a-b)\gamma x-2a\alpha z=0$ is also a circle.*

Solution. It can be easily shown that the equation of the cone is given by $\quad a(\alpha z-\gamma x)^2+b(\beta z-\gamma y)^2=(z-\gamma)^2.$ ...(1)

The section of (1) by the plane $x=0$ is given by

$$a\alpha^2z^2+b(\beta z-\gamma y)^2=(z-\gamma)^2,\ x=0. \quad ...(2)$$

The equations (2) will represent a circle if

the coeff. of y^2=the coeff. of z^2 and the coeff. of $yz=0$

i.e. if $\quad b\gamma^2=a\alpha^2+b\beta^2-1$ and $b\beta\gamma=0.$ ...(3)

But $b\neq0$ and also $\gamma\neq0$. Note that if we take $\gamma=0$ then the vertex (α, β, γ) of the cone will lie in its base which is impossible. Hence we must have $\beta=0$. Then the first relation of (3) provides

$$b\gamma^2=a\alpha^2-1,\ \beta=0. \quad ...(4)$$

$\therefore$ The vertex $P(\alpha, \beta, \gamma)$ lies on $ax^2-bz^2=1$, $y=0$. Again putting $\beta=0$ in (1), the equation of the cone becomes

$$a(\alpha z-\gamma x)^2+b\gamma^2y^2=(z-\gamma)^2$$

or $\quad a\alpha^2z^2+a\gamma^2x^2-2a\alpha\gamma zx+b\gamma^2y^2-z^2+2\gamma z-\gamma^2=0$

or $\quad a\gamma^2x^2+(b\gamma^2+1)z^2-z^2+b\gamma^2y^2-2a\alpha zx+2\gamma z+\gamma^2=0$

[Putting $a\alpha^2=b\gamma^2+1$ from (4)]

or $\quad \{b\gamma^2(x^2+y^2+z^2)+2\gamma z-\gamma^2\}+\gamma x[(a-b)\gamma x-2a\alpha z]=0.$ ...(5)

The equation (5) will represent a sphere if

$\gamma x[(a-b)\gamma x-2a\alpha z]=0$ *i.e.* $x=0$, $(a-b)\gamma x-2a\alpha z=0$,

Therefore the circular sections are given by

$$(a-b)\gamma x-2a\alpha z=0,\ x=0.$$

Ex. 16. *Find the equations to the circular sections of the conicoid*

$$yz\left(\frac{b}{c}+\frac{c}{b}\right)+zx\left(\frac{c}{a}+\frac{a}{c}\right)+xy\left(\frac{a}{b}+\frac{b}{a}\right)+1=0.$$

Solution. The equation of the given conicoid can be rewritten as

$$yz\left(\frac{b}{c}+\frac{c}{b}\right)+zx\left(\frac{c}{a}+\frac{a}{c}\right)+xy\left(\frac{a}{b}+\frac{b}{a}\right)+\lambda(x^2+y^2+z^2)$$
$$-\lambda(x^2+y^2+z^2-1/\lambda)=0. \quad ...(1)$$

The equation (1) will represent a surface passing through the intersection of a sphere and a pair of planes if the equation

$$yz\left(\frac{b}{c}+\frac{c}{b}\right)+zx\left(\frac{c}{a}+\frac{a}{c}\right)+xy\left(\frac{a}{b}+\frac{b}{a}\right)$$
$$+\lambda(x^2+y^2+z^2)=0 \quad \ldots(2)$$

respresents a pair of planes. The condition for this is

$$\begin{vmatrix} \lambda & \frac{a^2+b^2}{2ab} & \frac{c^2+a^2}{2ca} \\ \frac{a^2+b^2}{2ab} & \lambda & \frac{b^2+c^2}{2bc} \\ \frac{c^2+a^2}{2ca} & \frac{b^2+c^2}{2bc} & \lambda \end{vmatrix}=0.$$

Expanding the determinant, we get

$$\lambda^3-\lambda\left\{\left(\frac{b^2+c^2}{2bc}\right)^2+\left(\frac{c^2+a^2}{2ca}\right)^2+\left(\frac{a^2+b^2}{2ab}\right)^2\right\}$$
$$+2.\left(\frac{b^2+c^2}{2bc}\right)\left(\frac{c^2+a^2}{2ca}\right)\left(\frac{a^2+b^2}{2ab}\right)=0.$$

This is clearly satisfied by $\lambda=1$. Putting $\lambda=1$, the equation of the pair of planes is given by

$$x^2+y^2+z^2+yz\left(\frac{b}{c}+\frac{c}{b}\right)+zx\left(\frac{c}{a}+\frac{a}{c}\right)+xy\left(\frac{a}{b}+\frac{b}{a}\right)=0$$

or
$$(ax+by+cz)\left(\frac{x}{a}+\frac{y}{b}+\frac{z}{c}\right)=0.$$

$\therefore$ Central circular sections are

$$ax+by+cz=0,\ x/a+y/b+z/c=0. \quad \ldots(3)$$

The equations of any circular sections are given by

$$ax+by+cz=\lambda,\ x/a+y/b+z/c=\mu.$$

Ex. 17. *Find the conditions that the equations*

$$F(x, y, z)\equiv ax^2+by^2+cz^2+2fyz+2gzx+2hxy=1$$

and $lx+my+nz=0$ *should determine a circle.*

Solution. Proceeding exactly as in § 9, the equation

$$ax^2+by^2+cz^2+2fyz+2gzx+2hxy-\lambda(x^2+y^2+z^2)=0 \quad \ldots(1)$$

must represent two planes. But one of these planes is given to be $lx+my+nz=0$. So we rewrite the left hand side of the equation (1) as

$$(a-\lambda)x^2+(b-\lambda)y^2+(c-\lambda)z^2+2fyz+2gzx+2hxy$$
$$\equiv(lx+my+nz)\left\{\frac{(a-\lambda)}{l}x+\frac{(b-\lambda)}{m}y+\frac{(c-\lambda)}{n}z\right\}. \quad \ldots(2)$$

Now (2) is an identity, hence coefficients of like terms in x, y, z should be equal. We clearly see that the coefficients of x^2,

y^2, z^2 are equal and hence equating the coefficients of yz, zx and xy, we get

$$\left.\begin{array}{l} 2f=(b-\lambda)\, n/m+(c-\lambda)\, m/n,\ 2g=(a-\lambda)\, a/l+(c-\lambda)\, l/n \\ \text{and} \quad 2h=(a-\lambda)\, m/l+(b-\lambda)\, l/m. \end{array}\right\} \quad ...(3)$$

The first of the relations in (3) gives

$$\lambda\left(\frac{n}{m}+\frac{m}{n}\right)=\frac{bn}{m}+\frac{mc}{n}-2f.$$

$$\therefore \quad \lambda=\frac{bn^2+cm^2-2fmn}{m^2+n^2}=\frac{cl^2+an^2-2gnl}{n^2+l^2}=\frac{am^2+bl^2-2hlm}{l^2+m^2}.$$

(By symmetry)

These are the required conditions, it being assumed that neither of l, m, n is zero.

Ex. 18. *The normals to the ellipsoid* $x^2/a^2+y^2/b^2+z^2/c^2=1$ *at all points of a central circular section are parallel to a plane that makes an angle* $\cos^{-1}\left\{\dfrac{ac}{b\sqrt{(a^2-b^2+c^2)}}\right\}$ *with the section.*

Solution. One of the real central circular sections is

$$(x/a)\sqrt{(a^2-b^2)}+(z/c)\sqrt{(b^2-c^2)}=0. \quad ...(1)$$

Let the generators of the enveloping cylinder which touch along (1), be parallel to the line $x/l=y/m=z/n$.

$\therefore$ the diametral plane $lx/a^2+my/b^2+nz/c^2=0$ ...(2)
and the plane (1) should represent the same plane.

Hence on comparing (1) and (2), we get

$$\frac{l}{a\sqrt{(a^2-b^2)}}=\frac{m}{0}=\frac{n}{c\sqrt{(b^2-c^2)}}$$

Also the normals to the ellipsoid will be parallel to the normal section of the cylinder *i.e.* to the plane $lx+my+nz=0$

or $$a\sqrt{(a^2-b^2)}\, x+c\sqrt{(b^2-c^2)}\, z=0. \quad ...(3)$$

Now if θ be the angle between the planes (1) and (3), then we have

$$\cos\theta=\frac{(a^2-b^2)+(b^2-c^2)}{\left[\left(\dfrac{a^2-b^2}{a^2}+\dfrac{b^2-c^2}{c^2}\right)\{a^2(a^2-b^2)+c^2(b^2-c^2)\}\right]^{1/2}}$$

$$=\frac{ac\,(a^2-c^2)}{b\,[(a^2-c^2)\,(a^2-c^2)\,(a^2+c^2-b^2)]^{1/2}}$$

$$\therefore \quad \theta=\cos^{-1}\frac{ac\,(a^2-c^2)}{b\sqrt{(a^2-b^2+c^2)}}.$$

Ex. 19. *Find the real circular sections of the following paraboloids :* (i) $x^2+10z^2=2y$, (ii) $13y^2+4z^2=2x$.

Solution. (i) The equation $x^2+10z^2=2y$ of the paraboloid may be rewritten as $(x^2+y^2+z^2-2y)+(9z^2-y^2)=0$. ...(1)

The equation (1) will represent a surface passing through the intersection of a sphere and a pair of planes if the equation $9z^2-y^2=0$ represents a pair of planes. Clearly $9z^2-y^2=0$ gives $y\pm 3z=0$ as two planes. Hence the real central circular sections of the given paraboloid are $y\pm 3z=0$.

Hence the equations of any circular sections are

$$y+3z=\lambda \quad \text{and} \quad y-3z=\mu.$$

(ii) Writing the given equation as

$$4(x^2+y^2+z^2-x/2)+(9y^2-4x^2)=0$$

and proceeding as in part (i) above the real circular sections are given by $2x+3y=\lambda$, $2x-3y=\mu$.

UMBILICS

§ 11. Umbilics.

Definition. *Let P (α, β, γ) be a point on any conicoid. If the planes parallel to the tangent plane at the point P determine circular sections of the conicoid, then the tangent plane at the point P itself will be a circular section (i e. a point circular section) of radius zero. Such a point P is called an umbilic of the conicoid. Hence an umbilic is a point circle which lies on the conicoid.*

§ 12. To determine the real umbilics of the ellipsoid.

The equation of the ellipsoid is $x^2/a^2+y^2/b^2+z^2/c^2=1$. ...(1)

Let $P(\alpha, \beta, \gamma)$ be an umbilic of (1). The equation of the tangent plane to (1) at the point P is $\alpha x/a^2+\beta y/b^2+\gamma z/c^2=1$. ...(2)

The tangent plane (2) should be parallel to either of the real circular sections of (1) *i.e.* to either of the two planes

$$(x/a)\sqrt{(a^2-b^2)}\pm(z/c)\sqrt{(b^2-c^2)}=0. \quad ...(3)$$

On comparing (2) and (3), we have

$$\beta=0 \text{ and } \frac{\alpha}{a\sqrt{(a^2-b^2)}}=\pm\frac{\gamma}{c\sqrt{(b^2-c^2)}}=k \text{ (say)}. \quad ...(4)$$

Since $P(\alpha, \beta, \gamma)$ lies on (1), therefore

$$\alpha^2/a^2+\beta^2/b^2+\gamma^2/c^2=1. \quad ...(5)$$

Putting the values of α, β, γ from the relations (4) in (5), we get $k^2\{(a^2-b^2)+(b^2-c^2)\}=1$, or $k=\pm 1/\sqrt{(a^2-c^2)}$.

Putting the values of k in (4), the co-ordinates of the umbilics of the ellipsoid (1) are given by

$$\alpha=\pm\frac{a\sqrt{(a^2-b^2)}}{\sqrt{(a^2-c^2)}},\ \beta=0,\ \gamma=\pm\frac{c\sqrt{(b^2-c^2)}}{\sqrt{(a^2-c^2)}}. \quad ...(6)$$

Clearly (6) gives four real umbilics.

Corollary 1. *To show that the umbilics of the ellipsoid lie on a sphere.*

Squaring and adding the relations in (6), we get

$$\alpha^2+\beta^2+\gamma^2=\frac{a^2(a^2-b^2)}{a^2-c^2}+\frac{c^2(b^2-c^2)}{a^2-c^2}$$

$$=\frac{a^2(a^2-c^2)+c^2(a^2-c^2)-b^2(a^2-c^2)}{(a^2-c^2)}=a^2+c^2-b^2.$$

$\therefore$ The locus of $P(\alpha, \beta, \gamma)$ is $x^2+y^2+z^2=a^2-b^2+c^2$ which is the equation of the required sphere on which lie the umbilics of the ellipsoid (1).

Corollary 2. *To find the length p of the perpendicular distance from the centre to the tangent plane at an umbilic of the ellipsoid.*

Here p=the length of the perpendicular from the centre (0, 0, 0) of the ellipsoid to the tangent plane (2)

i.e. $$p=\frac{1}{\sqrt{(\alpha^2/a^4+\beta^2/b^4+\gamma^2/c^4)}}. \quad ...(7)$$

From (6), we have

$$\frac{\alpha^2}{a^4}+\frac{\beta^2}{b^4}+\frac{\gamma^2}{c^4}=\frac{1}{a^2-c^2}\left\{\frac{a^2-b^2}{a^2}+0+\frac{b^2-c^2}{c^2}\right\}=\frac{b^2}{a^2c^2}$$

$\therefore$ from (7), we have $p=ac/b$.

§ 13. To determine the real umbilics of the paraboloid.

The equation of the paraboloid is $ax^2+by^2=2cz$. ...(1)

$(a > b > 0)$

Let $P(\alpha, \beta, \gamma)$ be an umbilic of (1). The equation of the tangent plane at the point P is $a\alpha x+b\beta y-c(z+\gamma)=0$. ...(2)

The tangent plane (2) should be parallel to either of the real circular sections of (1) *i.e.* to either of the planes

$$x\sqrt{(a-b)}\pm z\sqrt{b}=0. \quad ...(3)$$

On comparing (2) and (3), we have

$$\beta=0,\ \frac{a\alpha}{\sqrt{(a-b)}}=\pm\frac{c}{\sqrt{b}}.\quad\therefore\quad \alpha=\pm\frac{c}{a}\sqrt{\left(\frac{a-b}{b}\right)} \quad ...(4)$$

Since $P(\alpha, \beta, \gamma)$ lies on (1), therefore $a\alpha^2+b\beta^2=2c\gamma$

or $$2c\gamma=\frac{c^2}{a}\left(\frac{a-b}{b}\right)+0 \text{ using (4), or } \gamma=\frac{c(a-b)}{2ab}.$$

Hence $\left(\pm\frac{c}{a}\sqrt{\left(\frac{a-b}{a}\right)},\ 0,\ \frac{c(a-b)}{2ab}\right)$ are the co-ordinates of two real umbilics of the paraboloid (1).

Corollary. *The umbilics of the paraboloid* $x^2/a^2+y^2/b^2=2cz$, $a>b$ *are given by* $(0, \pm bc\sqrt{(a^2-b^2)}, \frac{1}{2}c(a^2-b^2))$.

Proceed exactly as in § 13 above.

SOLVED EXAMPLES (E)

Ex. 1. *Prove that the central circular sections of the conicoid* $(a-b)x^2+ay^2+(a+b)z^2=1$ *are at right angles and that the umbilics are given by*

$$x=\pm\sqrt{\left\{\frac{a+b}{2a(a-b)}\right\}},\ y=0,\ z=\pm\sqrt{\left\{\frac{a-b}{2a(a+b)}\right\}}.$$

Solution. The given equation of the conicoid can be rewritten as
$$a(x^2+y^2+z^2)+b(z^2-x^2)=0 \qquad \ldots(1)$$

The equation (1) clearly shows that the circular sections of the given conicoid are $z^2-x^2=0$ or $z\pm x=0$ ...(2) which are at right angles.

Let $P(\alpha, \beta, \gamma)$ be an umbilic. The equation of the tangent plane at $P(\alpha, \beta, \gamma)$ is $(a-b)\alpha x+a\beta y+(a+b)\gamma z=1$. ...(3)

The tangent plane (3) must be parallel to either of the planes (2).

$$\therefore \quad \frac{(a-b)\alpha}{1}=\frac{\alpha\beta}{0}=\frac{(a+b)\gamma}{\pm 1}=k \text{ (say)}.$$

Hence $\alpha=k/(a-b),\ \beta=0,\ \gamma=\pm k/(a+b)$. ...(4)

Also $P(\alpha, \beta, \gamma)$ lies on the given conicoid, hence we have
$$(a-b)\alpha^2+a\beta^2+(a+b)\gamma^2=1$$

or
$$(a-b)\frac{k^2}{(a-b)^2}+0+(a+b)\frac{k^2}{(a+b)^2}=1$$

[Putting the values from (4)]

or
$$k^2=\frac{a^2-b^2}{2a} \text{ or } k=\pm\sqrt{\left(\frac{a^2-b^2}{2a}\right)}.$$

Putting the values of k in (4), the required umbilics are given by

$$\alpha=\pm\sqrt{\left\{\frac{a+b}{2a(a-b)}\right\}},\ \beta=0,\ \gamma=\pm\sqrt{\left\{\frac{a-b}{2a(a+b)}\right\}}.$$

Ex. 2. *Prove that the radius of the circle in which the plane* $(x/a)\sqrt{(a^2-b^2)}+(z/c)\sqrt{(b^2-c^2)}=\lambda$ *cuts the ellipsoid*

$$x^2/a^2+y^2/b^2+z^2/c^2=1 \text{ is } b\sqrt{\left(1-\frac{\lambda^2}{a^2-c^2}\right)}$$

Deduce the co-ordinates of the umbilics of the ellipsoid.

Solution. For the first part see Ex. 2 of the set solved examples (D) above. There we have proved that the radius r of the circular section $(x/a)\sqrt{(a^2-b^2)}+(z/c)\sqrt{(b^2-c^2)}=\lambda$ ...(1)
is $r=b\sqrt{\{1-\lambda^2/(a^2-c^2)\}}$.

For an umbilic, the radius r of the circle is zero.

Hence if $r=0$, we have $\lambda=\pm\sqrt{(a^2-c^2)}$ and the equation of the plane (1) becomes

$$(x/a)\sqrt{(a^2-b^2)}+(z/c)\sqrt{(b^2-c^2)}=\pm\sqrt{(a^2-c^2)}. \quad ...(2)$$

Now let (α, β, γ) be the co-ordinates of the umbilic. The tangent plane at (α, β, γ) to the ellipsoid is

$$\alpha x/a^2+\beta y/b^2+\gamma z/c^2=1. \quad ...(3)$$

The planes (2) and (3) should be the same.

$$\therefore \quad \frac{\alpha/a^2}{\sqrt{(a^2-b^2)}/a}=\frac{\beta/b^2}{0}=\frac{\gamma/c^2}{\sqrt{(b^2-c^2)}/c}=\frac{1}{\pm\sqrt{(a^2-c^2)}}$$

or $$\alpha=\frac{\pm a\sqrt{(a^2-b^2)}}{\sqrt{(a^2-c^2)}}, \beta=0, \gamma=\frac{\pm c\sqrt{(b^2-c^2)}}{\sqrt{(a^2-c^2)}}.$$

Ex. 3. *Find the real umbilics of the hyperboloid*

$$x^2/a^2-y^2/b^2-z^2/c^2=1.$$

Solution. Let the co-ordinates of the umbilic be (α, β, γ).

The tangent plane at (α, β, γ) is

$$\alpha x/a^2-\beta y/b^2-\gamma z/c^2=1. \quad ...(1)$$

The tangent plane (1) should be parallel to either of the real circular sections of the given hyperboloid of two sheets *i.e.* to either of the two planes

$$(x/a)\sqrt{(a^2+b^2)}\pm(z/c)\sqrt{(b^2-c^2)}=0. \quad ...(2)$$

$$\therefore \quad \frac{\alpha/a^2}{\sqrt{(a^2+b^2)}/a}=\frac{\beta/b^2}{0}=\frac{-\gamma/c^2}{\pm\sqrt{(b^2-c^2)}/c}=k \text{ (say)}.$$

$$\therefore \quad \alpha=ak\sqrt{(a^2+b^2)}, \beta=0, \gamma=\mp ck\sqrt{(b^2-c^2)}. \quad ...(3)$$

But (α, β, γ) lies on the given conicoid so that

$$\alpha^2/a^2-\beta^2/b^2-\gamma^2/c^2=1$$

or $$k^2\{(a^2+b^2)-(b^2-c^2)\}=1 \quad \text{or} \quad k=\pm 1/\sqrt{(a^2+c^2)}.$$

Putting the value of k in (3), the four real umbilics are given by

$$\alpha=\pm\frac{a\sqrt{(a^2+b^2)}}{\sqrt{(a^2+c^2)}}, \beta=0, \gamma=\frac{\mp c\sqrt{(b^2-c^2)}}{\sqrt{(a^2+c^2)}}$$

Ex. 4. *Prove that the umbilics of the conicoid*

$\dfrac{x^2}{a+b}+\dfrac{y^2}{a}+\dfrac{z^2}{a-b}=1$ *are the extremities of the equal conjugate diameters of the ellipse* $y=0$, $x^2/(a+b)+z^2/(a-b)=1$.

Solution. Replacing a^2 by $(a+b)$, b^2 by a and c^2 by $(a-b)$ in § 12, the umbilics (α, β, γ) of the given conicoid are given by

$$\alpha=\pm\sqrt{\left(\frac{a+b}{2}\right)}, \beta=0, \gamma=\pm\sqrt{\left(\frac{a-b}{2}\right)}. \quad ...(1)$$

Now the given ellipse is $\dfrac{x^2}{a+b}+\dfrac{z^2}{a-b}=1, y=0.$ ...(2)

Let $[\sqrt{(a+b)}\cos\theta, 0, \sqrt{(a-b)}\sin\theta]$ and $[-\sqrt{(a+b)}\sin\theta, 0, \sqrt{(a-b)}\cos\theta]$ be the extremities of equal conjugate diameters of the ellipse (2), so that we have

$$(a+b)\cos^2\theta+0+(a-b)\sin^2\theta=(a+b)\sin^2\theta+0+(a-b)\cos^2\theta$$

or $\quad 2b\cos^2\theta=2b\sin^2\theta$, or $\tan^2\theta=1$ or $\theta=\pm\frac{1}{4}\pi$.

Putting $\theta=\pm\frac{1}{4}\pi$, the extremities of the equal conjugate diameters are

$$[\sqrt{(a+b)}\cos(\pm\tfrac{1}{4}\pi), 0, \sqrt{(a-b)}\sin(\pm\tfrac{1}{4}\pi)]$$

and $\quad [-(a+b)\sin(\pm\frac{1}{4}\pi), 0, \sqrt{(a-b)}\cos(\pm\frac{1}{4}\pi)]$

i.e. $\quad \left[\pm\sqrt{\left(\dfrac{a+b}{2}\right)}, 0, \pm\sqrt{\left(\dfrac{a-b}{2}\right)}\right]$

which are also the co-ordinates of the umbilics given by (1).

———

5

Confocal Conicoids

§ 1. Confocal conicoids.

Definition. *Conicoids whose principal sections have the same foci are called the confocal conicoids. Or in other words conicoids whose principal sections are confocal conics are called confocal conicoids.*

Confocal conicoids of the ellipsoids and paraboloids.

(i) Le the equation of the ellipsoid be

$$x^2/a^2+y^2/b^2+z^2/c^2=1. \quad \text{...(1)}$$

Consider the equation $$\frac{x^2}{a^2-\lambda}+\frac{y^2}{b^2-\lambda}+\frac{z^2}{c^2-\lambda}=1. \quad \text{...(2)}$$

The section of (2) by the principal plane XOY *i.e.* by the plane $z=0$ is the conic $$\frac{x^2}{a^2-\lambda}+\frac{y^2}{b^2-\lambda}=1,\ z=0. \quad \text{...(3)}$$

The equation (3) represents the system of conics confocal to the ellipse $x^2/a^2+y^2/b^2=1,\ z=0.$

Similarly the sections of (2) by the principal planes $x=0$ and $y=0$ are confocal conics.

Hence the equation (2) represents, for all values of λ conicoids confocal with the ellipsoid (1).

Again if in the equation

$$\frac{x^2}{\alpha^2}+\frac{y^2}{\alpha^2-b^2}+\frac{z^2}{\alpha^2-c^2}=1 \quad \text{...(4)}$$

b and c are constants and α is a parameter, it **represents a system of confocal conicoids.** In this case α is called the **primary semi-axis.**

(ii) Let the equation of the paraboloid be

$$x^2/a^2+y^2/b^2=2z. \quad \text{...(5)}$$

Consider the equation $$\frac{x^2}{a^2-\lambda}+\frac{y^2}{b^2-\lambda}=2z-\lambda. \quad \text{...(6)}$$

Discussing as above, we see that the principal planes $x=0$ and $y=0$ cut the paraboloids (6) in confocal parabolas and hence the equation (6) represents paraboloids confocal with the paraboloid (5).

§ 2. Three confocals through a given point.

To prove that three conicoids, confocal with a given central conicoid, will pass through a given point ; and one of the three is an ellipsoid, one a hyperboloid of one sheet and one a hyperboloid of two sheets.

Let the equation of the central conicoid (ellipsoid say) be

$$x^2/a^2+y^2/b^2+z^2/c^2=1. \qquad ...(1)$$

Any conicoid confocal to (1) is

$$x^2/(a^2-\lambda)+y^2/(b^2-\lambda)+z^2/(c^2-\lambda)=1. \qquad ...(2)$$

Let (α, β, γ) be the given point. If (2) passes through the point (α, β, γ), we have

$$\alpha^2/(a^2-\lambda)+\beta^2/(b^2-\lambda)+\gamma^2/(c^2-\lambda)=1.$$

Simplifying, we have

$$f(\lambda)\equiv\alpha^2 (b^2-\lambda)(c^2-\lambda)+\beta^2 (a^2-\lambda)(c^2-\lambda)+\gamma^2 (a^2-\lambda)(b^2-\lambda)$$
$$-(a^2-\lambda)(b^2-\lambda)(c^2-\lambda)=0. \qquad ...(3)$$

This being a cubic equation in λ, gives three values of λ and corresponding to these three values of λ we have three confocal conicoids passing through the given point (α, β, γ).

Now let $a > b > c$. Let us take the help of theory of equations to test reality of the roots of the equation (3).

Putting in succession $\quad \lambda=\infty, a^2, b^2, c^2, -\infty$
in (3), we have $\quad f(\lambda)=+, +, -, +, -.$

We see that $f(\lambda)$ has three changes of signs (*i.e.* positive to negative, negative to positive and positive to negative) and hence the equation (3) *i.e.* $f(\lambda)=0$ has three real roots, say, $\lambda_1, \lambda_2, \lambda_3$ and are such that $\quad a^2 > \lambda_1 > b^2 > \lambda_2 > c^2 > \lambda_3.$

When $\lambda=\lambda_1$ *i.e.* λ is between a^2 and b^2 we have two coefficients of the equation (2) negative and hence (2) represents a **hyperboloid of two sheets.**

Similarly when $\lambda=\lambda_2$ *i.e.* λ is in between b^2 and c^2, one coefficient is $-$ve and the equation (2) represents a **hyperboloid of one sheet** ; and when $\lambda=\lambda_3$ *i.e.* λ is in between c^2 and $-\infty$ all the coefficients are $+$ve and the equation (2) represents an **ellipsoid.**

§ 3. Three paraboloids through a given point.

To prove that three paraboloids confocal with a given paraboloid pass through a given point—two elliptic and one hyperbolic.

Let the equation of the paraboloid be $x^2/a^2+y^2/b^2=2z$. ...(1)

Any paraboloid confocal to (1) is

$$x^2/(a^2-\lambda)+y^2/(b^2-\lambda)=2z-\lambda. \quad ...(2)$$

If (2) passes through the given point (α, β, γ), (say), we have

$$\alpha^2/(a^2-\lambda)+\beta^2/(b^2-\lambda)=2\gamma-\lambda.$$

Simplifying, we have

$$f(\lambda)\equiv\alpha^2(b^2-\lambda)+\beta^2(a^2-\lambda)-2\gamma(a^2-\lambda)(b^2-\lambda)$$
$$+\lambda(a^2-\lambda)(b^2-\lambda)=0. \quad ...(3)$$

The equation (3) being a cubic in λ gives three values of λ and corresponding to these three values of λ three paraboloids confocal to (1) pass through the given point (α, β, γ).

Now let $a > b$.

Putting in succession $\lambda=\infty, a^2, b^2, -\infty$

in (3), we have $f(\lambda)=+, -, +, -$.

Since $f(\lambda)$ has three changes of signs, the equation (3) *i.e.* $f(\lambda)=0$ has three real roots say λ_1, λ_2, λ_3 and are such that

$$\lambda_1 > a^2 > \lambda_2 > b^2 > \lambda_3.$$

Discussing as in § 2 above we see that for $\lambda=\lambda_1$ and $\lambda=\lambda_3$ the equation (2) represents elliptic paraboloids and for $\lambda=\lambda_2$ it represents a hyperbolic paraboloid.

§ 4. *To prove that one conicoid confocal with a given conicoid touches a given plane.*

The equation of any conicoid confocal to $x^2/a^2+y^2/b^2+z^2/c^2=1$ is

$$x^2/(a^2-\lambda)+y^2/(b^2-\lambda)+z^2/(c^2-\lambda)=1. \quad ...(1)$$

Let the given plane be $lx+my+nz=p$. ...(2)

The plane (2) will touch the confocal conicoid (1) if

$$l^2(a^2-\lambda)+m^2(b^2-\lambda)+n^2(c^2-\lambda)=p^2.$$

This being a linear equation in λ, gives only one value of λ. Hence only one confocal will touch the given plane.

§ 5. *To prove that two conicoids confocal with a given conicoid touch a given straight line.*

The equation of any conicoid confocal with

$$x^2/a^2+y^2/b^2+z^2/c^2=1$$

is

$$x^2/(a^2-\lambda)+y^2/(b^2-\lambda)+z^2/(c^2-\lambda)=1. \quad ...(1)$$

Let the given straight line be

$$(x-\alpha)/l=(y-\beta)/m=(z-\gamma)/n. \quad ...(2)$$

Any point on (2) is $(lr+\alpha, mr+\beta, nr+\gamma)$ and let the straight line (2) meet (1) in this point.

$$\therefore \quad (lr+\alpha)^2/(a^2-\lambda)+(mr+\beta)^2/(b^2-\lambda)+(nr+\gamma)^2/(c^2-\lambda)=1$$

or $$r^2\left(\frac{l^2}{a^2-\lambda}+\frac{m^2}{b^2-\lambda}+\frac{n^2}{c^2-\lambda}\right)+2r\left(\frac{l\alpha}{a^2-\lambda}+\frac{m\beta}{b^2-\lambda}+\frac{n\gamma}{c^2-\lambda}\right)$$
$$+\left(\frac{\alpha^2}{a^2-\lambda}+\frac{\beta^2}{b^2-\lambda}+\frac{\gamma^2}{c^2-\lambda}-1\right)=0. \quad ...(3)$$

This is a quadratic equation in r and gives two values of r. If the line (2) is a tangent line to (1), these two values of r coincide the condition for which is [by using the formula $B^2=4AC$]

$$\left(\frac{l\alpha}{a^2-\lambda}+\frac{m\beta}{b^2-\lambda}+\frac{n\gamma}{c^2-\lambda}\right)^2$$
$$=\left(\frac{l^2}{a^2-\lambda}+\frac{m^2}{b^2-\lambda}+\frac{n^2}{c^2-\lambda}\right)\left(\frac{\alpha^2}{a^2-\lambda}+\frac{\beta^2}{b^2-\lambda}+\frac{\gamma^2}{c^2-\lambda}-1\right)$$

or $$\frac{(\beta n-\gamma m)^2}{(b^2-\lambda)(c^2-\lambda)}+\frac{(\gamma l-\alpha n)^2}{(a^2-\lambda)(c^2-\lambda)}+\frac{(\alpha m-\beta l)^2}{(a^2-\lambda)(b^2-\lambda)}$$
$$=\frac{l^2}{a^2-\lambda}+\frac{m^2}{b^2-\lambda}+\frac{n^2}{c^2-\lambda} \quad ...(4)$$

which being a quadratic in λ, will give two values of λ and hence we have two confocals touching a given straight line.

Corollary *If a straight line touches two conicoids, the tangent planes at the points of contact will be at right angles.*

Let the roots of the equation (4) above be λ_1 and λ_2. Putting these values of λ in (1), the two confocal conicoids are

$$x^2/(a^2-\lambda_1)+y^2/(b^2-\lambda_1)+z^2/(c^2-\lambda_1)=1, \quad ...(5)$$

and $$x^2/(a^2-\lambda_2)+y^2/(b^2-\lambda_2)+z^2/(c^2-\lambda_2)=1. \quad ...(6)$$

If the confocal conicoids (5) and (6) touch the line (2) at the points $P(x_1, y_1, z_1)$ and $Q(x_2, y_2, z_2)$ respectively, then the line PQ lies in the tangent planes to the confocal conicoids (5) and (6) *i.e.* in the planes

$$xx_1/(a^2-\lambda_1)+yy_1/(b^2-\lambda_1)+zz_1/(c^2-\lambda_1)=1, \quad ...(7)$$

and $$xx_2/(a^2-\lambda_2)+yy_2/(b^2-\lambda_2)+zz_2/(c^2-\lambda_2)=1. \quad ...(8)$$

$$\therefore \quad x_1x_2/(a^2-\lambda_1)+y_1y_2/(b^2-\lambda_1)+z_1z_2/(c^2-\lambda_1)=1, \quad ...(9)$$

and $$x_1x_2/(a^2-\lambda_2)+y_1y_2/(b^2-\lambda_2)+z_1z_2/(c^2-\lambda_2)=1. \quad ...(10)$$

Subtracting (10) from (9), we get

$$\Sigma\,[x_1x_2\,\{1/(a^2-\lambda_1)-1/(a^2-\lambda_2)\}]=0$$

or $$(\lambda_1-\lambda_2)\,\Sigma\,[x_1x_2/\{(a^2-\lambda_1)\,(a^2-\lambda_2)\}]=0$$

or $$\frac{x_1x_2}{(a^2-\lambda_1)(a^2-\lambda_2)}+\frac{y_1y_2}{(b^2-\lambda_1)(b^2-\lambda_2)}+\frac{z_1z_2}{(c^2-\lambda_1)(c^2-\lambda_2)}=0$$

$$[\because \lambda_1 \neq \lambda_2] \quad ...(11)$$

which is the condition for the tangent planes (7) and (8) to be at right angles. Hence proved.

§ 6. *To prove that the confocal conicoids cut one another at right angles at all their common points, i.e. the tangent planes at any common point are at right angles.*

Let the two conicoids confocal to $x^2/a^2+y^2/b^2+z^2/c^2=1$ be given by

$$x^2/(a^2-\lambda_1)+y^2/(b^2-\lambda_1)+z^2/(c^2-\lambda_1)=1, \quad ...(1)$$

and $$x^2/(a^2-\lambda_2)+y^2/(b^2-\lambda_2)+z^2/(c^2-\lambda_2)=1. \quad ...(2)$$

Let (1) and (2) cut in the point (x_1, y_1, z_1). Then the point (x_1, y_1, z_1) lies on both (1) and (2) and so we have

$$x_1^2/(a^2-\lambda_1)+y_1^2/(b^2-\lambda_1)+z_1^2/(c^2-\lambda_1)=1, \quad ...(3)$$

and $$x_1^2/(a^2-\lambda_2)+y_1^2/(b^2-\lambda_2)+z_1^2/(c^2-\lambda_2)=1. \quad ...(4)$$

The equations of the tangent planes at (x_1, y_1, z_1) to (1) and (2) are

$$xx_1/(a^2-\lambda_1)+yy_1/(b^2-\lambda_1)+zz_1/(c^2-\lambda_1)=1, \quad ...(5)$$

and $$xx_1/(a^2-\lambda_2)+yy_1/(b^2-\lambda_2)+zz_1/(c^2-\lambda_2)=1. \quad ...(6)$$

Subtracting (4) from (3), we get

$$(\lambda_1-\lambda_2)\ \Sigma\ [x_1^2/\{(a^2-\lambda_1)\ (a^2-\lambda_2)\}]=0$$

or $$\frac{x_1^2}{(a^2-\lambda_1)(a^2-\lambda_2)}+\frac{y_1^2}{(b^2-\lambda_1)(b^2-\lambda_2)}+\frac{z_1^2}{(c^2-\lambda_1)\ (c^2-\lambda_2)}=0,$$

$[\because \quad \lambda_1 \neq \lambda_2]$

which is also the condition that the tangent planes (5) and (6) are at right angles. Hence proved.

Corollary. It immediately follows from § 6 above that the tangent planes at a point P to the three confocal conicoids which pass through it are mutually orthogonal.

§ 7. **Elliptic co-ordinates.**

Proceeding as in § 2 above upto equation (3), we have

$$f(\lambda)\equiv\alpha^2\ (b^2-\lambda)\ (c^2-\lambda)+\beta^2\ (a^2-\lambda)\ (c^2-\lambda)+\gamma^2\ (a^2-\lambda)\ (b^2-\lambda)$$
$$-(a^2-\lambda)\ (b^2-\lambda)\ (c^2-\lambda)=0. \quad ...(3)$$

If the roots of this equation are λ_1, λ_2, λ_3, then we may write

$$f(\lambda)=(\lambda-\lambda_1)\ (\lambda-\lambda_2)\ (\lambda-\lambda_3). \quad ...(4)$$

Dividing (3) by $(a^2-\lambda)\ (b^2-\lambda)\ (c^2-\lambda)$, we have

$$1-\frac{\alpha^2}{a^2-\lambda}-\frac{\beta^2}{b^2-\lambda}-\frac{\gamma^2}{c^2-\lambda}=\frac{-f(\lambda)}{(a^2-\lambda)\ (b^2-\lambda)\ (c^2-\lambda)}$$

or $$1-\frac{\alpha^2}{a^2-\lambda}-\frac{\beta^2}{b^2-\lambda}-\frac{\gamma^2}{c^2-\lambda}=\frac{-(\lambda-\lambda_1)(\lambda-\lambda_2)\ (\lambda-\lambda_3)}{(a^2-\lambda)\ (b^2-\lambda)\ (c^2-\lambda)}. \quad ...(5)$$

By resolving into partial fractions, the relation (5) may be written as

$$1-\frac{\alpha^2}{a^2-\lambda}-\frac{\beta^2}{b^2-\lambda}-\frac{\gamma^2}{c^2-\lambda}=1-\frac{(a^2-\lambda_1)(a^2-\lambda_2)(a^2-\lambda_3)}{(b^2-a^2)(c^2-a^2)(a^2-\lambda)}$$
$$-\frac{(b^2-\lambda_1)(b^2-\lambda_2)(b^2-\lambda_3)}{(c^2-b^2)(a^2-b^2)(b^2-\lambda)}-\frac{(c^2-\lambda_1)(c^2-\lambda_2)(c^2-\lambda_3)}{(a^2-c^2)(b^2-c^2)(c^2-\lambda)}.$$

Hence comparing the coefficients of $1/(a^2-\lambda)$, $1/(b^2-\lambda)$ and $1/(c^2-\lambda)$ on either side, we have

$$\left.\begin{aligned}\alpha^2&=\frac{(a^2-\lambda_1)(a^2-\lambda_2)(a^2-\lambda_3)}{(b^2-a^2)(c^2-a^2)}\\ \beta^2&=\frac{(b^2-\lambda_1)(b^2-\lambda_2)(b^2-\lambda_3)}{(c^2-b^2)(a^2-b^2)}\\ \gamma^2&=\frac{(c^2-\lambda_1)(c^2-\lambda_2)(c^2-\lambda_3)}{(a^2-c^2)(b^2-c^2)}\end{aligned}\right\}. \quad \text{...(6)}$$

These express the co-ordinates of the point $P(\alpha, \beta, \gamma)$ in terms of the parameters of the three confocal conicoids through the point P, *i.e.* if the parameters $\lambda_1, \lambda_2, \lambda_3$ are given, the position of the point P can be uniquely determined. Therefore $\lambda_1, \lambda_2, \lambda_3$ are called the **elliptic co-ordinates** of the point $P(\alpha, \beta, \gamma)$ with respect to the fundamental conicoid (1).

§ 8. Focal Conics.

Let $$x^2/(a^2-\lambda)+y^2/(b^2-\lambda)+z^2/(c^2-\lambda)=1 \quad \text{...(1)}$$
be the equation of any confocal conicoid. We have proved in § 2 above that if $\lambda < c^2$, the surface is an ellipsoid ; but the ellipsoid becomes flatter and flatter as λ approaches the value c^2. Hence the elliptic disc, whose equations are

$$x^2/(a^2-c^2)+y^2/(b^2-c^2)=1,\ z=0 \quad \text{...(2)}$$

is a limiting form of one of the confocals.

Again when $b^2 > \lambda > c^2$ and λ is very nearly equal to b^2, the hyperboloid of one sheet is very nearly coincident with that part of the plane $y=0$ which contains the centre and is bounded by the hyperbola

$$x^2/(a^2-b^2)+z^2/(c^2-b^2)=1,\ y=0. \quad \text{...(3)}$$

Also when $a^2 > \lambda > b^2$ and λ is very nearly equal to b^2, the hyperboloid of two sheets is very nearly coincident with that part of the plane $y=0$ which does not contain the centre and is bounded by the hyperbola

$$x^2/(a^2-b^2)+z^2/(c^2-b^2)=1,\ y=0$$

and in case λ tends to a^2, the confocal is imaginary.

The conics given by (2) and (3) are called the **focal conics**.

SOLVED EXAMPLES (A)

Ex. 1. *Prove that the equation to the confocal through the point of the focal ellipse whose eccentric angle is α, is*

$$\frac{x^2}{(a^2-b^2)\cos^2\alpha}-\frac{y^2}{(a^2-b^2)\sin^2\alpha}+\frac{z^2}{(c^2-a^2\sin^2\alpha-b^2\cos^2\alpha)}=1.$$

Solution. Let the equation of the confocal be

$$x^2/(a^2-\lambda)+y^2/(b^2-\lambda)+z^2/(c^2-\lambda)=1. \qquad \ldots(1)$$

The equations of the focal ellipse are [See equations (2), § 8]

$$x^2/(a^2-c^2)+y^2/(b^2-c^2)=1,\ z=0. \qquad \ldots(2)$$

Any point with eccentric angle α on (2) is $[\sqrt{(a^2-c^2)}\cos\alpha, \sqrt{(b^2-c^2)}\sin\alpha, 0]$. If (1) passes through this point, we have

$$(a^2-c^2)\cos^2\alpha/(a^2-\lambda)+(b^2-c^2)\sin^2\alpha/(b^2-\lambda)=1$$

or $$(a^2-\lambda)(b^2-\lambda)-(b^2-\lambda)(a^2-c^2)\cos^2\alpha-(a^2-\lambda)(b^2-c^2)\sin^2\alpha=0$$

or $$\lambda^2-\lambda(a^2\sin^2\alpha+b^2\cos^2\alpha+c^2)+c^2(a^2\sin^2\alpha+b^2\cos^2\alpha)=0$$

or $$(\lambda-a^2\sin^2\alpha-b^2\cos^2\alpha)(\lambda-c^2)=0$$

or $$\lambda=a^2\sin^2\alpha+b^2\cos^2\alpha,\ \lambda=c^2.$$

For $\lambda=c^2$, we get the confocal ellipse (2).

Hence the required confocal is obtained by putting $\lambda=a^2\sin^2\alpha+b^2\cos^2\alpha$ in (1) and is given by

$$\frac{x^2}{a^2-(a^2\sin^2\alpha+b^2\cos^2\alpha)}+\frac{y^2}{b^2-(a^2\sin^2\alpha+b^2\cos^2\alpha)}+\frac{z^2}{c^2-(a^2\sin^2\alpha+b^2\cos^2\alpha)}=1$$

or $$\frac{x^2}{(a^2-b^2)\cos^2\alpha}-\frac{y^2}{(a^2-b^2)\sin^2\alpha}+\frac{z^2}{(c^2-a^2\sin^2\alpha-b^2\cos^2\alpha)}=1.$$

Ex. 2. *Prove that the equation to the confocal which has a system of circular sections parallel to the plane x=y is*

$$\frac{x^2}{(c^2-a^2)(a^2-b^2)}+\frac{y^2}{(b^2-c^2)(a^2-b^2)}-\frac{z^2}{2(b^2-c^2)(c^2-a^2)}=\frac{1}{2c^2-(a^2+b^2)};$$

Solution. Let the equation of the confocal be

$$x^2/(a^2-\lambda)+y^2/(b^2-\lambda)+z^2/(c^2-\lambda)=1. \qquad \ldots(1)$$

The equation (1) can be rewritten as

$$\frac{1}{(c^2-\lambda)}\{x^2+y^2+z^2-(c^2-\lambda)\}+x^2\left(\frac{1}{a^2-\lambda}-\frac{1}{c^2-\lambda}\right)+y^2\left(\frac{1}{b^2-\lambda}-\frac{1}{c^2-\lambda}\right)=0. \qquad \ldots(2)$$

The equation (2) will represent a sphere if

$$x^2\{1/(a^2-\lambda)-1/(c^2-\lambda)\}+y^2\{1/(b^2-\lambda)-1/(c^2-\lambda)\}=0$$

or
$$\frac{x^2(c^2-a^2)}{(a^2-\lambda)(c^2-\lambda)}+\frac{y^2(c^2-b^2)}{(b^2-\lambda)(c^2-\lambda)}=0$$

or
$$x^2(b^2-\lambda)(c^2-a^2)=y^2(b^2-c^2)(a^2-\lambda). \quad \text{...(3)}$$

The equation (3) represents a pair of planes (assuming $a^2>b^2>c^2$), and hence the central circular sections are given by (3). The central circular sections (2) will be parallel to the plane $x=y$ if

$$(b^2-\lambda)(c^2-a^2)=(b^2-c^2)(a^2-\lambda) \text{ or } \lambda=\frac{2a^2b^2-b^2c^2-c^2a^2}{a^2+b^2-2c^2}.$$

Putting this value of λ in (1), the required confocal is given by

$$\frac{x^2}{a^2-\dfrac{2a^2b^2-b^2c^2-c^2a^2}{a^2+b^2-2c^2}}+\frac{y^2}{b^2-\dfrac{2a^2b^2-b^2c^2-c^2a^2}{a^2+b^2-2c^2}}+\frac{z^2}{c^2-\dfrac{2a^2b^2-b^2c^2-c^2a^2}{a^2+b^2-2c^2}}=1$$

or
$$\frac{x^2(a^2+b^2-2c^2)}{a^4-a^2b^2+b^2c^2-a^2c^2}+\frac{y^2(a^2+b^2-2c^2)}{b^4-a^2b^2-b^2c^2+c^2a^2}+\frac{z^2(a^2+b^2-2c^2)}{2(c^2a^2+b^2c^2-c^2-a^2b^2)}=1$$

or
$$\frac{x^2}{(c^2-a^2)(a^2-b^2)}+\frac{y^2}{(b^2-c^2)(a^2-b^2)}-\frac{z^2}{2(b^2-c^2)(c^2-a^2)}=\frac{1}{2c^2-a^2-b^2}.$$

Ex. 3. *A given plane and parallel tangent plane to a conicoid are at distances p and p_0 from the centre. Prove that the parameter of the confocal conicoid which touches the plane is $p_0^2-p^2$.*

Solution. Let the equation of the given plane be

$$lx+my+nz=p \quad \text{...(1)}$$

where l, m, n are actual d.c.'s so that $l^2+m^2+n^2=1$. ...(2)

Let the equation of the conicoid be

$$x^2/a^2+y^2/b^2+z^2/c^2=1 \quad \text{...(3)}$$

and that of the confocal conicoid be

$$\frac{x^2}{a^2-\lambda}+\frac{y^2}{b^2-\lambda}+\frac{z^2}{c^2-\lambda}=1. \quad \text{(4)}$$

The equation of the plane parallel to (1) and at a distance p_0 from the centre (0, 0, 0) is $lx+my+nz=p_0$. ...(5)

If the plane (5) touches (3), then

$$a^2l^2+b^2m^2+c^2n^2=p_0^2. \quad ...(6)$$

Again if the plane (1) touches the confocal (4), then

$$(a^2-\lambda)\, l^2+(b^2-\lambda)\, m^2+(c^2-\lambda)\, n^2=p^2$$

or $$(a^2l^2+b^2m^2+c^2n^2)-\lambda\,(l^2+m^2+n^2)=p^2$$

or $$p_0^2-\lambda .\, 1=p^2, \quad \text{using (2) and (6)}$$

or $$\lambda=p_0^2-p^2.$$ **Proved.**

Ex. 4. *Prove that the perpendiculars from the origin to the tangent planes to the ellipsoid which touch it along its curve of intersection with the confocal whose parameter is λ, lie on the cone*

$$a^2x^2/(a^2-\lambda)+b^2y^2/(b^2-\lambda)+c^2z^2/(c^2-\lambda)=0.$$

Solution. Let the equations to the ellipsoid and its confocal be

$$x^2/a^2+y^2/b^2+z^2/c^2=1, \quad ...(1)$$

and $$x^2/(a^2-\lambda)+y^2/(b^2-\lambda)+z^2/(c^2-\lambda)=1. \quad ...(2)$$

Let the co-ordinates of a point on the curve of intersection of (1) and (2) be (x', y', z').

The equation of the tangent plane at the point (x', y', z') to (1) is

$$xx'/a^2+yy'/b^2+zz'/c^2=1. \quad ...(3)$$

Now the equations of the perpendicular from the origin to the tangent plane (3) are

$$\frac{x}{x'/a^2}=\frac{y}{y'/b^2}=\frac{z}{z'/c^2}. \quad ..(4)$$

Since the point (x', y', z') must lie on (1) and (2), we have

$$\frac{x'^2}{a^2}+\frac{y'^2}{b^2}+\frac{z'^2}{c^2}=1 \text{ and } \frac{x'^2}{a^2-\lambda}+\frac{y'^2}{b^2-\lambda}+\frac{z'^2}{c^2-\lambda}=1.$$

Subtracting these two relations, we get

$$\frac{x'^2}{a^2\,(a^2-\lambda)}+\frac{y'^2}{b^2\,(b^2-\lambda)}+\frac{z'^2}{c^2\,(c^2-\lambda)}=0. \quad ...(5)$$

Hence the locus of (4) is obtained by eliminating x', y', z' between (4) and (5) *i.e.* (4) lies on the cone

$$a^2x^2/(a^2-\lambda)+b^2y^2/(b^2-\lambda)+c^2z^2/(c^2-\lambda)=0.$$

Ex. 5 *Find the locus of the point of intersection of three planes mutually at right angles, each of which touches one of three given confocals, is a sphere.*

Solution. Let the equations of three confocals be

$$x^2/(a^2-\lambda_r)+y^2/(b^2-\lambda_r)+z^2/(c^2-\lambda_r)=1, \ (r=1, 2, 3) \quad ...(1)$$

and let the equations of the three tangent planes touching the three confocal conicoids be

$$l_rx+m_ry+n_rz=\sqrt{[(a^2-\lambda_r)\, l_r^2+(b^2-\lambda_r)\, m_r^2+(c^2-\lambda_r)\, n_r^2]}. \quad ...(2)$$

Since the three tangent planes given by (2) are at right angles, we have

$$l_1^2+l_2^2+l_3^2=1,\ l_1^2+m_1^2+n_1^2=1,\ l_1m_1+l_2m_2+l_3m_3=0, \text{ etc.}$$

Now squaring and adding the equations of the three tangent planes given by (2), we have

$$x^2+y^2+z^2=(a^2+b^2+c^2)-(\lambda_1+\lambda_2+\lambda_3)$$

which is the required locus of the point of intersection and is clearly a sphere.

Ex. 6. *If a_1, a_2, a_3 are the primary semi-axes of the confocals to $x^2/a^2+y^2/b^2+z^2/c^2=1$ which pass through a point (α, β, γ), then*

$$\alpha^2=\frac{a_1^2a_2^2a_3^2}{(b^2-a^2)(c^2-a^2)},$$

$$\beta^2=\frac{(b^2-a^2+a_1^2)(b^2-a^2+a_2^2)(b^2-a^2+a_3^2)}{(c^2-b^2)(a^2-b^2)}$$

$$\gamma^2=\frac{(c^2-a^2+a_1^2)(c^2-a^2+a_2^2)(c^2-a^2+a_3^2)}{(a^2-c^2)(b^2-c^2)}.$$

Solution. From § 7, we have

$$\left.\begin{aligned}\alpha^2&=\frac{(a^2-\lambda_1)(a^2-\lambda_2)(a^2-\lambda_3)}{(b^2-a^2)(c^2-a^2)},\\ \beta^2&=\frac{(b^2-\lambda_1)(b^2-\lambda_2)(b^2-\lambda_3)}{(c^2-b^2)(a^2-b^2)}\\ \gamma^2&=\frac{(c^2-\lambda_1)(c^2-\lambda_2)(c^2-\lambda_3)}{(a^2-c^2)(b^2-c^2)}\end{aligned}\right\}\quad ...(1)$$

Here we are given primary semi-axes as a_1, a_2, a_3.

$$\therefore\quad a^2-\lambda_1=a_1^2,\ a^2-\lambda_2=a_2^2,\ a^2-\lambda_3=a_3^2$$

or

$$\lambda_1=a^2-a_1^2,\ \lambda_2=a^2-a_2^2,\ \lambda_3=a^2-a_3^2.$$

Putting these values of λ_1, λ_2, λ_3 in (1), we at once get the results stated.

Ex. 7. *Show that the two confocal paraboloids cut every where at right angles.*

Solution. Let the equations to two confocal paraboloids be

$$\frac{x^2}{a^2-\lambda_1}+\frac{y^2}{b^2-\lambda_1}=2z-\lambda_1,\quad ...(1)$$

and

$$\frac{x^2}{a^2-\lambda_2}+\frac{y^2}{b^2-\lambda_2}=2z-\lambda_2.\quad ...(2)$$

If (x_1, y_1, z_1) is a common point of (1) and (2), then we have

$$\frac{x_1^2}{a^2-\lambda_1}+\frac{y_1^2}{b^2-\lambda_1}=2z_1-\lambda_1,\quad ...(3)$$

and
$$\frac{x_1^2}{a^2-\lambda_2}+\frac{y_1^2}{b^2-\lambda_2}=2z_1-\lambda_2. \quad ...(4)$$

Subtracting (4) from (3), we get
$$\frac{x_1^2(\lambda_1-\lambda_2)}{(a^2-\lambda_1)(a^2-\lambda_2)}+\frac{y_1^2(\lambda_1-\lambda_2)}{(b^2-\lambda_1)(b^2-\lambda_2)}=-(\lambda_1-\lambda_2)$$

or
$$\frac{x_1^2}{(a^2-\lambda_1)(a^2-\lambda_2)}+\frac{y_1^2}{(b^2-\lambda_1)(b^2-\lambda_2)}=-1. \quad ...(5)$$

Again the equations to the tangent planes at (x_1, y_1, z_1) to the surfaces (1) and (2) are
$$\frac{xx_1}{a^2-\lambda_1}+\frac{yy_1}{b^2-\lambda_1}=(z+z_1)-\lambda_1 \quad ...(6)$$

and
$$\frac{xx_1}{a^2-\lambda_2}+\frac{yy_1}{b^2-\lambda_2}=(z+z_1)-\lambda_2. \quad ...(7)$$

If the planes (6) and (7) are to be at right angles, then we should have
$$\frac{x_1^2}{(a^2-\lambda_1)(a^2-\lambda_2)}+\frac{y_1^2}{(b^2-\lambda_1)(b^2-\lambda_2)}+1=0$$
which is true by virtue of (5). Hence proved.

Ex. 8. *Prove that the locus of the umbilici of a system of confocal ellipsoids is the focal hyperbola.*

Solution. Let the equation of the confocal ellipsoid be
$$x^2/(a^2-\lambda)+y^2/(b^2-\lambda)+z^2/(c^2-\lambda)=1. \quad ...(1)$$

If the umbilici of (1) are (α, β, γ) then
$$\alpha=\pm\frac{\sqrt{(a^2-\lambda)}\sqrt{(a^2-b^2)}}{\sqrt{(a^2-c^2)}},\ \beta=0,\ \gamma=\pm\frac{\sqrt{(c^2-\lambda)}\sqrt{(b^2-c^2)}}{\sqrt{(a^2-c^2)}}.$$

[Obtained by replacing a^2 by $a^2-\lambda$, b^2 by $b^2-\lambda$ and c^2 by $c^2-\lambda$ in the equations (6) of § 12 of the chapter 'The plane sections of conicoids'].
$$\therefore\ a^2-\lambda=\frac{\alpha^2(a^2-c^2)}{a^2-b^2},\ c^2-\lambda=\frac{\gamma^2(a^2-c^2)}{b^2-c^2},\ \beta=0.$$

Subtracting, thus eliminating λ, we get
$$\frac{\alpha^2}{(a^2-b^2)}-\frac{\gamma^2}{b^2-c^2}=1,\ \beta=0.$$

$\therefore$ The locus of the umbilici (α, β, γ) is given by
$$x^2/(a^2-b^2)-z^2/(b^2-c^2)=1,\ y=0$$
which represents a focal hyperbola.

§ 9. *To prove that the parameters of the two confocals through any point P of a conicoid are equal to the squares of the axes of the central section of the conicoid which is parallel to the tangent plane at P, and the normals at P to the confocals are parallel to the axes of that section.*

Let the conicoid be $x^2/a^2+y^2/b^2+z^2/c^2=1$. ...(1)

The equation of the confocal to (1) is

$$x^2/(a^2-\lambda)+y^2/(b^2-\lambda)+z^2/(c^2-\lambda)=1. \quad ...(2)$$

Let P (x_1, y_1, z_1) be a point on (1). Therefore the parameters of the confocals through P (x_1, y_1, z_1) are given by

$$\frac{x_1^2}{a^2-\lambda}+\frac{y_1^2}{b^2-\lambda}+\frac{z_1^2}{c^2-\lambda}=1=\frac{x_1^2}{a^2}+\frac{y_1^2}{b^2}+\frac{z_1^2}{c^2}$$

or
$$\frac{x_1^2}{a^2(a^2-\lambda)}+\frac{y_1^2}{b^2(b^2-\lambda)}+\frac{z_1^2}{c^2(c^2-\lambda)}=0. \quad ...(3)$$

The equation of the tangent plane at P (x_1, y_1, z_1) to (1) is

$$xx_1/a^2+yy_1/b^2+zz_1/c^2=1. \quad ...(4)$$

$\therefore$ the central section of (1) parallel to (4) is given by

$$xx_1/a^2+yy_1/b^2+zz_1/c^2=0. \quad ...(5)$$

Also the squares of the lengths (r) of the semi-axes of the section of (1) by the plane (5) are given by

$$\frac{x_1^2}{a^2(a^2-r^2)}+\frac{y_1^2}{b^2(b^2-r^2)}+\frac{z_1^2}{c^2(c^2-r^2)}=0. \quad ..(6)$$

Comparing (3) and (6) we see that $r^2=\lambda$, *i e.* the squares of the semi-axes of the section are the two values of the parameter λ.

Again the direction cosines l, m, n of the semi-axes of length r are given by

$$\frac{l}{x_1/(a^2-r^2)}=\frac{m}{y_1/(b^2-r^2)}=\frac{n}{z_1/(c^2-r^2)} \quad ...(7)$$

and the equations of the normal at $P(x_1, y_1, z_1)$ to the confocal (2) are

$$\frac{x-x_1}{x_1/(a^2-\lambda)}=\frac{y-y_1}{y_1/(b^2-\lambda)}=\frac{z-z_1}{z_1/(c^2-\lambda)}. \quad ...(8)$$

Since the values of λ are the values of r^2, hence in view of (7) and (8) we can say that the axis of the section is parallel to the normal at (x_1, y_1, z_1) to the confocal.

§ 10. *To prove that the locus of the poles of a given plane with respect to a system of confocal conicoids is a straight line.*

Let the equation of the given plane be

$$lx+my+nz=1. \quad ...(1)$$

Let the equation of the system of confocals be

$$x^2/(a^2-\lambda)+y^2/(b^2-\lambda)+z^2/(c^2-\lambda)=1. \quad ...(2)$$

Let the pole of (1) with respect to (2) be (α, β, γ). The equation of the polar plane of (α, β, γ) with respect to (2) is

$$\alpha x/(a^2-\lambda)+\beta y/(b^2-\lambda)+\gamma z/(c^2-\lambda)=1. \quad \ldots(3)$$

The planes represented by (1) and (3) should be the same and hence comparing their coefficients, we have

$$\frac{l}{\alpha/(a^2-\lambda)}=\frac{m}{\beta/(b^2-\lambda)}=\frac{n}{\gamma/(c^2-\lambda)}=1.$$

$$\therefore \quad \alpha/l=a^2-\lambda,\ \beta/m=b^2-\lambda,\ \gamma/n=c^2-\lambda$$

or
$$\frac{\alpha}{l}-a^2=\frac{\beta}{m}-b^2=\frac{\gamma}{n}-c^2=-\lambda,$$

or
$$\frac{\alpha-a^2l}{l}=\frac{\beta-b^2m}{m}=\frac{\gamma-c^2n}{n}.$$

$\therefore$ The locus of the pole (α, β, γ) is

$$(x-a^2l)/l=(y-b^2m)/m=(z-c^2n)/n \quad \ldots(4)$$

which is a straight line perpendicular to the plane (1).

Corollary. *To prove that the locus of the poles is the normal to the plane at the point of contact with the confocal which touches it.*

Proceeding as above we derive the equations (4).

Again if the plane (1) touches a confocal conicoid

$$x^2/(a^2-\mu)+y^2/(b^2-\mu)+z^2/(c^2-\mu)=1,$$

then the point of contact is $(a^2l+\mu l,\ b^2m+\mu m,\ c^2n+\mu n)$.

This point clearly satisfies the straight line (4). Hence the proposition.

§ 11. Corresponding points.

Consider a point $P(x_1, y_1, z_1)$ situated on the conicoid

$$x^2/a^2+y^2/b^2+z^2/c^2=1 \quad \ldots(1)$$

and a point $Q(\xi_1, \eta_1, \zeta_1)$ situated on the conicoid

$$x^2/\alpha^2+y^2/\beta^2+z^2/\gamma^2=1. \quad \ldots(2)$$

The points P and Q are called **corresponding points** if there exist the following relations between their co-ordinates ;

$$\frac{x_1}{a}=\frac{\xi_1}{\alpha},\ \frac{y_1}{b}=\frac{\eta_1}{\beta},\ \text{and}\ \frac{z_1}{c}=\frac{\zeta_1}{\gamma}. \quad \ldots(3)$$

Distance relation. *If there are any two points P and Q on a conicoid and P′ and Q′ are the corresponding points on a confocal conicoid then to prove that PQ′=P′Q.*

Let $P(x_1, y_1, z_1)$ and $Q(x_2, y_2, z_2)$ be the points on

$$x^2/a^2+y^2/b^2+z^2/c^2=1.$$

Again let $P'(\xi_1, \eta_1, \zeta_1)$ and $Q'(\xi_2, \eta_2, \zeta_2)$ be the corresponding points on the confocal conicoid

$$x^2/(a^2-\lambda)+y^2/(b^2-\lambda)+z^2/(c^2-\lambda)=1.$$

We are to prove that $PQ'=P'Q$ *i.e.* $(PQ')^2=(P'Q)^2$

i.e. $(x_1-\xi_2)^2+(y_1-\eta_2)^2+(z_1-\zeta_2)^2=(x_2-\xi_1)^2+(y_2-\eta_1)^2+(z_2-\zeta_1)^2$. ...(4)

Using the relations (3), in the present case, we have

$$\frac{x_1}{a}=\frac{\xi_1}{\sqrt{(a^2-\lambda)}}, \frac{y_1}{b}=\frac{\eta_1}{\sqrt{(b^2-\lambda)}}, \frac{z_1}{c}=\frac{\zeta_1}{\sqrt{(c^2-\lambda)}} \quad ...(5)$$

and $$\frac{x_2}{a}=\frac{\xi_2}{\sqrt{(a^2-\lambda)}}, \frac{y_2}{b}=\frac{\eta_2}{\sqrt{(b^2-\lambda)}}, \frac{z_2}{c}=\frac{\zeta_2}{\sqrt{(c^2-\lambda)}}. \quad ...(6)$$

Putting the values of x_1, y_1, z_1 and ξ_2, η_2, ζ_2 from relations (5) and (6) in (4), we get

$$\Sigma\left\{\frac{a\xi_1}{\sqrt{(a^2-\lambda)}}-\frac{x_2\sqrt{(a^2-\lambda)}}{a}\right\}^2=\Sigma\,(x_2-\xi_1)^2$$

or $$\Sigma\left\{\frac{a^2\xi_1^2}{(a^2-\lambda)}\right\}+\Sigma\left\{\frac{x_2^2\,(a^2-\lambda)}{a^2}\right\}-2\Sigma\xi_1x_2=\Sigma x_2^2+\Sigma\xi_1^2-2\Sigma\xi_1x_2$$

or $$\Sigma\xi_1^2\left\{\frac{a^2}{a^2-\lambda}-1\right\}+\Sigma x_2^2\left\{\frac{a^2-\lambda}{a^2}-1\right\}=0$$

or $$\lambda\Sigma\left\{\frac{\xi_1^2}{a^2-\lambda}-\frac{x_2^2}{a^2}\right\}=0$$

or $$\lambda\,(1-1)=0,$$

since the points lie on the conicoids.

This relation is identically true.

Hence $$PQ'=P'Q.$$

§ 12. Properties regarding the normals to three confocal conicoids through a given point P.

To prove the following properties :

(A) *Three conicoids confocal with a given conicoid* $x^2/a^2+y^2/b^2+z^2/c^2=1$ *pass through a given point P and PQ, PR, PS the normals at P to the confocals, meet the polar plane of P with respect to the given conicoid in Q, R, S. To prove that*

$$PQ=\lambda_1/p_1,\ PR=\lambda_2/p_2,\ PS=\lambda_3/p_3$$

where $\lambda_1, \lambda_2, \lambda_3$ *are the parameters of the confocals and* p_1, p_2, p_3 *are the perpendiculars from the centre to the tangent planes at the point P to the confocals.*

(B) *To prove that the tetrahedron PQRS is self polar with regard to the given conicoid.*

(C) *To prove that the normals to the three confocals through the point P are the axes of the enveloping cone with its vertex at P.*

(A) The equation of the given conicoid is

$$x^2/a^2+y^2/b^2+z^2/c^2=1. \quad ...(1)$$

Let the co-ordinates of the given point P be (α, β, γ). The equation of the polar plane of $P(\alpha, \beta, \gamma)$ w.r.t. (1) is

$$\alpha x/a^2+\beta y/b^2+\gamma z/c^2=1. \quad ...(2)$$

Let the equation of one conicoid confocal to (1) be

$$x^2/(a^2-\lambda_1)+y^2/(b^2-\lambda_1)+z^2/(c^2-\lambda_1)=1. \quad ...(3)$$

The equations of the normal PQ at P to (3) are

$$\frac{x-\alpha}{p_1\alpha/(a^2-\lambda_1)}=\frac{y-\beta}{p_1\beta/(b^2-\lambda_1)}=\frac{z-\gamma}{p_1\gamma/(c^2-\lambda_1)}=r \text{ (say)} \quad ..(4)$$

where p_1 is the length of the perpendicular from the centre (0, 0, 0) to the tangent plane.

The co-ordinates of Q, a point on (4) such that $PQ=r$, are

$$\left[\alpha\left(1+\frac{p_1r}{a^2-\lambda_1}\right), \beta\left(1+\frac{p_1r}{b^2-\lambda_1}\right), \gamma\left(1+\frac{p_1r}{c^2-\lambda_1}\right)\right].$$

If the normal PQ meets the polar plane (2) in the point Q, then the co-ordinates of Q will satisfy the equation (2) and hence we have

$$\frac{\alpha^2}{a^2}\left(1+\frac{p_1r}{a^2-\lambda_1}\right)+\frac{\beta^2}{b^2}\left(1+\frac{p_1r}{b^2-\lambda_1}\right)+\frac{\gamma^2}{c^2}\left(1+\frac{p_1r}{c^2-\lambda_1}\right)=1. \quad ..(5)$$

Also the point $P(\alpha, \beta, \gamma)$ lies on the confocal (3).

$$\therefore \quad \frac{\alpha^2}{a^2-\lambda_1}+\frac{\beta^2}{b^2-\lambda_1}+\frac{\gamma^2}{c^2-\lambda_1}=1. \quad ...(6)$$

Subtracting (6) from (5), we get

$$(p_1r-\lambda_1)\left\{\frac{\alpha^2}{a^2(a^2-\lambda_1)}+\frac{\beta^2}{b^2(b^2-\lambda_1)}+\frac{\gamma^2}{c^2(c^2-\lambda_1)}\right\}=0.$$

$\therefore \quad p_1r-\lambda_1=0$ or $r=\lambda_1/p_1$ or $PQ=\lambda_1/p_1 \quad [\because \quad r=PQ]$.

In a similar manner if we proceed for the confocals of parameters λ_2 and λ_3 we shall get $PR=\lambda_2/p_2$ and $PS=\lambda_3/p_3$.

(B) Now putting $p_1r=\lambda_1$, the co-ordinates of Q are given by

$$\left[\alpha\left(1+\frac{\lambda_1}{a^2-\lambda_1}\right), \beta\left(1+\frac{\lambda_1}{b^2-\lambda_1}\right), \gamma\left(1+\frac{\lambda_1}{c^2-\lambda_1}\right)\right]$$

or

$$\left(\frac{a^2\alpha}{a^2-\lambda_1}, \frac{b^2\beta}{b^2-\lambda_1}, \frac{c^2\gamma}{c^2-\lambda_1}\right)$$

Hence the equation of the polar plane of Q with regard to the conicoid (1) is

$$\frac{\alpha x}{a^2-\lambda_1}+\frac{\beta y}{b^2-\lambda_1}+\frac{\gamma z}{c^2-\lambda_1}=1$$

which is the same as the tangent plane to the confocal (3) at the point $P(\alpha, \beta, \gamma)$. This tangent plane contains the normals PR and PS. Hence the polar plane of Q is the plane PRS. In a similar manner we can prove that the polar plane of R is the plane PQS, the polar plane of S is the plane PQR and the polar plane of P is the plane QRS. Hence we conclude that the tetrahedron $PQRS$ is self polar with respect to the given conicoid (1).

(C) We have shown above that the tetrahedron $PQRS$ is self polar with regard to the conicoid (1). It follows from it that the triangle QRS is self polar with regard to the common section of the conicoid (1) and the enveloping cone by the plane QRS. Hence the normals PQ, PR and PS are the conjugate diameters of the enveloping cone with the vertex at P. Since PQ, PR and PS are mutually orthogonal, they are the principal axes of the enveloping cone with the vertex at the point P.

§ **13.** *To find the equation of the enveloping cone of a conicoid in its simplest form.*

Consider the three normals PQ, PR and PS through a given point P (see § 12 above). The simplest form of the equation to the enveloping cone with the vertex at P is when the normals PQ, PR and PS are its principal axes. Let the equation of the cone be

$$Ax^2+By^2+Cz^2=0. \qquad \text{...(1)}$$

Also the tangent planes to the confocals at the point whose distances from the centre O of the given conicoid are p_1, p_2, p_3 will be the co-ordinate planes.

$\therefore$ The co-ordinates of O with respect to PQ, PR, PS as axes are $(-p_1, -p_2, -p_3)$.

$\therefore$ The equations to PQ are $x/p_1=y/p_2=z/p_3$.

Again the centre of the section of the cone or conicoid by the plane QRS lies on PO. Let its co-ordinates be (kp_1, kp_2, kp_3). Therefore the equation of the plane whose section with the cone has its centre at (kp_1, kp_2, kp_3) is

$$Ap_1(x-kp_1)+Bp_2(y-kp_2)+Cp_3(z-kp_3)=0. \qquad \text{...(2)}$$

Hence it should be the equation of the plane QRS.

Again since the plane QRS makes intercepts $\lambda_1/p_1, \lambda_2/p_2, \lambda_3/p_3$ on the normals (*i.e.* new axes), its equation is also given by

$$p_1x/\lambda_1+p_2y/\lambda_2+p_3z/\lambda_3=1. \qquad \text{...(3)}$$

Comparing the equations (2) and (3), we get

$$\frac{Ap_1}{p_1/\lambda_1}=\frac{Bp_2}{p_2/\lambda_2}=\frac{Cp_3}{p_3/\lambda_3}, \text{ or } \frac{A}{1/\lambda_1}=\frac{B}{1/\lambda_2}=\frac{C}{1/\lambda_3}. \quad ...(4)$$

Eliminating A, B, C between (1) and (4), the equation of the required enveloping cone is $x^2/\lambda_1+y^2/\lambda_2+z^2/\lambda_3=0$.

§ **14.** *To find the equation to the given conicoid referred to the normals to the confocals through a given point P as co-ordinate axes.*

Take the four points P, Q, R, S as in § 12 so that PQ, PR and PS are the three normals through P. Now we are to find the equation of the conicoid with reference to the normals PQ, PR and PS as co-ordinate axes.

The conicoid will be having contact with the cone along the section of the cone and the plane QRS [See § 13] and hence the equation of the conicoid will be of the form

$$\left(\frac{x^2}{\lambda_1}+\frac{y^2}{\lambda_2}+\frac{z^2}{\lambda_3}\right)=k\left(\frac{p_1x}{\lambda_1}+\frac{p_2y}{\lambda_2}+\frac{p_3z}{\lambda_3}-1\right)^2. \quad ...(1)$$

The centre $O(-p_1, -p_2, -p_3)$ of the conicoid bisects all chords passing through it. The equations of the chord parallel to x-axis (*i.e.* PQ) are given by

$$\frac{x+p_1}{1}=\frac{y+p_2}{0}=\frac{z+p_3}{0}=r \text{ (say)}. \quad ..(2)$$

Let the chord (2) meet the conicoid (1) in the point $(r-p_1, -p_2, -p_3)$. We have then

$$\frac{(r-p_1)^2}{\lambda_1}+\frac{p_2^2}{\lambda_2}+\frac{p_3^2}{\lambda_3}=k\left\{\frac{p_1(r-p_1)}{\lambda_1}-\frac{p_2^2}{\lambda_2}-\frac{p_3^2}{\lambda_3}-1\right\}^2. \quad ...(3)$$

The equation (3) being a quadratic in r shows that the chord (2) meets the conicoid (1) in two points. Since the centre is the middle point of the chord, the two values of r should be equal in magnitude but opposite in signs. Hence if r_1 and r_2 are the roots of (3) then r_1+r_2 is zero.

Also $r_1+r_2=-$(the coeff. of r)/(the coeff. of r^2)$=0$.

$\therefore$ the coeff. of $r=0$

or
$$\frac{-2p_1}{\lambda_1}+\frac{2kp_1}{\lambda_1}\left(\frac{p_1^2}{\lambda_1}+\frac{p_2^2}{\lambda_2}+\frac{p_3^2}{\lambda_3}+1\right)=0$$

or
$$1/k=p_1^2/\lambda_1+p_2^2/\lambda_2+p_3^2/\lambda_3+1.$$

Putting this value of k in (1), the required equation of the conicoid is

$$\left(\frac{x^2}{\lambda_1}+\frac{y^2}{\lambda_2}+\frac{z^2}{\lambda_3}\right)\left(\frac{p_1^2}{\lambda_1}+\frac{p_2^2}{\lambda_2}+\frac{p_3^2}{\lambda_3}+1\right)=\left(\frac{p_1x}{\lambda_1}+\frac{p_2y}{\lambda_2}+\frac{p_3z}{\lambda_3}-1\right)^2.$$

SOLVED EXAMPLES (B)

Ex. 1. *If λ and μ are the parameters of the confocal hyperboloids through a point P on the ellipsoid $x^2/a^2+y^2/b^2+z^2/c^2=1$, then prove that the perpendicular from the centre to the tangent plane at P to the ellipsoid is $abc/\sqrt{(\lambda\mu)}$. Prove also that the perpendiculars to the tangent planes to the hyperboloids are*

$$\sqrt{\left\{\frac{(a^2-\lambda)(b^2-\lambda)(c^2-\lambda)}{\lambda(\lambda-\mu)}\right\}} \text{ and } \sqrt{\left\{\frac{(a^2-\mu)(b^2-\mu)(c^2-\mu)}{\mu(\mu-\lambda)}\right\}}.$$

Solution. We know that the parameters of the confocals are equal to the squares of the semi-axes of the central section which is parallel to the tangent plane at P to the conicoid. If p is the perpendicular from the centre to the tangent plane, then

$$p\sqrt{(\lambda\mu)}=abc \quad \text{or} \quad p=abc/\sqrt{(\lambda\mu)}. \quad ...(1)$$

Now $\quad x^2/(a^2-\lambda)+y^2/(b^2-\lambda)+z^2/(c^2-\lambda)=1 \quad ...(2)$

has $\quad x^2/a^2+y^2/b^2+z^2/c^2=1 \quad ...(3)$

and $\quad x^2/(a^2-\mu)+y^2/(b^2-\mu)+z^2/(c^2-\mu)=1 \quad ...(4)$

as confocal conicoids. Hence the parameters of the conicoids (3) and (4) confocal to (2) are $-\lambda$ and $\mu-\lambda$ respectively.

$\therefore$ The length of the perpendicular from the centre to the tangent plane of (2)

$$=\sqrt{\left\{\frac{(a^2-\lambda)(b^2-\lambda)(c^2-\lambda)}{-\lambda(\lambda-\mu)}\right\}}, \text{ using (1)}$$

$$=\sqrt{[(a^2-\lambda)(b^2-\lambda)(c^2-\lambda)/\{\lambda(\lambda-\mu)\}]}.$$

Similarly for the conicoid (4), the perpendicular

$$=\sqrt{\left\{\frac{(a^2-\mu)(b^2-\mu)(c^2-\mu)}{\mu(\mu-\lambda)}\right\}}.$$

Ex. 2. *If $\lambda_1, \lambda_2, \lambda_3$ are the parameters of three confocals to $x^2/a^2+y^2/b^2+z^2/c^2=1$ that pass through P, prove that the perpendiculars from the centre to the tangent plane at P are*

$$\sqrt{\left\{\frac{(a^2-\lambda_1)(b^2-\lambda_1)(c^2-\lambda_1)}{(\lambda_2-\lambda_1)(\lambda_3-\lambda_1)}\right\}}, \text{ etc.}$$

Solution. The equations of the three confocals to $x^2/a^2+y^2/b^2+z^2/c^2=1$ that pass through P are

$$x^2/(a^2-\lambda_1)+y^2/(b^2-\lambda_1)+z^2/(c^2-\lambda_1)=1, \quad ...(1)$$

$$x^2/(a^2-\lambda_2)+y^2/(b^2-\lambda_2)+z^2/(c^2-\lambda_2)=1, \quad ...(2)$$

and $\quad x^2/(a^2-\lambda_3)+y^2/(b^2-\lambda_3)+z^2/(c^2-\lambda_3)=1 \quad ...(3)$

with $\lambda_1, \lambda_2, \lambda_3$ as their respective parameters.

Now the parameters of (2) and (3) with respect to (1) are $\lambda_2-\lambda_1$ and $\lambda_3-\lambda_1$ respectively.

Hence the length of the perpendicular from the centre to the tangent plane of (1) at P

$$=\sqrt{\left\{\frac{(a^2-\lambda_1)(b^2-\lambda_1)(c^2-\lambda_1)}{(\lambda_2-\lambda_1)(\lambda_3-\lambda_1)}\right\}}.$$

[using formula (1) of Ex. 1 above]

Again the parameters of (1) and (3) with respect to (2) are $\lambda_1-\lambda_2$ and $\lambda_3-\lambda_2$ respectively. Hence the length of the perpendicular from the centre to the tangent plane of (2) at P

$$=\sqrt{\left\{\frac{(a^2-\lambda_2)(b^2-\lambda_2)(c^2-\lambda_2)}{(\lambda_1-\lambda_2)(\lambda_3-\lambda_2)}\right\}}.$$

Similarly the length of the perpendicular from the centre to the tangent plane of (3) at P

$$=\sqrt{\left\{\frac{(a^2-\lambda_3)(b^2-\lambda_3)(c^2-\lambda_3)}{(\lambda_2-\lambda_3)(\lambda_1-\lambda_3)}\right\}}.$$

Ex. 3. *If $a_1, b_1, c_1; a_2, b_2, c_2; a_3, b_3, c_3$ are the axes of the confocals to $x^2/\alpha^2+y^2/\beta^2+z^2/\gamma^2=1$ which pass through a point (ξ, η, ζ) and p_1, p_2, p_3 are the perpendiculars from the centre to the tangent planes to the confocals at the point, prove that*

$$\xi^2+\eta^2+\zeta^2=a_1^2+b_2^2+c_3^2,\ p_1^2/a_1^2+p_2^2/a_2^2+p_3^2/a_3^2=1,$$

$$\frac{p_1^2}{a_1^2-\alpha^2}+\frac{p_2^2}{a_2^2-\alpha^2}+\frac{p_3^2}{a_3^2-\alpha^2}-1=\frac{\alpha^2\beta^2\gamma^2}{(a_1^2-\alpha^2)(a_2^2-\alpha^2)(a_3^2-\alpha^2)}.$$

Solution. The equation of the ellipsoid is

$$x^2/\alpha^2+y^2/\beta^2+z^2/\gamma^2=1. \qquad ...(1)$$

Let the equation of its any confocal be

$$x^2/(\alpha^2-\lambda)+y^2/(\beta^2-\lambda)+z^2/(\gamma^2-\lambda)=1. \qquad ...(2)$$

If (2) passes through the point (ξ, η, ζ), then

$$\xi^2/(\alpha^2-\lambda)+\eta^2/(\beta^2-\lambda)+\zeta^2/(\gamma^2-\lambda)=1$$

or $$(\alpha^2-\lambda)(\beta^2-\lambda)(\gamma^2-\lambda)-\xi^2(\beta^2-\lambda)(\gamma^2-\lambda)-\eta^2(\alpha^2-\lambda)(\gamma^2-\lambda)$$
$$-\zeta^2(\alpha^2-\lambda)(\beta^2-\lambda)=0$$

or $$\lambda^3-\lambda^2\{(\alpha^2+\beta^2+\gamma^2)-(\xi^2+\eta^2+\zeta^2)\}+\lambda(\ )+...=0.$$

This is a cubic equation in λ and has three roots, say, $\lambda_1, \lambda_2, \lambda_3$.

$$\therefore\quad \lambda_1+\lambda_2+\lambda_3=\alpha^2+\beta^2+\gamma^2-(\xi^2+\eta^2+\zeta^2)$$

or $$\xi^2+\eta^2+\zeta^2=(\alpha^2-\lambda_1)+(\beta^2-\lambda_2)+(\gamma^2-\lambda_3). \qquad ...(3)$$

But as given in the problem, we have

$$\left.\begin{array}{l}\alpha^2-\lambda_1=a_1^2,\ \beta^2-\lambda_1=b_1^2,\ \gamma^2-\lambda_1=c_1^2\\ \alpha^2-\lambda_2=a_2^2,\ \beta^2-\lambda_2=b_2^2,\ \gamma^2-\lambda_2=c_2^2\\ \alpha^2-\lambda_3=a_3^2,\ \beta^2-\lambda_3=b_3^2,\ \gamma^2-\lambda_3=c_3^2\end{array}\right\} \quad \ldots(4)$$

Using the relations (4) in (3), we get

$$\xi^2+\eta^2+\zeta^2=a_1^2+b_2^2+c_3^2.$$

This proves the first part.

Again by Ex. 2 above, we have

$$p_1=\sqrt{\left\{\frac{(\alpha^2-\lambda_1)(\beta^2-\lambda_1)(\gamma^2-\lambda_1)}{(\lambda_2-\lambda_1)(\lambda_3-\lambda_1)}\right\}}$$

or $$p_1^2=\frac{a_1^2(\beta^2-\lambda_1)(\gamma^2-\lambda_1)}{(\lambda_2-\lambda_1)(\lambda_3-\lambda_1)} \qquad [\because\ \alpha^2-\lambda_1=a_1^2, \text{ by } (4)]$$

or $$\frac{p_1^2}{a_1^2}=\frac{(\beta^2-\lambda_1)(\gamma^2-\lambda_1)}{(\lambda_2-\lambda_1)(\lambda_3-\lambda_1)}$$

or $$\frac{p_1^2}{a_1^2}=1+\frac{(\beta^2-\lambda_2)(\gamma^2-\lambda_2)}{(\lambda_3-\lambda_2)(\lambda_2-\lambda_1)}+\frac{(\beta^2-\lambda_3)(\gamma^2-\lambda_3)}{(\lambda_2-\lambda_3)(\lambda_3-\lambda_1)},$$

by resolving into partial fractions

or $$\frac{p_1^2}{a_1^2}=1-\frac{(\beta^2-\lambda_2)(\gamma^2-\lambda_2)}{(\lambda_3-\lambda_2)(\lambda_1-\lambda_2)}-\frac{(\beta^2-\lambda_3)(\gamma^2-\lambda_3)}{(\lambda_1-\lambda_3)(\lambda_2-\lambda_3)}. \quad \ldots(5)$$

Also $$p_2^2=\frac{(\alpha^2-\lambda_2)(\beta^2-\lambda_2)(\gamma^2-\lambda_2)}{(\lambda_1-\lambda_2)(\lambda_3-\lambda_2)}$$

or $$\frac{p_2^2}{a_2^2}=\frac{(\beta^2-\lambda_2)(\gamma^2-\lambda_2)}{(\lambda_1-\lambda_2)(\lambda_3-\lambda_2)}. \qquad [\because\ \alpha^2-\lambda_2=a_2^2, \text{ by } (4)] \quad \ldots(6)$$

Similarly $$\frac{p_3^2}{a_3^2}=\frac{(\beta^2-\lambda_3)(\gamma^2-\lambda_3)}{(\lambda_1-\lambda_3)(\lambda_2-\lambda_3)}. \quad \ldots(7)$$

Adding (5), (6) and (7), we have

$$p_1^2/a_1^2+p_2^2/a_2^2+p_3^2/a_3^2=1.$$

This proves the second part.

Again $$\frac{p_1^2}{a_1^2-\alpha^2}=\frac{p_1^2}{-\lambda_1}=\frac{(\alpha^2-\lambda_1)(\beta^2-\lambda_1)(\gamma^2-\lambda_1)}{-\lambda_1(\lambda_2-\lambda_1)(\lambda_3-\lambda_1)}$$

[Putting for p_1^2]

or $$\frac{p_1^2}{a_1^2-\alpha^2}=1-\frac{\alpha^2\beta^2\gamma^2}{\lambda_1\lambda_2\lambda_3}-\frac{(\alpha^2-\lambda_2)(\beta^2-\lambda_2)(\gamma^2-\lambda_2)}{\lambda_2(\lambda_3-\lambda_2)(\lambda_3-\lambda_1)}$$

$$-\frac{(\alpha^2-\lambda_3)(\beta^2-\lambda_3)(\gamma^2-\lambda_3)}{\lambda_3(\lambda_2-\lambda_3)(\lambda_3-\lambda_1)} \quad \ldots(8)$$

Also

$$\frac{p_2^2}{a_2^2-\alpha^2}=\frac{(\alpha^2-\lambda_2)(\beta^2-\lambda_2)(\gamma^2-\lambda_2)}{-\lambda_2(\lambda_1-\lambda_2)(\lambda_3-\lambda_2)}=\frac{(\alpha^2-\lambda_2)(\beta^2-\lambda_2)(\gamma^2-\lambda_2)}{\lambda_2(\lambda_3-\lambda_2)(\lambda_2-\lambda_1)} \quad \ldots(9)$$

and $$\frac{p_3^2}{a_3^2-\alpha^2}=\frac{(\alpha^2-\lambda_3)(\beta^2-\lambda_3)(\gamma^2-\lambda_3)}{-\lambda_3(\lambda_2-\lambda_3)(\lambda_1-\lambda_3)}=\frac{(\alpha^2-\lambda_3)(\beta^2-\lambda_3)(\gamma^2-\lambda_3)}{\lambda_3(\lambda_2-\lambda_3)(\lambda_3-\lambda_1)} \quad ...(10)$$

Adding (8), (9) and (10), we get

$$\sum\left\{\frac{p_1^2}{a_1^2-\alpha^2}\right\}=1-\frac{\alpha^2\beta^2\gamma^2}{\lambda_1\lambda_2\lambda_3},$$

or $$\sum\left\{\frac{p_1^2}{a_1^2-\alpha^2}\right\}-1=\frac{\alpha^2\beta^2\gamma^2}{(a_1^2-\alpha^2)(a_2^2-\alpha^2)(a_3^2-\alpha^2)}.$$

This proves the third part.

Ex. 4. *If P is a point on an ellipsoid and P′ is the corresponding point on a confocal whose parameter is λ, then prove that $OP^2-OP'^2=\lambda$, where O is the centre.*

Solution. Let $P(\alpha, \beta, \gamma)$ be a point on the ellipsoid

$$x^2/a^2+y^2/b^2+z^2/c^2=1 \quad ...(1)$$

and $P'(\xi, \eta, \zeta)$ be the corresponding point on its confocal

$$x^2/(a^2-\lambda)+y^2/(b^2-\lambda)+z^2/(c^2-\lambda)=1. \quad ...(2)$$

Hence by definition [See § 11] we have

$$\frac{\alpha}{a}=\frac{\xi}{\sqrt{(a^2-\lambda)}},\ \frac{\beta}{b}=\frac{\eta}{\sqrt{(b^2-\lambda)}},\ \frac{\gamma}{c}=\frac{\zeta}{\sqrt{(c^2-\lambda)}}.$$

Also the centre O is (0, 0, 0). Therefore

$$OP^2-OP'^2=\{(\alpha-0)^2+(\beta-0)^2+(\gamma-0)^2\}-\{(\xi-0)^2+(\eta-0)^2+(\zeta-0)^2\}$$

$$=\alpha^2+\beta^2+\gamma^2-\xi^2-\eta^2-\zeta^2$$

$$=(\alpha^2+\beta^2+\gamma^2)-\frac{(a^2-\lambda)\alpha^2}{a^2}-\frac{(b^2-\lambda)\beta^2}{b^2}-\frac{(c^2-\lambda)\gamma^2}{c^2}$$

$$=\lambda\left(\frac{\alpha^2}{a^2}+\frac{\beta^2}{b^2}+\frac{\gamma^2}{c^2}\right)$$

$$=\lambda\times1=\lambda. \quad [\because P(\alpha, \beta, \gamma) \text{ lies on } (1)]$$

§ 15. The foci of conicoids.

(A) Definition of a conicoid due to Mac Cullagh.

A conicoid is the locus of a point which moves so that its distance from a fixed piont, called the focus, is in a constant ratio to its distance (measured parallel to a fixed plane) from a fixed straight line, called the directrix.

To find foci by the above definition. Let the origin be the focus and $z=0$ be the fixed plane.

Let the equations of the directrix be given by

$$(x-f)/l=(y-g)/m=(z-h)/n. \quad ...(1)$$

Let (ξ, η, ζ) be the co-ordinates of any given point P on the locus. The equation of the plane through $P(\xi, \eta, \zeta)$ and parallel to the plane $z=0$ is $z=\zeta$. ...(2)

The line (1) meets the plane (2) in the point M (say) whose co-ordinates are given by

$$\frac{x-f}{l}=\frac{y-g}{m}=\frac{\zeta-h}{n},\ z=\zeta$$

i.e. M is the point $\left[f+\dfrac{l(\zeta-h)}{n},\ g+\dfrac{m(\zeta-h)}{n},\ \zeta\right]$.

According to the above definition,

$$OP/PM=\text{constant}=e \text{ (say)}.$$

$$\therefore\quad OP^2=e^2\,PM^2$$

or $\xi^2+\eta^2+\zeta^2=e^2\left[\left\{\xi-f-\dfrac{l}{n}(\zeta-h)\right\}^2+\left\{\eta-g-\dfrac{m}{n}(\zeta-h)\right\}^2+0^2\right]$.

$\therefore$ The equation of the locus of the point $P(\xi, \eta, \zeta)$ is

$x^2+y^2+z^2=e^2\,[\{x-f-(l/n)(z-h)\}^2+\{y-g-(m/n)(z-h)\}^2]$ ...(3)

which represents a conicoid.

If we change the axes in any manner, the equation (3) of the conicoid will be of the form

$$(x-\alpha)^2+(y-\beta)^2+(z-\gamma)^2-A=0$$

where A is the sum of two squares or is the product of two imaginary factors.

Hence we can determine the foci of any given conicoid whose equation is $S=0$, from the consideration that

$$S-\lambda\,\{(x-\alpha)^2+(y-\beta)^2+(z-\gamma)^2\}$$

will be the product of imaginary linear factors if (α, β, γ) be a focus, provided a suitable value be given to λ.

(B) Definition of a conicoid due to Salmon.

A conicoid is the locus of a point the square of whose distance from a fixed point, called a focus, varies as the product of its distances from two fixed planes.

Let the equation of the two fixed planes be

$$lx+my+nz+p=0 \quad\text{and}\quad l'x+m'y+n'z+p'=0.$$

Then the equation of the locus is of the form

$$(x-\alpha)^2+(y-\beta)^2+(z-\gamma)^2$$
$$=k^2\,(lx+my+nz+p)\,(l'x+m'y+n'z+p').$$

Hence we can determine the foci of any conicoid according to the above definition by the consideration that

$$S-\lambda\,\{(x-\alpha)^2+(y-\beta)^2+(z-\gamma)^2\}$$

will be the product of real linear factors if (α, β, γ) be a focus provided a suitable value be given to λ.

(C) To find the foci of the conicoid whose equation is

$$ax^2+by^2+cz^2=1.$$

Let (α, β, γ) be the co-ordinates of the focus.

Here $S \equiv ax^2+by^2+cz^2-1=0$.

Hence using $S-\lambda\{(x-\alpha)^2+(y-\beta)^2+(z-\gamma)^2\}=0$, we have

$$(ax^2+by^2+cz^2-1)-\lambda\{(x-\alpha)^2+(y-\beta)^2+(z-\gamma)^2\}=0$$

or $$(a-\lambda)\,x^2+(b-\lambda)\,y^2+(c-\lambda)\,z^2+2\lambda\,(\alpha x+\beta y+\gamma z)$$
$$-\lambda\,(\alpha^2+\beta^2+\gamma^2)-1=0. \quad \ldots(1)$$

The left hand side of (1) should be a product of linear factors and for it λ should be equal to a, b, or c.

If $\lambda=a$, the equation (1) becomes

$$(b-a)\,y^2+(c-a)\,z^2+2a\alpha x+2a\beta y+2a\gamma z-a\,(\alpha^2+\beta^2+\gamma^2)-1=0$$

or $$(b-a)\left(y+\frac{a\beta}{b-a}\right)^2+(c-a)\left(z+\frac{a\gamma}{c-a}\right)^2$$
$$+2a\alpha x-a\alpha^2-\frac{ab\beta^2}{b-a}-\frac{ac\gamma^2}{c-a}-1=0.$$

Hence in order that the left hand side of (1) may be a product of linear factors, we have $\alpha=0$ and

$$\frac{ab\beta^2}{b-a}+\frac{ac\gamma^2}{c-a}=1 \;\; i.e. \;\; \frac{\beta^2}{1/b-1/a}+\frac{\gamma^2}{1/c-1/a}=1.$$

Similarly if $b=0$, we have $\beta=0$ and $\dfrac{\alpha^2}{1/a-1/b}+\dfrac{\gamma^2}{1/c-1/b}=1$

and if $\lambda=c$, we have $\gamma=0$ and $\dfrac{\alpha^2}{1/a-1/c}+\dfrac{\beta^2}{1/b-1/c}=1.$

Hence there are three conics, one in each principal plane, on which the foci lie. The equations of these conics are given by

$$x=0, \frac{y^2}{1/b-1/a}+\frac{z^2}{1/c-1/a}=1, \quad \ldots(2)$$

$$y=0, \frac{x^2}{1/a-1/b}+\frac{z^2}{1/c-1/b}=1, \quad \ldots(3)$$

and $$z=0, \frac{x^2}{1/a-1/c}+\frac{y^2}{1/b-1/c}=1. \quad \ldots(4)$$

In case the surface is the ellipsoid $x^2/a^2+y^2/b^2+z^2/c^2=1$, *the equations of the conics on which foci lie are* [replacing $1/a$, $1/b$, $1/c$ by a^2, b^2, c^2 respectively in the equations (2), (3), (4)]

$$x=0,\ \frac{y^2}{b^2-a^2}+\frac{z^2}{c^2-a^2}=1, \qquad \ldots(5)$$

$$y=0,\ \frac{x^2}{a^2-b^2}+\frac{z^2}{c^2-b^2}=1, \qquad \ldots(6)$$

and $$z=0,\ \frac{x^2}{a^2-c^2}+\frac{y^2}{b^2-c^2}=1. \qquad \ldots(7)$$

If $a > b > c$, (5) is an imaginary ellipsoid, (6) is a hyperbola and (7) is an ellipse. These conics are called **focal conics.**

(D) Focal conics of the cone $ax^2+by^2+cz^2=0$.

In view of equations of the focal conics (2), (3) and (4) of § 15 (C) above, the focal conics of the cone $ax^2+by^2+cz^2=0$ are

$$x=0,\ \frac{y^2}{1/b-1/a}+\frac{z^2}{1/c-1/a}=0 \qquad \ldots(1)$$

$$y=0,\ \frac{z^2}{1/c-1/b}+\frac{x^2}{1/a-1/b}=0 \qquad \ldots(2)$$

$$z=0,\ \frac{x^2}{1/a-1/c}+\frac{y^2}{1/b-1/c}=0. \qquad \ldots(3)$$

Hence we observe that one of the focal conics of a cone is a pair of real straight lines which are called the **focal lines.**

SOLVED EXAMPLES (C)

Ex. 1. *Find the equations to the focal conics of the hyperboloid* $x^2+yz-2=0$.

Solution. Here $S \equiv x^2+yz-2=0$.

$\therefore$ the foci (α, β, γ) lie on the planes given by

$$x^2+yz-2-\lambda\{(x-\alpha)^2+(y-\beta)^2+(z-\gamma)^2\}=0 \qquad \ldots(1)$$

or $$f(x, y, z) \equiv x^2(1-\lambda)-\lambda y^2-\lambda z^2+yz+2\lambda\alpha x+2\lambda\beta y+2\lambda\gamma z -\lambda(\alpha^2+\beta^2+\gamma^2)-2=0.$$

If it represents a pair of planes, then

$$\begin{vmatrix} 1-\lambda & 0 & 0 \\ 0 & -\lambda & \frac{1}{2} \\ 0 & \frac{1}{2} & -\lambda \end{vmatrix}=0 \quad \text{or} \quad (1-\lambda)\{\lambda^2-\tfrac{1}{4}\}=0 \quad \text{or} \quad \lambda=1, \pm\tfrac{1}{2}.$$

Also the line of intersection is given by

$$\frac{\partial f}{\partial x}=2x(1-\lambda)+2\lambda\alpha=0 \qquad \ldots(2)$$

$$\frac{\partial f}{\partial y}=-2\lambda y+2\lambda\beta+z=0 \qquad \ldots(3)$$

$$\frac{\partial f}{\partial z}=-2\lambda z+2\lambda\gamma+y=0. \qquad \ldots(4)$$

If $\lambda=1$, the above equations give

$$\alpha=0,\ -2y+2\beta+z=0,\ -2z+2\gamma+y=0.$$

$$\therefore\quad y=(4\beta+2\gamma)/3,\ z=(2\beta+4\gamma)/3.$$

If (ξ, η, ζ) is a point on it, then for pair of planes we have $u\xi+v\eta+w\zeta+d=0$.

Hence if $\lambda=1$, we have

$$\alpha=0,\ 0+\beta\times\frac{4\beta+2\gamma}{3}+\gamma\times\frac{4\gamma+2\beta}{3}-(\alpha^2+\beta^2+\gamma^2-2)=0$$

or $\alpha=0,\ \beta^2+4\beta\gamma+\gamma^2=6.$

$\therefore$ One of the focal conics is $x=0,\ y^2+4yz+z^2=6.$

If $\lambda=-\frac{1}{2}$,

$$f(x, y, z)=\tfrac{3}{2}x^2+\tfrac{1}{2}y^2+\tfrac{1}{2}z^2+yz-\alpha x-\beta y-\gamma z$$
$$+\tfrac{1}{2}(\alpha^2+\beta^2+\gamma^2)-2=0.$$

If it is a pair of planes, the line of intersection is given by [Putting $\lambda=-\frac{1}{2}$ in (2), (3) and (4) above]

$$3x-\alpha=0\ \ ...(5),\quad y+z-\beta=0\ \ ...(6),\quad y+z-\gamma=0.\quad ...(7)$$

From (5), $x=\frac{1}{3}\alpha$.

From (6) and (7), $\beta=\gamma$.

Let $\quad z=0,\ y=\beta.$

$\therefore$ $(\frac{1}{3}\alpha, \beta, 0)$ is a point on the line of intersection.

$$\therefore\quad -\tfrac{1}{2}\alpha\times\tfrac{1}{3}\alpha-\tfrac{1}{2}\beta\times\beta+\tfrac{1}{2}(\alpha^2+\beta^2+\gamma^2)-2=0$$

or
$$2\alpha^2+3\beta^2=12.$$

$$\therefore\quad \beta=\gamma,\ 2\alpha^2+3\beta^2=12.$$

Hence the other focal conic is $y=z,\ 2x^2+3y^2=12.$

If $\lambda=\frac{1}{2}$, the focal conic is the imaginary ellipse.

Therefore the focal conics are

$$\left.\begin{aligned} x=0,\ y^2+z^2+4yz=0 \\ \text{and}\quad y=z,\ 2x^2+3y^2=12. \end{aligned}\right\}$$

Ans.

6

Reduction of General Equation of Second Degree

§ 1. **Introduction.** The most general equation of the second degree is given by

$$F(x, y, z) \equiv ax^2+by^2+cz^2+2fyz+2gzx+2hxy$$
$$+2ux+2vy+2wz+d=0. \qquad ...(1)$$

It can be reduced to either of the following two forms, by the transformation of axes :

First form : $\lambda_1 x^2+\lambda_2 y^2+\lambda_3 z^2=\mu$ ...(2)

Second form : $\lambda_1 x^2+\lambda_2 y^2=2\mu z.$ ...(3)

By giving different values to λ_1, λ_2, λ_3 and μ the forms (2) and (3) will give rise to different types of surfaces. Now we are giving below all types of such surfaces.

First form. The equation $\lambda_1 x^2+\lambda_2 y^2+\lambda_3 z^2=\mu$ will be of any of the following forms.

(i)	$Ax^2+By^2+Cz^2=1$	Ellipsoid
(ii)	$A(x^2+y^2)+Cz^2=1$	Ellipsoid of revolution
(iii)	$A(x^2+y^2+z^2)=1$	Sphere
(iv)	$Ax^2+By^2-Cz^2=1$	Hyperboloid of one sheet
(v)	$Ax^2-By^2-Cz^2=1$	Hyperboloid of two sheets
(vi)	$A(x^2-z^2)+By^2=1$	Hyperboloid of revolution
(vii)	$Ax^2+By^2+Cz^2=0$	Cone
(viii)	$Ax^2+By^2=1$	Elliptic cylinder
(ix)	$Ax^2-By^2=1$	Hyperbolic cylinder
(x)	$Ax^2-By^2=0$	Pair of intersecting planes
(xi)	$Ax^2=1$ or $By^2=1$ or $Cz^2=1$	Pair of parallel planes.

Second form. The equation $\lambda_1 x^2+\lambda_2 y^2=2\mu z$ will be of any of the following forms :

(i)	$Ax^2+By^2=2Cz$	Elliptic paraboloid
(ii)	$Ax^2-By^2=2Cz$	Hyperbolic paraboloid
(iii)	$A(x^2+y^2)=2Cz$	Paraboloid of revolution
(iv)	$Ax^2=\pm 2Cz$	Parabolic cylinder.

Remark. In the rest of the chapter we shall denote the homogeneous part of the equation (1) by $f(x, y, z)$ until otherwise stated, thus

$$f(x, y, z)=ax^2+by^2+cz^2+2fyz+2gzx+2hxy \quad \text{.. (A)}$$

$$\therefore \; f(l, m, n)=al^2+bm^2+cn^2+2fmn+2gnl+2hlm \quad \text{...(B)}$$

And
$$\left.\begin{aligned} \frac{\partial f}{\partial x}&=2(ax+hy+gz), & \frac{\partial f}{\partial l}&=2(al+hm+gn) \\ \frac{\partial f}{\partial y}&=2(hx+by+fz), & \frac{\partial f}{\partial m}&=2(hl+bm+fn) \\ \frac{\partial f}{\partial z}&=2(gx+fy+cz), & \frac{\partial f}{\partial n}&=2(gl+fm+cn) \end{aligned}\right\} \quad \text{.. (C)}$$

Also $\dfrac{\partial F}{\partial x}=2(ax+hy+gz+u)$, etc.

§ 2. **Points of intersection.** *To find the points of intersection of a given line* $\dfrac{x-\alpha}{l}=\dfrac{y-\beta}{m}=\dfrac{z-\gamma}{n}$ *with the surface* $F(x, y, z)=0$.

The equations of the given line are

$$\frac{x-\alpha}{l}=\frac{y-\beta}{m}=\frac{z-\gamma}{n}=r \text{ (say)}. \quad \text{...(1)}$$

This is a line passing through the point (α, β, γ) and having direction ratios l, m, n. Any point on the line (1) is $(lr+\alpha, mr+\beta, nr+\gamma)$ and it will lie on the given surface $F(x, y, z)=0$ if

$$F(lr+\alpha, mr+\beta, nr+\gamma)=0$$

or if
$$a(lr+\alpha)^2+b(mr+\beta)^2+c(nr+\gamma)^2+2f(mr+\beta)(nr+\gamma)$$
$$+2g(nr+\gamma)(lr+\gamma)+2h(lr+\alpha)(mr+\beta)+2u(lr+\alpha)$$
$$+2v(mr+\beta)+2w(nr+\gamma)+d=0$$

or if
$$r^2(al^2+bm^2+cn^2+2fmn+2gnl+2hlm)+2r\{l(a\alpha+h\beta+g\gamma)$$
$$+m(h\alpha+b\beta+f\gamma)+n(g\alpha+f\beta+c\gamma)\}+F(\alpha, \beta, \gamma)=0$$

or if
$$r^2 f(l, m, n)+r\left(l\frac{\partial F}{\partial \alpha}+m\frac{\partial F}{\partial \beta}+n\frac{\partial F}{\partial \gamma}\right)+F(\alpha, \beta, \gamma)=0. \quad \text{...(2)}$$

This is a quadratic equation in r and hence the straight line (1) cuts the surface $F(x, y, z)=0$ in two points *i.e.* all the straight lines coplanar with a particular plane cut the surface in two points This shows that *all the plane sections of a surface of second degree are conics. On account of this property a surface of second degree is called a conicoid.*

§ 3. **The tangent plane.** *To find the equation of the tangent plane at any point* (α, β, γ) *of a conicoid* $F(x, y, z)=0$.

The equation of the given conicoid is

$$F(x, y, z) \equiv f(x, y, z) + 2ux + 2vy + 2wz + d = 0. \quad \text{...(1)}$$

Since the point (α, β, γ) lies on (1), $F(\alpha, \beta, \gamma) = 0$. ...(2)

Now the equations of any straight line through the point (α, β, γ) are $(x-\alpha)/l = (y-\beta)/m = (z-\gamma)/n$. ...(3)

Proceeding exactly as in § 2 above, the points of intersection of (1) and (3) are given by the two values of r, given by [See equation (2) of § 2 above]

$$r^2 . f(l, m, n) + r\left(l\frac{\partial F}{\partial \alpha} + m\frac{\partial F}{\partial \beta} + n\frac{\partial F}{\partial \gamma}\right) + F(\alpha, \beta, \gamma) = 0$$

or $$r^2 f(l, m, n) + r\left(l\frac{\partial F}{\partial \alpha} + m\frac{\partial F}{\partial \beta} + n\frac{\partial F}{\partial \gamma}\right) = 0, \text{ using (2)}. \quad \text{...(4)}$$

The equation (4) shows that one value of r is zero. If (3) is a tangent line then the other value of r should also be zero, the condition for which is $l\frac{\partial F}{\partial \alpha} + m\frac{\partial F}{\partial \beta} + n\frac{\partial F}{\partial \gamma} = 0$. ...(5)

Hence the locus of the tangent lines through (α, β, γ) *i.e.* the equation of the tangent plane at (α, β, γ) is

$$(x-\alpha)\frac{\partial F}{\partial \alpha} + (y-\beta)\frac{\partial F}{\partial \beta} + (z-\gamma)\frac{\partial F}{\partial \gamma} = 0 \quad \text{...(6)}$$

The equation (6) of the tangent plane at (α, β, γ) may also be written as

$$x\frac{\partial F}{\partial \alpha} + y\frac{\partial F}{\partial \beta} + z\frac{\partial F}{\partial \gamma} = \alpha\frac{\partial F}{\partial \alpha} + \beta\frac{\partial F}{\partial \beta} + \gamma\frac{\partial F}{\partial \gamma}. \quad \text{...(7)}$$

Again if $F(x, y, z)$ be made homogeneous by introducing a new variable t (which is put equal to zero after differentiation), the equation (7) of the tangent plane at (α, β, γ) becomes

$$x\frac{\partial F}{\partial \alpha} + y\frac{\partial F}{\partial \beta} + z\frac{\partial F}{\partial \gamma} + t\frac{\partial F}{\partial t} = 0. \quad \text{...(8)}$$

§ 4. The Normal. *To find the equations of the normal at (α, β, γ) to the surface $F(x, y, z) = 0$.*

The normal at any point (α, β, γ) is a straight line through the point (α, β, γ) perpendicular to the tangent plane at (α, β, γ) to the surface $F(x, y, z) = 0$. Hence the required equations of the normal at (α, β, γ) are given by

$$\frac{x-\alpha}{\partial F/\partial \alpha} = \frac{y-\beta}{\partial F/\partial \beta} = \frac{z-\gamma}{\partial F/\partial \gamma}. \quad \text{...(1)}$$

§ 5. The Polar Plane. Definition. *If any secant through a point A meets the given conicoid in the points P and Q and if a point*

R (on the secant) is harmonic conjugate to A with respect to the points P and Q i.e. AP, AR and AQ are in harmonic progression, then the locus of R is called the polar of A.

The equation of polar plane. *To find the polar plane of* $A(\alpha, \beta, \gamma)$ *with respect to the conicoid* $F(x, y, z)=0$.

Let the equations to any secant through $A(\alpha, \beta, \gamma)$ be

$$(x-\alpha)/l=(y-\beta)/m=(z-\gamma)/n. \quad ...(1)$$

If the line (1) meets the surface $F(x, y, z)=0$ in the points P and Q then proceeding exactly as in § 2 above, we have

$$r^2.f(l, m, n)+r\left(l\frac{\partial F}{\partial \alpha}+m\frac{\partial F}{\partial \beta}+n\frac{\partial F}{\partial \gamma}\right)+F(\alpha, \beta, \gamma)=0. \quad ..(2)$$

If r_1 and r_2 are the roots of (2), then let $r_1=AP$ and $r_2=AQ$. Let the co-ordinates of the point R [mentioned in the definition] be (x_1, y_1, z_1). Suppose $AR=\rho$.

Now if AP, AR, AQ i.e. r_1, ρ, r_2 are in harmonic progression, we have

$$\rho=\frac{2r_1r_2}{r_1+r_2}=-\frac{2F(\alpha, \beta, \gamma)}{l\dfrac{\partial F}{\partial \alpha}+m\dfrac{\partial F}{\partial \beta}+n\dfrac{\partial F}{\partial \gamma}}. \quad ...(3)$$

Since $R(x_1, y_1, z_1)$ lies on (1), we have

$$x_1-\alpha=\rho l,\ y_1-\beta=\rho m,\ z_1-\gamma=\rho n. \quad ..(4)$$

From (3), we get

$$\rho l\frac{\partial F}{\partial \alpha}+\rho m\frac{\partial F}{\partial \beta}+\rho n\frac{\partial F}{\partial \gamma}=-2F(\alpha, \beta, \gamma)$$

or $$(x_1-\alpha)\frac{\partial F}{\partial \alpha}+(y_1-\beta)\frac{\partial F}{\partial \beta}+(z_1-\gamma)\frac{\partial F}{\partial \gamma}=-2F(\alpha, \beta, \gamma),$$ using (4).

$\therefore$ The locus of $R(x_1, y_1, z_1)$ i.e. the equation of the polar plane of $A(\alpha, \beta, \gamma)$ is

$$(x-\alpha)\frac{\partial F}{\partial \alpha}+(y-\beta)\frac{\partial F}{\partial \beta}+(z-\gamma)\frac{\partial F}{\partial \gamma}=-2F(\alpha, \beta, \gamma) \quad ...(5)$$

Again if $F(x, y, z)$ be made homogeneous by introducing a new variable t (which is put equal to zero after differentiation), the equation (5) of the polar plane of $A(\alpha, \beta, \gamma)$ becomes

$$x\frac{\partial F}{\partial \alpha}+y\frac{\partial F}{\partial \beta}+z\frac{\partial F}{\partial \gamma}+t\frac{\partial F}{\partial t}=0. \quad ...(6)$$

§ 6. **The enveloping cone.** *To find the equation of the enveloping cone from a given point* $A(\alpha, \beta, \gamma)$.

Any line through $A(\alpha, \beta, \gamma)$ is $\dfrac{x-\alpha}{l}=\dfrac{y-\beta}{m}=\dfrac{z-\gamma}{n}$. $\quad ...(1)$

Proceed exactly as in § 2 above upto equation (2), namely the equation

$$r^2.f(l, m, n)+r\left(l\frac{\partial F}{\partial \alpha}+m\frac{\partial F}{\partial \beta}+n\frac{\partial F}{\partial \gamma}\right)+F(\alpha, \beta, \gamma)=0. \quad ...(2)$$

The line (1) will touch the conicoid $F(x, y, z)=0$ if the roots of (2) are equal, the condition for which is

$$\left(l\frac{\partial F}{\partial \alpha}+m\frac{\partial F}{\partial \beta}+n\frac{\partial F}{\partial \gamma}\right)^2=4F(\alpha, \beta, \gamma)\, f(l, m, n). \quad ..(3)$$

Hence the locus of the tangents (1) *i.e.* the equation to the enveloping cone is

$$\left\{(x-\alpha)\frac{\partial F}{\partial \alpha}+(y-\beta)\frac{\partial F}{\partial \beta}+(z-\gamma)\frac{\partial F}{\partial \gamma}\right\}^2$$
$$=4F(\alpha, \beta, \gamma)\, f\{(x-\alpha), (y-\beta), (z-\gamma)\}. \quad ...(4)$$

§ 7. **The enveloping cylinder.** In this case any point (α, β, γ) on the tangent drawn parallel to the fixed line $x/l=y/m=z/n$ lies on the cylinder [obtained from equation (3) of § 6 above]

$$4F(x, y, z)\, f(l, m, n)=\left(l\frac{\partial F}{\partial x}+m\frac{\partial F}{\partial y}+n\frac{\partial F}{\partial z}\right)^2. \quad ...(1)$$

§ 8. *To find the locus of the chords which are bisected at a given point* (α, β, γ).

The equations of any chord through (α, β, γ) are

$$(x-\alpha)/l=(y-\beta)/m=(z-\gamma)/n. \quad ...(1)$$

The points of intersection of (1) with $F(x, y, z)=0$ are given by [See equation (2) of § 2 above]

$$r^2.f(l, m, n)+r\left(l\frac{\partial F}{\partial \alpha}+m\frac{\partial F}{\partial \beta}+n\frac{\partial F}{\partial \gamma}\right)+F(\alpha, \beta, \gamma)=0. \quad ...(2)$$

If (α, β, γ), the given point, is the middle point of the chord (1) then the two roots r_1 and r_2 (say) of (2) will be equal in magnitude but opposite in signs. Hence

$$r_1+r_2=0 \text{ i.e. } l\frac{\partial F}{\partial \alpha}+m\frac{\partial F}{\partial \beta}+n\frac{\partial F}{\partial \gamma}=0. \quad ...(3)$$

Now eliminating l, m, n between (1) and (3), the required locus is given by

$$(x-\alpha)\frac{\partial F}{\partial \alpha}+(y-\beta)\frac{\partial F}{\partial \beta}+(z-\gamma)\frac{\partial F}{\partial \gamma}=0. \quad ...(4)$$

Therefore all the chords which are bisected at the point (α, β, γ) lie in the plane given by the equation (4) above. Clearly the section of the conicoid $F(x, y, z)=0$ by the plane (4) is a conic with (α, β, γ) as centre.

§ 9. **The diametral plane. Definition**. *Let $x/l=y/m=z/n$ be a fixed line. The locus of the middle points of all the chords parallel to the fixed line $x/l=y/m=z/n$ is called the diametral plane of the line $x/l=y/m=z/n$. It is also called the diametral plane conjugate to the direction l, m, n.*

The equation of the diametral plane of a line.

Let $x/l=y/m=z/n$ be a given line. Let $\frac{x-\alpha}{l}=\frac{y-\beta}{m}=\frac{z-\gamma}{n}$ be a a straight line parallel to the given line intersecting the given conicoid $F(x, y, z)=0$ in two points. Let (α, β, γ) be the middle point of these two points. Then proceeding as in § 8 above, we have

$$l\frac{\partial F}{\partial \alpha}+m\frac{\partial F}{\partial \beta}+n\frac{\partial F}{\partial \gamma}=0.$$

Hence the locus of (α, β, ν) *i.e.* the required equation of the diametral plane is given by

$$l\frac{\partial F}{\partial x}+m\frac{\partial F}{\partial y}+n\frac{\partial F}{\partial z}=0. \quad \text{.. (1)}$$

SOLVED EXAMPLES (A)

Ex. 1. *Find the condition that the plane $lx+my+nz+p=0$ may touch the conicoid $F(x, y, z)=0$.*

Solution. Let the plane $lx+my+nz+p=0$ ...(1)
touch the surface $F(x, y, z)=0$ at the point (α, β, γ).

We have $F(x, y, z)\equiv ax^2+by^2+cz^2+2fyz+2gzx+2hxy$
$+2(ux+vy+wz)+d=0.$ (2)

Making (2) homogeneous with the help of a new variable t, we have

$$F(x, y, z, t)\equiv ax^2+by^2+cz^2+2fyz+2gzx+2hxy +2(ux+vy+wz)t+d.t^2=0.$$

$$\left.\begin{aligned} \text{Now}\quad & \frac{\partial F}{\partial x}=2(ax+hy+gz+ut);\\ \therefore\quad & \frac{\partial F}{\partial \alpha}=2(a\alpha+h\beta+g\gamma+u) \text{ at } t=1.\\ \text{Similarly}\quad & \frac{\partial F}{\partial \beta}=2(h\alpha+b\beta+f\gamma+v),\\ & \frac{\partial F}{\partial \gamma}=2(g\alpha+f\beta+c\gamma+w)\\ & \frac{\partial F}{\partial t}=2(ux+vy+wz+dt)\\ & \quad=2(ux+vy+wz+d) \text{ at } t=1. \end{aligned}\right\} \quad \text{...(A)}$$

The equation of the tangent plane at (α, β, γ) [See equation (8), § 3 above] is given by

$$x\frac{\partial F}{\partial \alpha}+y\frac{\partial F}{\partial \beta}+z\frac{\partial F}{\partial \gamma}+t\frac{\partial F}{\partial t}=0. \qquad \ldots(3)$$

If the plane (1) is a tangent plane then the equation (1) and (3) should represent the same plane. Hence comparing (1) and (3), we get

$$\frac{\partial F/\partial \alpha}{l}=\frac{\partial F/\partial \beta}{m}=\frac{\partial F/\partial \gamma}{n}=\frac{\partial F/\partial t}{p}=2k \text{ (say)}$$

or
$$a\alpha+h\beta+g\gamma+u-kl=0, \qquad \ldots(4)$$
$$h\alpha+b\beta+f\gamma+v-km=0, \qquad \ldots(5)$$
$$g\alpha+f\beta+c\gamma+w-kn=0, \qquad \ldots(6)$$
and
$$u\alpha+v\beta+w\gamma+d-kp=0. \qquad \ldots(7)$$

Since (α, β, γ) lies on (1), therefore $l\alpha+m\beta+n\gamma+p=0$

or
$$l\alpha+m\beta+n\gamma+p-k\times 0=0. \qquad (8)$$

Eliminating α, β, γ and $-k$ by the method of determinants, the required condition of tangency is given by

$$\begin{vmatrix} a & h & g & u & l \\ h & b & f & v & m \\ g & f & c & w & n \\ u & v & w & d & p \\ l & m & n & p & 0 \end{vmatrix}=0$$

or
$$Al^2+Bm^2+Cn^2+2Fmn+2Gnl+2Hlm$$
$$+2Ulp+2Vmp+2Wnp+p^2D=0$$

where the capital letters A, B, C etc. are the cofactors of the corresponding small letters in

$$\begin{vmatrix} a & h & g & u \\ h & b & f & v \\ g & f & c & w \\ u & v & w & d \end{vmatrix}$$

Ex. 2. *Prove that the plane $lx+my+nz=p$ touches the surface $f(x, y, z)=1$ if $Al^2+Bm^2+Cn^2+2Fmn+2Hlm+2Gnl=p^2D$ where A, B, C etc. are the cofactors of the corresponding small letters in the determinant D given by*

$$D=\begin{vmatrix} a & h & g \\ h & b & f \\ g & f & c \end{vmatrix}.$$

Solution. The equation of the given surface is $f(x, y, z)=1$

i.e. $ax^2+by^2+cz^2+2fyz+2gzx+2hxy-1=0.$ .. (1)

Let the plane $lx+my+nz=p$ ...(2)

touch the surface (1) at the point (α, β, γ). The equation of the tangent plane at (α, β, γ) is

$$x\frac{\partial f}{\partial \alpha}+y\frac{\partial f}{\partial \beta}+z\frac{\partial f}{\partial \gamma}+t\frac{\partial f}{\partial t}=0. \qquad ...(3)$$

If the plane (2) is the tangent plane at (α, β, γ), then the equations (2) and (3) should represent the same plane. Hence comparing (2) and (3), we get

$$\frac{\partial f/\partial \alpha}{l}=\frac{\partial f/\partial \beta}{m}=\frac{\partial f/\partial \gamma}{n}=\frac{\partial f/\partial t}{-p}$$

or $$\frac{2(a\alpha+h\beta+g\gamma)}{l}=\frac{2(h\alpha+b\beta+f\gamma)}{m}=\frac{2(g\alpha+f\beta+c\gamma)}{n}=\frac{-2}{-p}. \qquad ...(4)$$

[$\because$ the equation of the surface can be written as

$f(x, y, z, t)\equiv ax^2+by^2+cz^2+2fyz+2gzx+2hxy-t^2=0$;

$\therefore \partial f/\partial t=-2$ at $t=1$].

Now the relations (4) give

$p(a\alpha+h\beta+g\gamma)-l=0,$ ...(5)

$p(h\alpha+b\beta+f\gamma)-m=0,$ ...(6)

and $p(g\alpha+f\beta+c\gamma)-n=0.$ ...(7)

Since (α, β, γ) lies on (2), therefore

$p(l\alpha+m\beta+n\gamma)-p^2=0.$ ...(8)

Eliminating $p\alpha$, $p\beta$, $p\gamma$ and (-1), the condition of tangency is given by

$$\begin{vmatrix} a & h & g & l \\ h & b & f & m \\ g & f & c & n \\ l & m & n & p^2 \end{vmatrix}=0$$

or $Al^2+Bm^2+Cn^2+2Fmn+2Gnl+2Hlm=p^2D$

where A, B, C etc. are the co-factors of the corresponding small letters in the determinant

$$D=\begin{vmatrix} a & h & g \\ h & b & f \\ g & f & c \end{vmatrix}. \quad \left[\text{We also note that } A=\frac{\partial D}{\partial a} \text{ etc.}\right]$$

Ex. 3. *Show that the locus of the point of intersection of three mutually perpendicular tangent planes to the surface* $f(x, y, z)=1$ *is the sphere* $D(x^2+y^2+z^2)=A+B+C$.

Solution. Proceeding as in Ex. 2. above, the plane $lx+my+nz=p$ touches the surface

$$f(x, y, z)\equiv ax^2+by^2+cz^2+2fyz+2gzx+2hxy=1 \qquad (1)$$

if $$Al^2+Bm^2+Cn^2+2Fmn+2Gnl+2Hlm=p^2D. \qquad ..(2)$$

In other words $lx+my+nz=p$ is the equation of the tangent plane to (1) where p is given by (2).

Now let $$l_rx+m_ry+n_rz=p_r,\ (r=1, 2, 3) \qquad ...(3)$$

be the equations of three mutually perpendicular tangent planes. Hence p_r is given by

$$Al_r^2+Bm_r^2+Cn_r^2+2Fm_rn_r+2Gn_rl_r+2Hl_rm_r=p_r^2D. \qquad ..(4)$$

Putting $r=1, 2, 3$ in (3), squaring and adding the resulting equations, we get

$$x^2(l_1^2+l_2^2+l_3^2)+y^2\,\Sigma m_1^2+z^2\,\Sigma n_1^2=p_1^2+p_2^2+p_3^2$$

or $$x^2+y^2+z^2=(1/D)\{A\Sigma l_1^2+B\Sigma m_1^2+C\Sigma n_1^2+2F\Sigma m_1n_1 + 2G\Sigma n_1l_1+2H\Sigma l_1m_1\}=0, \quad \text{using (4)}$$

or $$D(x^2+y^2+z^2)=A+B+C.$$

This is the equation of the required locus and clearly represents a sphere concentric with the given conicoid and is called the **Director Sphere.**

Ex. 4. *If the axes are rectangular, prove that the locus of the feet of the perpendiculars from the origin to the tangent planes to* $f(x, y, z)=1$ *is*

$$Ax^2+By^2+Cz^2+2Fyz+2Gzx+2Hxy=D\ (x^2+y^2+z^2)^2.$$

Solution. Proceeding as in Ex. (2) above the plane

$$lx+my+nz=p \qquad ...(1)$$

touches $$f(x, y, z)\equiv ax^2+by^2+cz^2+2fyz+2gzx+2hxy=1 \qquad ...(2)$$

if $$Al^2+Bm^2+Cn^2+2Fmn+2Gnl+2Hlm=p^2D. \qquad ...(3)$$

Again the equations of the perpendicular from the origin to the tangent plane are

$$\frac{x}{l}=\frac{y}{m}=\frac{z}{n}=r=\frac{\sqrt{(x^2+y^2+z^2)}}{1} \qquad ...(4)$$

where l, m, n are the actual direction cosines. The foot of the perpendicular is (lr, mr, nr) and its locus is obtained by eliminating l, m, n between (3) and (4) and is given by

$$A(x/r)^2+B(y/r)^2+C(z/r)^2+2F(y/r)(z/r)+2G(z/r)(x/r)$$
$$+2H(x/r)(y/r)=p^2D$$

or $$Ax^2+By^2+Cz^2+2Fyz+2Gzx+2Hxy=r^2p^2D. \quad ...(5)$$

Now r=the length of the perpendicular from (0, 0, 0) to (1)

i.e. $r=\pm p/\sqrt{(l^2+m^2+n^2)}$ or $r^2=p^2$

or $p^2r^2=r^4=(x^2+y^2+z^2)^2$, using (4).

$\therefore$ The required locus (5) is given by

$$Ax^2+By^2+Cz^2+2Fyz+2Gzx+2Hxy=D(x^2+y^2+z^2)^2.$$

Ex. 5. *If two conicoids have a common generator, then they touch at two points of the generator.*

Solution. Let the equations of the two conicoids be given by

$$F_1(x, y, z)\equiv a_1x^2+b_1y^2+c_1z^2+2f_1yz+2g_1zx+2h_1xy$$
$$+2u_1x+2v_1y+2w_1z+d_1=0, \quad ...(1)$$

and $$F_2(x, y, z)\equiv a_2x^2+b_2y^2+c_2z^2+2f_2yz+2g_2zx+2h_2xy$$
$$+2u_2x+2v_2y+2w_2z+d_2=0. \quad ...(2)$$

Let the common generator be taken as x-axis, so that

$$\frac{x}{1}=\frac{y}{0}=\frac{z}{0}=r \text{ (say)} \quad (3)$$

will meet each of the above two conicoids in three points.

Now (3) meets (1) in three points, therefore

$a_1r^2+2u_1r+d_1=0$ is identically satisfied.

Hence $a_1=0,\ u_1=0,\ d_1=0.$

Similarly (3) meets (2) in three points, therefore $a_2=0$, $u_2=0$, $d_2=0$.

$\therefore$ the conicoids with x-axis as their common generators are given by the equations

$$b_1y^2+c_1z^2+2f_1yz+2g_1zx+2h_1xy+2v_1y+2w_1z=0, \quad ...(4)$$

and $$b_2y^2+c_2z^2+2f_2yz+2g_2zx+2h_2xy+2v_2y+2w_2z=0. \quad ...(5)$$

Again $(\alpha, 0, 0)$ is any point on the x-axis i.e. on the common generator. The equation of the tangent plane at $(\alpha, 0, 0)$ to (4) is

$$(x-\alpha)\frac{\partial F_1}{\partial \alpha}+(y-0)\frac{\partial F_1}{\partial \beta}+(z-0)\frac{\partial F_1}{\partial \gamma}=0 \quad [\because \beta=0, \gamma=0]$$

or $$(x-\alpha)(0+0)+y(0+0+2h_1\alpha+2v_1)+z(0+0+2g_1\alpha+2w_1)=0$$

or $$y(h_1\alpha+v_1)+z(g_1\alpha+w_1)=0 \quad ...(6)$$

In a similar way the equation of the tangent plane at $(\alpha, 0, 0)$ to (5) is $$y(h_2\alpha+v_2)+z(g_2\alpha+w_2)=0. \quad ...(7)$$

If the two conicoids touch along the common generator (*i.e.* along the x-axis here) the tangent planes (6) and (7) will be the same. Hence $\dfrac{h_1\alpha+v_1}{h_2\alpha+v_2}=\dfrac{g_1\alpha+w_1}{g_2\alpha+w_2}$

or $$(h_1\alpha+v_1)(g_2\alpha+w_2)=(g_1\alpha+w_1)(h_2\alpha+v_2).$$

This being a quadratic equation in α, gives two values of α and hence the conicoids touch at two points of the generator.

Ex. 6. *Show that the equation of the tangent plane at* (x', y', z') *on* $xy=cz$ *is* $x/x'+y/y'-z/z'=1$.

Hence show that the plane $lx+my+nz=p$ *will touch* $xy=cz$ *if* $clm+np=0$.

Solution. Proceed as in § 3 above.

Here $F(x, y, z, t)\equiv xy-czt=0$, etc.

§ 10. Principal planes and the principal directions.

Consider the diametral plane of the system of chords parallel to the line $$x/l=y/m=z/n.$$

A principal plane is a diametral plane at right angles to the chords it bisects, and the principal direction is the corresponding direction l, m, n *of the chords.*

The equation of the principal plane. The equation of the diametral plane bisecting the chords parallel to

$$x/l=y/m=z/n \qquad ...(1)$$

is given by $$l\frac{\partial F}{\partial x}+m\frac{\partial F}{\partial y}+n\frac{\partial F}{\partial z}=0 \qquad \text{[See § 9, above]}$$

or $$x(al+hm+gn)+y(hl+bm+fn)+z(gl+fm+cn)$$
$$+(ul+vm+wn)=0. \qquad ...(2)$$

If (2) is a principal plane, then (2) is at right angles to the chords (1) and so, we have

$$\frac{al+hm+gn}{l}=\frac{hl+bm+fn}{m}=\frac{gl+fm+cn}{n}=\lambda \text{ (say)}. \qquad ...(A)$$

$$\therefore \left.\begin{aligned} &(a-\lambda)l+hm+gn=0,\\ &hl+(b-\lambda)m+fn=0,\\ \text{and}\quad &gl+fm+(c-\lambda)n=0.\end{aligned}\right\} \qquad ...(3)$$

Since l, m, n cannot be all zero, so eliminating l, m, n between the relations (4), we see that λ is a root of the equation

$$\begin{vmatrix} a-\lambda & h & g \\ h & b-\lambda & f \\ g & f & c-\lambda \end{vmatrix}=0 \qquad ..(4)$$

or $\lambda^3-(a+b+c)\lambda^2+(bc+ca+ab-f^2-g^2-h^2)\lambda$
$$-(abc+2fgh-af^2-bg^2-ch^2)=0$$

or $$\lambda^3-(a+b+c)\lambda^2+(A+B+C)\lambda-D=0 \quad ...(5)$$

where A, B, C are the co-factors of a, b, c in

$$D\equiv\begin{vmatrix} a & h & g \\ h & b & f \\ g & f & c \end{vmatrix}. \quad [\because \; A=bc-f^2,\ B=ca-g^2,\ C=ab-h^2]$$

The equation (5) [or (4)] is a cubic equation in λ and is called the **'Discriminating cubic'**, its roots are called **characteristic roots. There exists at least one principal plane** since *one root of a cubic is always real.*

Now using (3), the equation (2) becomes

$$\lambda(lx+my+nz)+(ul+vm+wn)=0. \quad ...(6)$$

The equation (6) gives three principal planes corresponding to three values of λ [as obtained from (5)] and the corresponding values of l, m, n give the principal directions.

§ 11. The roots of the discriminating cubic are all real.

Let the general equation of the second degree be $F(x, y, z)=0$. If λ is a root of its discriminating cubic *i.e.* of the cubic

$$\lambda^3-(a+b+c)\lambda^2+(A+B+C)\lambda-D=0, \quad ...(1)$$

then l, m, n not all zero are given by [See § 10, above]

$$al+hm+gn=l\lambda \quad ...(2)$$
$$hl+bm+fn=m\lambda \quad ...(3)$$
$$gl+fm+cn=n\lambda. \quad ...(4)$$

Since λ has not been proved real, so l, m, n cannot be assumed as real quantities. Let the conjugate complexes of l, m, n be l', m', n' respectively.

Now multiplying the equations (2), (3) and (4) by l', m' and n' respectively and adding, we obtain

$$all'+bmm'+cnn'+h(lm'+l'm)+g(nl'+n'l)$$
$$+f(mn'+m'n)=\lambda(ll'+mm'+nn'). \quad ...(5)$$

But ll', mm', nn' are real. Also lm' is conjugate complex of $l'm$ and so $lm'+l'm$ is real. Similarly $mn'+m'n$ and $nl'+n'l$ are real. Again $ll'+mm'+nn'$ is a non-zero real number. Consequently (5) shows that λ is the ratio of two real numbers and hence λ is a real number *i.e.* the roots of the discriminating cubic of $F(x, y, z)=0$ are all real.

It follows that the quantities l, m, n corresponding to each value of λ are also real.

§ 12. Orthogonality of the principal directions.

To show that the principal directions corresponding to two distinct roots of the discriminating cubic are orthogonal.

Let λ_1, λ_2 be the two distinct roots of the discriminating cubic and the two corresponding principal directions be l_1, m_1, n_1 and l_2, m_2, n_2. We have [See equations (A) of § 10 above]

$$\frac{\partial f/\partial l_1}{2l_1}=\frac{\partial f/\partial m_1}{2m_1}=\frac{\partial f/\partial n_1}{2n_1}=\lambda_1 \text{ and } \frac{\partial f/\partial l_2}{2l_2}=\frac{\partial f/\partial m_2}{2m_2}=\frac{\partial f/\partial n_2}{2n_2}=\lambda_2.$$

$$\therefore\ 2l_1\lambda_1=\frac{\partial f}{\partial l_1},\ 2m_1\lambda_1=\frac{\partial f}{\partial m_1},\ 2n_1\lambda_1=\frac{\partial f}{\partial n_1},\ 2l_2\lambda_2=\frac{\partial f}{\partial l_2} \text{ etc.}$$

But we know that

$$l_1\frac{\partial f}{\partial l_2}+m_1\frac{\partial f}{\partial m_2}+n_1\frac{\partial f}{\partial n_2}=l_2\frac{\partial f}{\partial l_1}+m_2\frac{\partial f}{\partial m_1}+n_2\frac{\partial f}{\partial n_1}$$

or $$2(l_1l_2+m_1m_2+n_1n_2)\lambda_2=2(l_2l_1+m_2m_1+n_2n_1)\lambda_1$$

or $$(\lambda_2-\lambda_1)(l_1l_2+m_1m_2+n_1n_2)=0$$

or $$l_1l_2+m_1m_2+n_1n_2=0 \qquad [\because\ \lambda_1\neq\lambda_2]$$

It shows that the two principal directions are at right angles to each other.

§ 13. Transformation of f(x, y, z).

(A) *To prove that by rotation of axes the expression*

$$f(x,y,z)=ax^2+by^2+cz^2+2fyz+2gzx+2hxy$$

transforms to $\lambda_1x^2+\lambda_2y^2+\lambda_3z^2$ *where* $\lambda_1, \lambda_2, \lambda_3$ *are the roots of the equation*

$$\begin{vmatrix} a-\lambda & h & g \\ h & b-\lambda & f \\ g & f & c-\lambda \end{vmatrix}=0$$

or $$\lambda^3-\lambda^2(a+b+c)(bc+ca+ab-f^2-g^2-h^2)$$
$$-(abc+2fgh-af^2-bg^2-ch^2)=0.$$

Suppose we make the following transformation

$$x=l_1x+m_1y+n_1z,\ y=l_2x+m_2y+n_2z,\ z=l_3x+m_3y+n_3z.$$

Under this transformation the expression $x^2+y^2+z^2$ remains unchanged. Hence if the axes are rotated in such a manner that the expression $ax^2+by^2+cz^2+2fyz+2gzx+2hxy$ transforms to $\lambda_1x^2+\lambda_2y^2+\lambda_3z^2$, then the expression

$$ax^2+by^2+cz^2+2fyz+2gzx+2hxy-\lambda(x^2+y^2+z^2) \quad ...(1)$$

should become $\lambda_1x^2+\lambda_2y^2+\lambda_3z^2-\lambda(x^2+y^2+z^2)$. ...(2)

Now for the same value of λ, the expressions (1) and (2) both will be the product of two linear factors. The expression (1) *i.e.* $(a-\lambda)x^2+(b-\lambda)y^2+(c-\lambda)z^2+2fyz+2gzx+2hxy$ will be the product of two linear factors if

$$\begin{vmatrix} a-\lambda & h & g \\ h & b-\lambda & f \\ g & f & c-\lambda \end{vmatrix}=0 \quad ...(3)$$

or $\lambda^3-\lambda^2(a+b+c)+\lambda(bc+ca+ab-f^2-g^2-h^2)$

$$-(abc+2fgh-af^2-bg^2-ch^2)=0 \quad ...(3')$$

or $$\lambda^3-\lambda^2(a+b+c)+\lambda(A+B+C)-D=0 \quad ...(4)$$

where $$D=\begin{vmatrix} a & h & g \\ h & b & f \\ g & f & c \end{vmatrix}$$

and A, B, C are the cofactors of a, b and c in the determinant D so that $A=bc-f^2$, $B=ca-g^2$, $C=ab-h^2$.

Again the expression (2) *i.e.* $(\lambda_1-\lambda)x^2+(\lambda_2-\lambda)y^2+(\lambda_3-\lambda)z^2$ will be the product of two linear factors if

$$\begin{vmatrix} \lambda_1-\lambda & 0 & 0 \\ 0 & \lambda_2-\lambda & 0 \\ 0 & 0 & \lambda_3-\lambda \end{vmatrix}=0, \text{ i.e. } (\lambda_1-\lambda)(\lambda_2-\lambda)(\lambda_3-\lambda)=0$$

i.e. $\lambda=\lambda_1$, λ_2 or λ_3.

Hence we see that the expression (2) will be the product of two linear factors if the value of λ is equal to either λ_1, λ_2 or λ_3. Therefore, the values of λ from equation (3) will also be the same *i.e.* λ_1, λ_2 and λ_3.

Thus we conclude that if by rotation of axes the expression $f(x, y, z)$ is transformed to $\lambda_1x^2+\lambda_2y^2+\lambda_3z^2$ then λ_1, λ_3, λ_3 are the roots of the equation (3).

The equation (3) [or (3′) or (4)] is called the **discriminating cubic.**

Second Method. Suppose by the transformation

$$x=l_1x+m_1y+n_1z,\ y=l_2x+m_2y+n_2z,\ z=l_3x+m_3y+n_3z$$

the expression $ax^2+by^2+cz^2+2fyz+2gzx+2hxy$ transforms to $\lambda_1x^2+\lambda_2y^2+\lambda_3z^2$.

$\therefore\quad \lambda_1 x^2+\lambda_2 y^2+\lambda_3 z^2$
$=\lambda_1(l_1x+m_1y+n_1z)^2+\lambda_2(l_2x+m_2y+n_2z)^2+\lambda_3(l_3x+m_3y+n_3z)^2$
$\equiv ax^2+by^2+cz^2+2fyz+2gzx+2hxy.$

$$\therefore\quad \left.\begin{aligned} a&=\lambda_1 l_1^2+\lambda_2 l_2^2+\lambda_3 l_3^2, & f&=\lambda_1 m_1 n_1+\lambda_2 m_2 n_2+\lambda_3 m_3 n_3\\ b&=\lambda_1 m_1^2+\lambda_2 m_2^2+\lambda_3 m_3^2, & g&=\lambda_1 n_1 l_1+\lambda_2 n_2 l_2+\lambda_3 n_3 l_3\\ c&=\lambda_1 n_1^2+\lambda_2 n_2^2+\lambda_3 n_3^2, & h&=\lambda_1 l_1 m_1+\lambda_2 l_2 m_2+\lambda_3 l_3 m_3 \end{aligned}\right\}. \quad \ldots(5)$$

$\therefore\quad a+b+c=\lambda_1+\lambda_2+\lambda_3$ [Since $\Sigma l_1^2=\Sigma l_2^2=\Sigma l_3^2=1$]. ...(6)

Also $bc-f^2=\lambda_2\lambda_3\,(m_2n_3-m_3n_2)^2+\lambda_3\lambda_1\,(m_3n_1-m_1n_3)^2$
$\qquad\qquad+\lambda_1\lambda_2\,(m_2n_1-m_1n_2)^2$
$\qquad=\lambda_2\lambda_3 l_1^2+\lambda_3\lambda_1 l_2^2+\lambda_1\lambda_2 l_3^2$, since $m_2n_3-m_3n_2=l_1$.

Similarly $ca-g^2=\lambda_2\lambda_3 m_1^2+\lambda_3\lambda_1 m_2^2+\lambda_1\lambda_2 m_3^2$,

and $\qquad ab-h^2=\lambda_2\lambda_3 n_1^2+\lambda_3\lambda_1 n_2^2+\lambda_1\lambda_2 n_3^2.$

$\therefore\quad bc+ca+ab-f^2-g^2-h^2=\lambda_2\lambda_3+\lambda_3\lambda_1+\lambda_1\lambda_2.$ ...(7)

Also
$$\begin{vmatrix} l_1 & l_2 & l_3\\ m_1 & m_2 & m_3\\ n_1 & n_2 & n_3 \end{vmatrix}\times\begin{vmatrix} \lambda_1 l_1 & \lambda_2 l_2 & \lambda_3 l_3\\ \lambda_1 m_1 & \lambda_2 m_2 & \lambda_3 m_3\\ \lambda_1 n_1 & \lambda_2 n_2 & \lambda_3 n_3 \end{vmatrix}$$
$$=\begin{vmatrix} \Sigma\lambda_1 l_1^2 & \Sigma\lambda_1 l_1 m_1 & \Sigma\lambda_1 n_1 l_1\\ \Sigma\lambda_1 l_1 m_1 & \Sigma\lambda_1 m_1^2 & \Sigma\lambda_1 m_1 n_1\\ \Sigma\lambda_1 n_1 l_1 & \Sigma\lambda_1 m_1 n_1 & \Sigma\lambda_1 n_1^2 \end{vmatrix}$$

or
$$\lambda_1\lambda_2\lambda_3\begin{vmatrix} l_1 & m_1 & n_1\\ l_2 & m_2 & n_2\\ l_3 & m_3 & n_3 \end{vmatrix}^2=\begin{vmatrix} a & h & g\\ h & b & f\\ g & f & c \end{vmatrix}$$

[Putting the values from the relations (5)]

or
$$\lambda_1\lambda_2\lambda_3=\begin{vmatrix} a & h & g\\ h & b & f\\ g & f & c \end{vmatrix}=D \text{ (say), since } \begin{vmatrix} l_1 & m_1 & n_1\\ l_2 & m_2 & n_2\\ l_3 & m_3 & n_3 \end{vmatrix}=1.$$

The equation whose roots are $\lambda_1, \lambda_2, \lambda_3$ is given by

$$\lambda^3-(\lambda_1+\lambda_2+\lambda_3)\,\lambda^2+(\lambda_1\lambda_2+\lambda_2\lambda_3+\lambda_3\lambda_1)\,\lambda-\lambda_1\lambda_2\lambda_3=0$$

i.e. $\quad \lambda^3-(a+b+c)\,\lambda^2+(bc+ca+ab-f^2-g^2-h^2)\,\lambda-D=0$

i.e. $\quad \lambda^3-(a+b+c)\,\lambda^2+(bc+ca+ab-f^2-g^2-h^2)\,\lambda$
$\qquad\qquad -(abc+2fgh-af^2-bg^2-ch^2)=0.$

(B) *To find the direction cosines of the new axes :*

Let l_1, m_1, n_1 ; l_2, m_2, n_2 ; l_3, m_3, n_3 be the d.c.'s of the new axes. From relations (5) of § 13 (A) above, we have

$$al_1+hm_1+gn_1=\lambda_1 l_1 (l_1^2+m_1^2+n_1^2)+\lambda_2 l_2 (l_1 l_2+m_1 m_2+n_1 n_2)$$
$$+\lambda_3 l_3 (l_3 l_1+m_3 m_1+n_3 n_1)$$
$$=\lambda_1 l_1, \text{ since } \Sigma l_1^2=1, \Sigma l_1 l_2=\Sigma l_3 l_1=0.$$

$\therefore \quad (al_1+hm_1+gn_1)/l_1=\lambda_1.$

Similarly $(hl_1+bm_1+fn_1)/m_1=\lambda_1$ and $(gl_1+fm_1+cn_1)/n_1=\lambda_1$.

Also we get similar expressions for l_2, m_2, n_2 and l_3, m_3, n_3.

Hence the d.c.'s of the axes are given by the equations

$$\frac{al+hm+gn}{l}=\frac{hl+bm+fn}{m}=\frac{gl+fm+cn}{n}=\lambda \quad \text{...(8)}$$

where λ is the corresponding root of the discriminating cubic.

§ 14. The centre of the surface F (x, y, z)=0

To find the co-ordinates of the surface

$$F(x, y, z)\equiv ax^2+by^2+cz^2+2fyz+2gzx+2hxy+2ux+2vy$$
$$+2wz+d=0. \quad \text{...(1)}$$

Let (α, β, γ) be its centre. Shifting the origin to (α, β, γ), the equation (1) transforms to

$$a(x+\alpha)^2+b(y+\beta)^2+c(z+\gamma)^2+2f(y+\beta)(z+\gamma)+2g(z+\gamma)(x+\alpha)$$
$$+2h(x+\alpha)(y+\beta)+2u(x+\alpha)+2v(y+\beta)+2w(z+\gamma)+d=0.$$
$$\text{...(2)}$$

Now the centre of (2) is the origin and hence it will be a homogeneous equation. Therefore the first degree terms should vani h, so we have

$$\left.\begin{array}{l} a\alpha+h\beta+g\gamma+u=0 \text{ i.e. } \tfrac{1}{2}\partial F/\partial\alpha=0, \text{ i.e. } \partial F/\partial\alpha=0 \\ h\alpha+b\beta+f\gamma+v=0 \text{ i.e. } \tfrac{1}{2}\partial F/\partial\beta=0, \text{ i.e. } \partial F/\partial\beta=0 \\ g\alpha+f\beta+c\gamma+w=0 \text{ i.e. } \tfrac{1}{2}\partial F/\partial\gamma=0, \text{ i.e. } \partial F/\partial\gamma=0 \end{array}\right\}. \quad \text{...(3)}$$

Also the constant term in (2) is

$$=a\alpha^2+b\beta^2+c\gamma^2+2f\beta\gamma+2g\gamma\alpha+2h\alpha\beta+2u\alpha+2v\beta+2w\gamma+d$$
$$=\alpha(a\alpha+h\beta+g\gamma+u)+\beta(h\alpha+b\beta+f\gamma+v)+\gamma(g\alpha+f\beta+c\gamma+w)$$
$$+u\alpha+v\beta+w\gamma+d$$

$=u\alpha+v\beta+w\gamma+d$, using the relations (3)

$=d'$ (say).

Hence the transformed equation (2) reduces to

$$ax^2+by^2+cz^2+2fyz+2gzx+2hxy+d'=0$$

where $d'=u\alpha+v\beta+w\gamma+d$ and the centre (α, β, γ) of (1) is given by the equations (3) *i.e.* by the equations

$$\frac{\partial F}{\partial \alpha}=0, \frac{\partial F}{\partial \beta}=0, \frac{\partial F}{\partial \gamma}=0.$$

Working rule. We shall follow the following procedure to determine the centre of the given conicoid.

(i) If the given equation is homogeneous, then the centre of the given surface is origin.

(ii) If the given equation is not homogeneous then denote it by $F(x, y, z)=0$ and the co-ordinates of the centre of the surface are found by solving the equations

$$\frac{\partial F}{\partial x}=0, \frac{\partial F}{\partial y}=0, \frac{\partial F}{\partial z}=0.$$

§ 15. *Process of* **reducing a general equation** *to the standard form and to* **discuss the nature.**

Now without going in much details we give below the process of reducing a general equation $F(x, y, z)=0$ of second degree to the standard form *provided the terms of second degree do not form a perfect square.*

(S_1) Form the discriminating cubic and solve it.

(S_2) If all the three characteristic roots (say λ_1, λ_2 and λ_3) are different from zero, then find the co-ordinates (α, β, γ) of the centre by solving the equations (the equations of the central planes)

$$\frac{\partial F}{\partial x}=0, \frac{\partial F}{\partial y}=0, \frac{\partial F}{\partial z}=0.$$

(S_3) Shifting the origin to the centre (α, β, γ) and then rotating the axes, the reduced equation becomes

$$\lambda_1 x^2+\lambda_2 y^2+\lambda_3 z^2=\mu$$

where $\mu=-(u\alpha+v\beta+w\gamma+d)$.

(S_4) If one root (say) $\lambda_3=0$, then corresponding to this value (*i.e.* $\lambda_3=0$) find the principal directions l_3, m_3, n_3 from any two of the following equations ;

$$\left.\begin{aligned} al_3+hm_3+gn_3&=0\\ hl_3+bm_3+fn_3&=0\\ gl_3+fm_3+cn_3&=0\end{aligned}\right\} \quad \ldots(A)$$

and evaluate $k=ul_3+vm_3+wn_3$.

If $k \neq 0$. The reduced equation is $\lambda_1 x^2+\lambda_2 y^2+2kz=0$, and represents an elliptic or hyperbolic paraboloid whose vertex is given by solving any two of the following equations (1), (2) and (3) along with the equation (4) [Note that the equation (4) below is to be used in all cases in finding the co-ordinates of the vertex].

$$ax+hy+gz-l_3k+u=0 \quad ...(1)$$
$$hx+by+fz-m_3k+v=0 \quad ...(2)$$
$$gx+fy+cz-n_3k+w=0 \quad ...(3)$$
$$k\,(l_3x+m_3y+n_3z)+ux+vy+wz+d=0. \quad ...(4)$$

(S_6) If k=0. There is a line of centres, given by any two of the equations $\frac{\partial F}{\partial x}=0, \frac{\partial F}{\partial y}=0, \frac{\partial F}{\partial z}=0.$

Let any point (α, β, γ) on the line of centres be chosen as centre ; then the reduced equation is

$$\lambda_1x^2+\lambda_2y^2=\mu$$

where $\mu=-(u\alpha+v\beta+w\gamma+d).$

SOLVED EXAMPLES (B)

Case 1. When all the characterisitic roots are different from zero.

Ex. 1. *Reduce the equation*

$$2x^2-7y^2+2z^2-10\,yz-8zx-10xy+6x+12y-6z+5=0$$

to the standard form.

Solution. Comparing the given equation with the general equation $F(x, y, z)=0$ of second degree, we get

$a=2,\ b=-7,\ c=2,\ f=-5,\ g=-4,\ h=-5,\ u=3,$
$v=6,\ w=-3,\ d=5.$

We have,

$$D=\begin{vmatrix} a & h & g \\ h & b & f \\ g & f & c \end{vmatrix}=\begin{vmatrix} 2 & -5 & -4 \\ -5 & -7 & -5 \\ -4 & -5 & 2 \end{vmatrix}=-216.$$

$\therefore$ the discriminating cubic is

$$\lambda^3-(a+b+c)\,\lambda^2+(bc+ca+ab-f^2-g^2-h^2)\,\lambda-D=0$$

or $\lambda^3-(-3)\,\lambda^2+(-90)\,\lambda+216=0$

or $\lambda^3+3\lambda^2-90\lambda+216=0$

or $(\lambda-3)\,(\lambda^2+6\lambda-72)=0$

or $(\lambda-3)\,(\lambda+12)\,(\lambda-6)=0.$

$\therefore\ \lambda=3,\ 6 \text{ or } -12.$

centre (α, β, γ) is given by the equations

$$\left.\begin{aligned} \tfrac{1}{2}\frac{\partial F}{\partial \alpha} &= 2\alpha-5\beta-4\gamma+3=0 \\ \tfrac{1}{2}\frac{\partial F}{\partial \beta} &= -5\alpha-7\beta-5\gamma+6=0 \\ \tfrac{1}{2}\frac{\partial F}{\partial \gamma} &= -4\alpha-5\beta+2\gamma-3=0 \end{aligned}\right\}$$

Solving these equations, the centre is $(\frac{1}{3}, -\frac{1}{3}, \frac{4}{3})$.

Also $\mu = -(u\alpha + v\beta + w\gamma + d)$

or $\mu = -[3.(\frac{1}{3}) + 6.(-\frac{1}{3}) + (-3).(\frac{4}{3}) + 5] = 0.$

Hence the reduced equation (*i.e.* equation in standard form) is

$$\lambda_1 x^2 + \lambda_2 y^2 + \lambda_3 z^2 = \mu$$

or $$3x^2 + 6y^2 - 12z^2 = 0, \text{ or } x^2 + 2y^2 - 4z^2 = 0$$

which is the equation of a cone with its vertex at $(\frac{1}{3}, -\frac{1}{3}, \frac{4}{3})$.

Ex. 2. *Reduce the equation*

$$11x^2 + 10y^2 + 6z^2 - 8yz + 4zx - 12xy + 72x - 72y + 36z + 150 = 0$$

to the standard form and give the nature of the surface. Also find the equations of its axes.

Solution. Comparing the given equation with $F(x, y, z) = 0$, we have

$a = 11, b = 10, c = 6, f = -4, g = 2, h = -6, u = 36, v = -36, w = 18,$
$d = 150.$

The discriminating cubic is [See equation (3), § 13 (A)]

$$\begin{vmatrix} a-\lambda & h & g \\ h & b-\lambda & f \\ g & f & c-\lambda \end{vmatrix} = 0, \text{ or } \begin{vmatrix} 1-\lambda & -6 & 2 \\ -6 & 10-\lambda & -4 \\ 2 & -4 & 6-\lambda \end{vmatrix} = 0$$

or $\lambda^3 - 27\lambda^2 + 180\lambda - 324 = 0$, or $(\lambda - 3)(\lambda - 6)(\lambda - 18) = 0.$

$$\therefore \lambda = 3, 6, 18.$$

The centre (α, β, γ) is given by the equations

$$\left.\begin{aligned} \tfrac{1}{2}\frac{\partial F}{\partial \alpha} &= 11\alpha - 6\beta + 2\gamma + 36 = 0 \\ \tfrac{1}{2}\frac{\partial F}{\partial \beta} &= -6\alpha + 10\beta - 4\gamma - 36 = 0 \\ \tfrac{1}{2}\frac{\partial F}{\partial \gamma} &= 2\alpha - 4\beta + 6\gamma + 18 = 0 \end{aligned}\right\}$$

Solving these equations, the centre is $(-2, 2, -1)$.

Also $\mu = -(u\alpha + v\beta + w\gamma + d)$

or $\mu = -[36(-2) + (-36)(2) + 18(-1) + 150] = 12.$

Hence the reduced equation (*i.e.* the equation in standard form) is

$$\lambda_1 x^2 + \lambda_2 y^2 + \lambda_3 z^2 = \mu$$

or $$3x^2 + 6y^2 + 18z^2 = 12$$

or $$\frac{x^2}{4} + \frac{y^2}{2} + \frac{z^2}{2/3} = 1 \quad \ldots(1)$$

which is the equation of an ellipsoid.

Let l, m, n be the d.c.'s of the principal direction (*i.e.* the direction cosines of the axis) corresponding to $\lambda=3$. These are given by [See equations (8), § 13 or (3) of § 10]

$$\left.\begin{array}{l}(a-\lambda)\, l+hm+gn=0\\ hl+(b-\lambda)\, m+fn=0\\ gl+fm+(c-\lambda)\, n=0\end{array}\right\} \text{ or } \left.\begin{array}{r}8l-6m+2n=0\\ -6l+7m-4n=0\\ 2l-4m+3n=0\end{array}\right\}$$

Solving any two, we have $\dfrac{l}{1}=\dfrac{m}{2}=\dfrac{n}{2}=\dfrac{1}{\sqrt{(1^2+2^2+2^2)}}=\dfrac{1}{3}$

$$\therefore \quad l=\tfrac{1}{3},\ m=\tfrac{2}{3},\ n=\tfrac{2}{3}.$$

Hence the equations of the axis through the centre $(-2, 2, -1)$ and whose d.c.'s are $\frac{1}{3}, \frac{2}{3}, \frac{2}{3}$ are given by

$$\frac{x+2}{1}=\frac{y-2}{2}=\frac{z+1}{2}$$

Similarly, the equations of the other two axes corresponding to the other two values of λ are found as

$$\frac{x+2}{2}=\frac{y-2}{1}=\frac{z+1}{-2} \text{ and } \frac{x+2}{-2}=\frac{y-2}{2}=\frac{z+1}{-1}.$$

Some more examples for practice.

Reduce the following equations to the standard forms :

1. $3x^2+5y^2+3z^2+2yz+2zx+2xy-4x-8z+5=0.$
   [**Ans.** $3x^2+2y^2+6z^2=1$, ellipsoid].
2. $3x^2-y^2-z^2+6yz-6x+6y-2z-2=0.$
   [**Ans.** $3x^2+2y^2-4z^2=4$ hyperboloid of one sheet].
3. $3x^2+7y^2+3z^2+10yz-2zx+10xy+4x-12y-4z+1=0.$
   [**Ans.** $3x^2-4y^2-12z^2=1$, hyperboloid of two sheets].
4. $x^2+3y^2+3z^2-2yz-2x-2y+6z+3=0.$
   [**Ans.** $x^2+2y^2+4z^2=1$, ellipsoid].

Case II. When two roots of the discriminating cubic are equal. In this case the surface $F(x, y, z)=0$ represents a surface of revolution and the axis of rotation is obtained by taking into consideration that value of λ which is different from the equal values of λ.

SOLVED EXAMPLES (C)

Ex. 1. *Prove that the equation*

$$x^2+y^2+z^2+yz+zx+xy+3x+y+4z+4=0$$

represents an ellipsoid the squares of whose semi-axes are 2, 2, $\frac{1}{2}$. *Show that its principal axis is given by* $x+1=y-1=z+2$.

Solution. Multiplying the given equation of the surface by 2, we get

$$2x^2+2y^2+2z^2+2yz+2zx+2xy+6x+2y+8z+8=0.$$

$\therefore$ $a=2, b=2, c=2, f=1, g=1, h=1, u=3, v=1, w=4, d=4.$

The discriminating cubic is

$$\begin{vmatrix} a-\lambda & h & g \\ h & b-\lambda & f \\ g & f & c-\lambda \end{vmatrix}=0, \text{ or } \begin{vmatrix} 2-\lambda & 1 & 1 \\ 1 & 2-\lambda & 1 \\ 1 & 1 & 2-\lambda \end{vmatrix}=0$$

or $\lambda^3-6\lambda^2+9\lambda-4=0$ or $(\lambda-1)(\lambda-1)(\lambda-4)=0.$

$$\therefore \lambda=1, 1, 4.$$

Since two roots are equal, hence the given surface is a surface of revolution.

The centre (α, β, γ) is given by the equations

$$\left.\begin{aligned} \tfrac{1}{2}\frac{\partial F}{\partial \alpha}&=2\alpha+\beta+\gamma+3=0 \\ \tfrac{1}{2}\frac{\partial F}{\partial \beta}&=\alpha+2\beta+\gamma+1=0 \\ \tfrac{1}{2}\frac{\partial F}{\partial \gamma}&=\alpha+\beta+2\gamma+4=0 \end{aligned}\right\}.$$

Solving these equations, the centre is $(-1, 1, -2)$.

Also $\mu=-(u\alpha+v\beta+w\gamma+d)$

$$=-[3.(-1)+1.(1)+4.(-2)+8]=2.$$

Hence the reduced equation (*i.e.* the standard form) is

$$\lambda_1x^2+\lambda_2y^2+\lambda_3z^2=\mu, \text{ or } x^2+y^2+4z^2=2$$

or $$\frac{x^2}{2}+\frac{y^2}{2}+\frac{z^2}{\frac{1}{2}}=1$$

which represents an ellipsoid of revolution, the squares of whose semi-axes are 2, 2, $\frac{1}{2}$.

The d.c.'s l, m, n of the principal axis corresponding to $\lambda=4$ (which is non-repeated root) are given by

$$\frac{al+hm+gn}{l}=\frac{hl+bm+fn}{m}=\frac{gl+fm+cn}{n}=4$$

or $$\frac{2l+m+n}{l}=\frac{l+2m+n}{m}=\frac{l+m+2n}{n}=4$$

or $$-2l+m+n=0,\ l-2m+n=0,\ l+m-2n=0.$$

Solving, we have $\dfrac{l}{1}=\dfrac{m}{1}=\dfrac{n}{1}=\dfrac{1}{\sqrt{(1^2+1^2+1^2)}}=\dfrac{1}{\sqrt{(3)}}.$

Hence the equations of the axis of rotation *i.e.*, the equations of the principal axis corresponding to the non-repeated value *i.e.*

the equations of the straight line through the centre $(-1, 1, -2)$ and with d.c.'s proportional to 1, 1, 1 are given by

$$\frac{x+1}{1}=\frac{y-1}{1}=\frac{z+2}{1} \text{ i.e. } x+1=y-1=z+2.$$

Ex. 2. *Show that the equation* $x^2+y^2+z^2+yz+zx+xy=1$ *represents an ellipsoid the squares of whose semi-axes are* 2, 2, $\frac{1}{2}$. *Show also that the equation of its axis of revolution is* $x=y=z$.

Solution. Multiplying by 2, the given equation becomes

$$2x^2+2y^2+2z^2+2yz+2zx+2xy-2=0.$$

The discriminating cubic is

$$\begin{vmatrix} 2-\lambda & 1 & 1 \\ 1 & 2-\lambda & 1 \\ 1 & 1 & 2-\lambda \end{vmatrix}=0 \text{ or } \lambda^3-6\lambda^2+9\lambda-4=0$$
$$\text{or } (\lambda-1)^2(\lambda-4)=0.$$

$$\therefore \quad \lambda=1, 1, 4.$$

The centre (α, β, γ) is given by [as in Ex. 1 above]

$$2\alpha+\beta+\gamma=0,\ \alpha+2\beta+\gamma=0,\ \alpha+\beta+2\gamma=0.$$

Solving these equations, the centre is (0, 0, 0).

Also $\mu=-(u\alpha+v\beta+w\gamma+d)=2$, as $\alpha=\beta=\gamma=0$.

Hence the reduced equation (*i.e.* the equation in standard form) is

$$\lambda_1x^2+\lambda_2y^2+\lambda_3z^2=\mu \text{ or } x^2+y^2+4z^2=2$$

or
$$\frac{x^2}{2}+\frac{y^2}{2}+\frac{z^2}{\frac{1}{2}}=1$$

which represents an ellipsoid of revolution, the squares of whose semi-axes are 2, 2, $\frac{1}{2}$.

The d.c.'s l, m, n of the axis of revolution *i.e.* of the principal axis corresponding to the non-repeated root $\lambda=4$ are given by

$$\frac{al+hm+gn}{l}=\frac{hl+bm+fn}{m}=\frac{gl+fm+cn}{n}=4$$

or
$$\frac{2l+m+n}{l}=\frac{l+2m+n}{m}=\frac{l+m+2n}{n}=4$$

or
$$-2l+m+n=0,\ l-2m+n=0,\ l+m-2n=0.$$

Solving, we have $l=m=n=1$. $\therefore l=m=n=1/\sqrt{3}$.

$\therefore$ the equations of the axis of revolution are

$$\frac{x-0}{1}=\frac{y-0}{1}=\frac{z-0}{1} \text{ i.e. } x=y=z.$$

Ex. 3. *Show that the equation* $2y^2+4zx+2x-4y+6z+5=0$ *represents a right circular cone. Show also that the semi-vertical angle of this cone is* $\frac{1}{4}\pi$ *and that its axis is given by*

$$x+z+2=0,\ y=1.$$

Solution. Here $a=2, b=2, c=0, f=0, g=2, h=0, u=1,$
$v=-2, w=3, d=5.$

The discriminating cubic is

$$\begin{vmatrix} 0-\lambda & 0 & 2 \\ 0 & 2-\lambda & 0 \\ 2 & 0 & 0-\lambda \end{vmatrix}=0 \text{ or } (2-\lambda)(\lambda^2-4)=0.$$

$$\therefore\ \lambda=2, 2, -2.$$

Since two roots are equal, the given surface is a surface of revolution.

The centre (α, β, γ) is given by the equations

$$\left.\begin{aligned} 2\gamma+1=0, \\ 2\beta-2=0, \\ 2\alpha+3=0. \end{aligned}\right\}$$

Solving these equations, the centre is $(-\frac{3}{2}, 1, -\frac{1}{2})$.

Also $\mu=-(u\alpha+v\beta+w\gamma+d)$

or $\mu=-[1.(-\frac{3}{2})+(-2).1+3.(-\frac{1}{2})+5]=0.$

Hence the reduced equation is $\lambda_1x^2+\lambda_2y^2+\lambda_3z^2=\mu$

or $2x^2+2y^2-2z^2=0$

or $x^2+y^2=z^2$, or $x^2+y^2=z^2\tan^2 45°$ ...(1)

which represents a right circular cone whose semi-vertical angle is 45° and vertex is $(-\frac{3}{2}, 1, -\frac{1}{2})$.

The d.c.'s l, m, n of the axis are given by

$$\frac{al+hm+gn}{l}=\frac{hl+bm+fn}{m}=\frac{gl+fm+cn}{n}=-2$$

or $\dfrac{2n}{l}=\dfrac{2m}{m}=\dfrac{2l}{n}=-2$ or $\dfrac{n}{l}=-1,\ 2m=-2m$

or $n=-l,\ 4m=0$ or $n=-l,\ m=0$ or $\dfrac{l}{-1}=\dfrac{m}{0}=\dfrac{n}{1}$.

$\therefore$ the equations of the axis of the cone, which being a line through the vertex $(-\frac{3}{2}, 1, -\frac{1}{2})$, are given by

$$\frac{x+\frac{3}{2}}{-1}=\frac{y-1}{0}=\frac{z+\frac{1}{2}}{1} \text{ or } x+z+2=0,\ y=1.$$

Note. *If the surface is a cone then the centre of the surface is the vertex of the cone.*

Ex. 4. *Determine the nature of the surface*

$$\sqrt{x}+\sqrt{y}+\sqrt{z}=0.$$

Solution. Rewriting the given equation as

$$(\sqrt{x}+\sqrt{y})=-\sqrt{z}.$$

Squaring, $x+y+2\sqrt{(xy)}=z$

or $x+y-z=-2\sqrt{(xy)}.$

Squaring again, $x^2+y^2+z^2-2xy-2yz-2zx=0.$

Here $a=b=c=1, f=g=h=-1, u=v=w=d=0.$

The discriminating cubic is $\lambda^3-3\lambda^2+4=0$

or $(\lambda+1)(\lambda-2)^2=0. \quad \therefore \quad \lambda=2, 2, -1.$

The centre (α, β, γ) is given by the equations

$$\alpha-\beta-\gamma=0, \ -\alpha+\beta-\gamma=0, \ -\alpha-\beta+\gamma=0.$$

Solving these equations, the centre is (0, 0, 0).

Also $\mu=-(u\alpha+v\beta+w\gamma+d)=0.$

$\therefore$ The reduced equation is $2(x^2+y^2)-z^2=0$, which represents a right circular cone with its vertex as (0, 0, 0).

Proceeding as in Ex. 3 above the equations of the axis of the cone are $x=y=z.$

Some more examples for practice.

1. *Reduce the following equation to the standard form :*

$$x^2+2yz-4x+6y+2z=0.$$

[**Ans.** $x^2+y^2-z^2=10$, hyperboloid of revolution]

Discuss the nature of the following surfaces :

2. $xy+yz+zx=a^2.$

[**Ans.** Here $\lambda=2, -1, -1$; centre is (0, 0, 0). **Standard form** is $2x^2-y^2-z^2=2a^2$, which is a hyperboloid of revolution with its axis of revolution as the line $x=y=z$].

3. $2x^2+5y^2+10z^2+12yz+6zx+4xy-1=0.$

[**Ans.** Here $\lambda=1, 1, 15$; centre is (0, 0, 0). Reduced equation is $x^2+y^2+15z^2=1$, which is an ellipsoid of revolution, its axis of revolution being the line $\frac{x}{1}=\frac{y}{2}=\frac{z}{3}$].

4. $7x^2+y^2+z^2+16yz+8zx-8xy+2x+4y-40z-14=0.$

[**Ans.** Here $\lambda=9, 9, -9$; centre is (1, 2, 0). Reduced equation is $x^2+y^2-z^2=1$, which is a hyperboloid of revolution, its axis of revolution being the line $\frac{x-1}{1}=\frac{y-2}{2}=\frac{z-0}{-2}$].

5. $2y^2+4zx-6x-8y+2z+5=0$.

[**Ans.** Here $\lambda=-2, 2, 2$. The reduced equation is $x^2=y^2+z^2$, representing a cone with its vertex (*i.e.* centre) as the point $(-1, 2, \frac{3}{2})$, its axis of revolution parallel to the line

$$x+z=0,\ y=0].$$

Case III. When one root of the discriminating cubic is zero and $k \neq 0$.

SOLVED EXAMPLES (D)

Ex. 1. *Show that* $2x^2+2y^2+z^2+2yz-2zx-4xy+x+y=0$ *represents a paraboloid. Find the reduced equation, the co-ordinates of the vertex and the equations to the axis.*

Solution. Here $a=2, b=2, c=1, f=1, g=-1, h=-2, u=\frac{1}{2}$,

$$v=\tfrac{1}{2},\ w=0,\ d=0.$$

The discriminating cubic is

$$\begin{vmatrix} 2-\lambda & -2 & -1 \\ -2 & 2-\lambda & 1 \\ -1 & 1 & 1-\lambda \end{vmatrix}=0, \quad \text{or} \quad \lambda^3-5\lambda^2+2\lambda=0$$

or $\lambda(\lambda^2-5\lambda+2)=0$.

$\therefore$ $\lambda=0, \frac{1}{2}\{5 \pm \sqrt{(17)}\}$.

The d.c.'s l, m, n of the axis corresponding to $\lambda=0$ are given by [See equations (A) of § 15 (S_4)]

$$\left.\begin{array}{l} al+hm+gn=0 \\ hl+bm+fn=0 \\ gl+fm+cn=0 \end{array}\right] \quad \text{or} \quad \begin{array}{ll} 2l-2m-n=0 & \quad ...(1) \\ -2l+2m+n=0 & \quad ...(2) \\ -l+m+n=0. & \quad ...(3) \end{array}$$

Solving (1) and (3) [since (1) and (2) are identical], we have

$$\frac{l}{1}=\frac{m}{1}=\frac{n}{0}=\frac{1}{\sqrt{2}}. \quad ...(4)$$

$$\therefore \quad k=ul+vm+wn=\tfrac{1}{2}\left(\frac{1}{\sqrt{2}}\right)+\tfrac{1}{2}\left(\frac{1}{\sqrt{2}}\right)+0=\frac{1}{\sqrt{2}} \neq 0.$$

The reduced equation is $\lambda_1 x^2+\lambda_2 y^2+2kz=0$

or $$\tfrac{1}{2}(5+\sqrt{17})\,x^2+\tfrac{1}{2}(5-\sqrt{17})\,y^2+\sqrt{2}z=0. \quad ...(5)$$

Since $(5+\sqrt{17})$ and $(5-\sqrt{17})$ are both positive *i.e.* of the same sign, therefore (5) represents an elliptic paraboloid.

The vertex is given by [See S_4 of § 15] any two of

$$ax+hy+gz-lk+u=0,\ hx+by+fz-mk+v=0,$$
$$gx+fy+cz-nk+w=0$$

along with $k(lx+my+nz)+ux+vy+wz+d=0$

i.e. by $2x-2y-z-\frac{1}{2}+\frac{1}{2}=0,\ -2x+2y+z-\frac{1}{2}+\frac{1}{2}=0,$

$$-x+y+z-0+0=0$$

along with $\frac{1}{2}x+\frac{1}{2}y+0+\frac{1}{2}x+\frac{1}{2}y+0+0=0$

i.e. by $2x-2y-z=0,\ -x+y+z=0,\ x+y=0.$

These equations clearly give $x=y=z=0$.

Hence the vertex is (0, 0, 0).

The equations to the axis *i.e.* to the line through the vertex (0, 0, 0) and having its d.c.'s l, m, n given by the equations (4), are

$$\frac{x-0}{1}=\frac{y-0}{1}=\frac{z-0}{0} \quad \text{or} \quad x=y,\ z=0.$$

Ex. 2. *Prove that* $x^2+y^2+z^2-yz-zx-xy-3x-6y-9z+21=0$ *represents a paraboloid of revolution and find the co-ordinates of its focus. Also find the equations to its axis.*

Solution. Here $a=b=c=1, f=g=h=-\frac{1}{2}, u=-\frac{3}{2}, v=-3,$
$w=-\frac{9}{2}, d=21.$

The discriminating cubic is

$$\lambda^3-3\lambda^2+\tfrac{9}{4}\lambda=0, \quad \text{or} \quad \lambda\,(4\lambda^2-12\lambda+9)=0$$

or $$\lambda\,(2\lambda-3)^2=0. \quad \therefore \quad \lambda=0, \tfrac{3}{2}, \tfrac{3}{2}.$$

Since two roots are equal, the conicoid is a surface of revolution.

The d.c.'s l, m, n of the axis corresponding to $\lambda=0$ are given by

$$\left.\begin{aligned} al+hm+gn=0 \\ hl+bm+fn=0 \\ gl+fm+cn=0 \end{aligned}\right] \quad \text{or} \quad \begin{aligned} 2l-m-n&=0 &\quad ...(1) \\ -l+2m-n&=0 &\quad ...(2) \\ -l-m+2n&=0. &\quad ...(3) \end{aligned}$$

Solving (1) and (2),

$$\frac{l}{1+2}=\frac{m}{1+2}=\frac{n}{4-1} \quad \text{or} \quad \frac{l}{1}=\frac{m}{1}=\frac{n}{1}=\frac{1}{\sqrt{3}}. \qquad ...(4)$$

We have, $k=ul+vm+wn=-\frac{3}{2}\cdot\frac{1}{\sqrt{3}}-3.\frac{1}{\sqrt{3}}-\frac{9}{2}\cdot\frac{1}{\sqrt{3}}$
$=-3\sqrt{3}.$

$\therefore$ the reduced equation is $\lambda_1x^2+\lambda_2y^2+2kz=0$

or $\frac{3}{2}x^2+\frac{3}{2}y^2-6\sqrt{3}z=0$ or $x^2+y^2=4\sqrt{3}z.$ ...(5)

The vertex is given by any two of

$$ax+hy+gz-lk+u=0,\ hx+by+fz-mk+v=0,$$
$$gx+fy+cz-nk+w=0$$

along with $k\,(lx+my+nz)+ux+vy+wz+d=0$

i.e., by $x-\frac{1}{2}y-\frac{1}{2}z+3-\frac{3}{2}=0,\ -\frac{1}{2}x+y-\frac{1}{2}z+3-3=0,$
$-\frac{1}{2}x-\frac{1}{2}y+z+3-\frac{9}{2}=0$

along with $-3(x+y+z)-\frac{3}{2}x-3y-\frac{9}{2}z+21=0$

i.e., by $2x-y-z+3=0,\ -x+2y-z=0$

along with $3x+4y+5z-14=0.$

Solving these, we get $x=0,\ y=1,\ z=2.$

Hence the vertex is (0, 1, 2).

The equations to its axis are

$$\frac{x-0}{1/\sqrt{3}}=\frac{y-1}{1/\sqrt{3}}=\frac{z-2}{1/\sqrt{3}}=r \text{ (say)} \quad ...(6)$$

or $x=y-1=z-2.$

Now from (5) it follows that the length of the latus rectum is $4\sqrt{3}$, hence the focus lies on the axis (6) at a distance $\frac{1}{4}(4\sqrt{3})$ *i.e.* $\sqrt{3}$ from the vertex.

Therefore putting $r=\sqrt{3}$ in (6), the co-ordinates of the focus are given by

$$\left(\sqrt{3}.\frac{1}{\sqrt{3}},\ 1+\sqrt{3}.\frac{1}{\sqrt{3}},\ 2+\sqrt{3}.\frac{1}{\sqrt{3}}\right) \text{ i.e. } (1, 2, 3).$$

Ex. 3. *Reduce* $3z^2-6yz-6zx-7x-5y-6z+3=0$ *to standard form and find the nature of the surface represented by this equation.*

Solution. Here $a=b=0,\ c=3,\ f=-3,\ g=-3,\ h=0,\ u=-\frac{7}{2},$
$v=-\frac{5}{2},\ w=-3,\ d=3.$

The discriminating cubic is

$$\begin{vmatrix} -\lambda & 0 & -3 \\ 0 & -\lambda & -3 \\ -3 & -3 & 3-\lambda \end{vmatrix}=0 \quad \text{or} \quad \lambda^3-3\lambda^2-18\lambda=0$$

$$\text{or} \quad \lambda(\lambda-6)(\lambda+3)=0.$$

$$\therefore \quad \lambda=0,\ 6,\ -3.$$

The d.c.'s l, m, n of the axis corresponding to $\lambda=0$ are given by

$$\left.\begin{aligned} al+hm+gn=0 \\ hl+bm+fn=0 \\ gl+fm+cn=0 \end{aligned}\right] \quad \text{or} \quad \begin{aligned} -3n=0 \\ -3n=0 \\ -3l-3m+3n=0. \end{aligned}$$

Solving these, $n=0,\ l=-m,$

$$\therefore \quad \frac{l}{1}=\frac{m}{-1}=\frac{n}{0}=\frac{1}{\sqrt{2}}. \quad ...(1)$$

We have, $k=ul+vm+wn=-\frac{7}{2}\cdot\frac{1}{\sqrt{2}}+\frac{5}{2}\cdot\frac{1}{\sqrt{2}}+0=-\frac{1}{\sqrt{2}}.$

$\therefore$ the reduced equation is $\lambda_1x^2+\lambda_2y^2+2kz=0$

or $6x^2-3y^2+2\left(-\frac{1}{\sqrt{2}}\right)z=0$ or $6x^2-3y^2=\sqrt{2}z$. ...(2)

This represents a hyperbolic paraboloid, the latera recta of the principal parabolas *i.e.* of $6x^2=\sqrt{2}z$ and $3y^2=-\sqrt{2}z$ being $\frac{1}{6}\sqrt{2}$ and $\frac{1}{3}\sqrt{2}$ respectively.

Ex. 4. *Find the nature of the surface whose equation is* $3x^2+4y^2+9z^2+12yz+6zx+4xy+4x+6y+2z+1=0$.

Solution. Here $a=3, b=4, c=9, f=6, g=3, h=2, u=2,$
$v=3, w=1, d=1$.

The discriminating cubic is

$$\begin{vmatrix} 3-\lambda & 2 & 3 \\ 2 & 4-\lambda & 6 \\ 3 & 6 & 9-\lambda \end{vmatrix}=0 \text{ or } \lambda^3-16\lambda^2+26\lambda=0$$

or $\lambda(\lambda^2-16\lambda+26)=0$.

$\therefore \lambda=0, 8\pm\sqrt{(38)}$.

The d.c.'s l, m, n of the axis corresponding to $\lambda=0$ are given by

$$\left.\begin{array}{l} al+hm+gn=0 \\ hl+bm+fn=0 \\ gl+fm+cn=0 \end{array}\right] \text{ or } \begin{array}{ll} 3l+2m+3n=0 & ...(1) \\ 2l+4m+6n=0 & ...(2) \\ 3l+6m+9n=0. & ...(3) \end{array}$$

Solving (1) and (2), we get

$$\frac{l}{0}=\frac{m}{-12}=\frac{n}{8} \text{ or } \frac{l}{0}=\frac{m}{-3}=\frac{n}{2}=\frac{1}{\sqrt{(13)}} \quad ...(4)$$

$$\therefore \quad k=ul+vm+wn=0+3.\left(\frac{-3}{\sqrt{13}}\right)+1.\frac{2}{\sqrt{(13)}}=\frac{-7}{\sqrt{(13)}}.$$

$\therefore$ the reduced equation is $\lambda_1x^2+\lambda_2y^2+2kz=0$

or $(8+\sqrt{38})x^2+(8-\sqrt{38})y^2=\{14/\sqrt{(13)}\}z$

which represents an elliptic paraboloid, the latera recta of the principal parabolas *i.e.* of $(8+\sqrt{38})x^2=\{14/\sqrt{13})z$ and $(8-\sqrt{38})y^2=\{14/\sqrt{13}\}z$ being $\frac{14}{\sqrt{13}(8+\sqrt{38})}$ and $\frac{14}{\sqrt{13}(8-\sqrt{38})}$ respectively.

Some more examples for practice.

1. *Show that the surface whose equation is*

$$16x^2+4y^2+4z^2+4yz-8zx+8xy+4x+4y-16z-24=0$$

is an elliptic paraboloid. Find the co-ordinates of its vertex, and the equation to its axis.

[**Ans.** $\lambda=0, 18, 6$; reduced equation is $6x^2+18y^2-12z=0$

i.e. $x^2+3y^2=2z$. Vertex is $(-1, 2, -1)$; the equations of the axis are $\frac{x+1}{1}=\frac{y-2}{-2}=\frac{z+1}{2}$]

2. *Reduce the following equation of a hyperbolic paraboloid to standard form :*

$$5x^2-16y^2+5z^2+8yz-14zx+8xy+4x+20y+4z-24=0.$$

Find also the co-ordinates of the vertex and the equations to its axis.

[Ans. $\lambda=0, 12, -18$; reduced equation is $2x^2-3y^2+2z=0$, vertex is $(1, 1, 1)$; the equations of the axis are

$$\frac{x-1}{2}=\frac{y-1}{1}=\frac{z-1}{2}\Big].$$

3. *Show that the surface whose equation is*

$$4x^2-y^2-z^2+2yz-8x-4y+8z-2=0$$

is a hyperbolic paraboloid. Find its vertex and axis.

[Ans. $\lambda=0, 4, -2$; reduced equation is $2x^2-y^2+\sqrt{2}z=0$, which is a hyperbolic paraboloid. Vertex is $(1, -\frac{9}{4}, \frac{3}{4})$. The equations of the axis are $\frac{x-1}{0}=\frac{y+(9/4)}{1}=\frac{z-(3/4)}{1}$].

4. *Reduce to standard form the equation*

$6y^2-18yz-6zx+2xy-9x+5y-5z+2=0$. *Find its nature.*

[Ans. $\lambda=0, 26, -14$; reduced equation is $14x^2-26y^2=2\sqrt{(91)}\,z$, which is a hyperbolic paraboloid].

5. *Reduce to standard form the equation*

$$x^2-y^2+2yz-2zx-x-y+z=0.$$

[Ans. $3x^2-3y^2=z$, which is a hyperbolic paraboloid].

6. *Reduce to standard form the equation*

$4y^2+4z^2+4yz-2x-14y-22z+33=0$. *Give its vertex and axis.*

[Ans. $\lambda=0, 2, 6$; reduced equation is $x^2+3y^2=z$, which is an elliptic paraboloid. Vertex is $(1, \frac{1}{2}, \frac{5}{2})$; axis is the line

$$\frac{x-1}{1}=\frac{y-\frac{1}{2}}{0}=\frac{z-5/2}{0}\Big]$$

7. *Reduce to standard form the equation*

$2x^2+2y^2-4z^2-2yz-2zx-5xy-2x-2y+z=0$. *Give its vertex and axis.*

[**Ans.** $\lambda=0, 9, -9$; reduced equation is $3(x^2-y^2)=2z$, which is a hyperbolic paraboloid. Vertex is (0, 0, 0), axis is

$$\frac{x}{2}=\frac{y}{2}=\frac{z}{-1}\Big].$$

8. *Reduce to standard form the equation*

$$2x^2+20y^2+18z^2-12yz+12xy+22x+6y-2z-2=0.$$

[**Ans.** $\lambda=0, 14, 26$; reduced equation is $14x^2+26y^2=2\sqrt{(91)}\,z$, which is an elliptic paraboloid].

Case IV. When one root of the discriminating cubic is zero and $k=0$.

[*Also refer* S_5 *of* § 15]

SOLVED EXAMPLES (E)

Ex. 1. *Reduce the following equation to the standard form :*

$$2x^2+5y^2+2z^2-2yz+4zx-2xy+14x-16y+14z+26=0.$$

Solution. Here $a=2, b=5, c=2, f=-1, g=2, h=-1, u=7, v=-8, w=7, d=26.$

The discriminating cubic is

$$\begin{vmatrix} 2-\lambda & -1 & 2 \\ -1 & 5-\lambda & -1 \\ 2 & -1 & 2-\lambda \end{vmatrix}=0, \quad \text{or } \lambda^3-9\lambda^2+18\lambda=0$$
$$\text{or } \lambda(\lambda-3)(\lambda-6)=0.$$
$$\therefore \lambda=0, 3, 6.$$

The d.c.'s l, m, n of the axis corresponding to $\lambda=0$ are given by

$$\left.\begin{aligned} al+hm+gn&=0 \\ hl+bm+fn&=0 \\ gl+fm+cn&=0 \end{aligned}\right] \quad \text{or} \quad \begin{aligned} 2l-m+2n&=0 && \dots(1) \\ -l+5m-n&=0 && \dots(2) \\ 2l-m+2n&=0. && \dots(3) \end{aligned}$$

Solving (1) and (2), $\dfrac{l}{-9}=\dfrac{m}{0}=\dfrac{n}{9}$ or $\dfrac{l}{-1}=\dfrac{m}{0}=\dfrac{n}{1}=\dfrac{1}{\sqrt{2}}$. ...(4)

$$\therefore \quad k=ul+vm+wn=7.\left(-\frac{1}{\sqrt{2}}\right)-8.(0)+7.\left(\frac{1}{\sqrt{2}}\right)=0.$$

Since $k=0$, the surface has no unique centre. It has a line of centres which is given by any two of the following equations ;

$$\tfrac{1}{2}\frac{\partial F}{\partial x}=2x-y+2z+7=0 \qquad \dots(5)$$

$$\tfrac{1}{2}\frac{\partial F}{\partial y}=-x+5y-z-8=0 \qquad \dots(6)$$

$$\tfrac{1}{2}\frac{\partial F}{\partial z}=2x-y+2z+7=0. \qquad \dots(7)$$

Since the equations (5) and (7) are the same, therefore there are only two independent equations [namely (5) and (6)] giving the centre.

Assuming $z=0$, the equations (5) and (6) become

$2x-y+7=0$ and $-x+5y-8=0$. $\therefore$ $x=-3, y=1$.

$\therefore$ any point (α, β, γ) on the line of centres is $(-3, 1, 0)$.

$\therefore$ $\mu=-(u\alpha+v\beta+w\gamma+d)=-[7.(-3)-8.(1)+0+26]=3$.

$\therefore$ the reduced equation is $\lambda_1 x^2+\lambda_2 y^2=\mu$

or $3x^2+6y^2=3$ or $x^2+2y^2=1$

which is an elliptic cylinder.

The equations to the axis. The axis of the surface being the line of centres, its equations in non-symmetrical form are given by the equations (5) and (6) *i.e.* by

$$2x-y+2z+7=0=x-5y+z+8.$$

Its symmetrical form can be obtained from these equations as usual. The symmetrical form of the axis can be written directly as

$$\frac{x+3}{-1}=\frac{y-1}{0}=\frac{z-0}{1}$$

because the axis is passing through any centre $(-3, 1, 0)$ and has d.c.'s as given by (4).

Ex. 2. *Reduce to its principal axes*

$$2y^2-2yz+2zx-2xy-x-2y+3z-2=0.$$

Find also the equations to its axis.

Solution. Here $a=0$, $b=2$, $c=0$, $f=-1$, $g=1$, $h=-1$,

$u=-\frac{1}{2}$, $v=-1$, $w=\frac{3}{2}$, $d=-2$.

The discriminating cubic is

$$\begin{vmatrix} -\lambda & -1 & 1 \\ -1 & 2-\lambda & -1 \\ 1 & -1 & -\lambda \end{vmatrix}=0 \quad \text{or} \quad \lambda^3-2\lambda^2-3\lambda=0$$

or $\lambda(\lambda-3)(\lambda+1)=0$.

$\therefore$ $\lambda=0, 3, -1$.

The d.c.'s l, m, n, of the axis corresponding to $\lambda=0$ are given by

$$\left.\begin{aligned} al+hm+gn&=0 \\ hl+bm+fn&=0 \\ gl+fm+cn&=0 \end{aligned}\right\} \quad \text{or} \quad \begin{aligned} -m+n&=0 && \quad ...(1) \\ -l+2m-n&=0 && \quad ...(2) \\ l-m&=0. && \quad ...(3) \end{aligned}$$

Solving (1) and (3), $\dfrac{l}{1}=\dfrac{m}{1}=\dfrac{n}{1}=\dfrac{1}{\sqrt{3}}$. ...(4)

$$\therefore \quad k=ul+vm+wn=-\tfrac{1}{2}.\frac{1}{\sqrt{3}}-1.\frac{1}{\sqrt{3}}+\tfrac{3}{2}.\frac{1}{\sqrt{3}}=0.$$

Since $k=0$, the surface has no unique centre. It has a line of centres given by any two of the following equations :

$$\frac{\partial F}{\partial x}=-2y+2z-1=0 \quad ..(5)$$

$$\frac{\partial F}{\partial y}=-2x+4y-2z-2=0 \quad ...(6)$$

$$\frac{\partial F}{\partial z}=2x-2y+3=0$$

or $$-2x+2y-3=0. \quad ...(7)$$

If we add the equations (5) and (6) we get the equation (7) and hence there are only two independent equations.

Taking $z=0$, from (5) and (6) we get $y=-\frac{1}{2}$, $x=-2$.

$\therefore$ any centre (α, β, γ) on the line of centres is $(-2, -\frac{1}{2}, 0)$.

$$\therefore \quad \mu=-(u\alpha+v\beta+w\gamma+d)$$

$$=-[-\tfrac{1}{2}(-2)+(-1)(-\tfrac{1}{2})+0-2]=\tfrac{1}{2}.$$

The reduced equation is $\lambda_1 x^2+\lambda_2 y^2=\mu$

or $$3x^2-y^2=\tfrac{1}{2} \quad \text{or} \quad 6x^2-2y^2=1$$

which respresents a hyperbolic cylinder. Its axis, being a line through any centre $(-2, -\frac{1}{2}, 0)$ and having d.c.'s l, m, n as given by (4), has its equations given by

$$\frac{x+2}{1}=\frac{y+\frac{1}{2}}{1}=\frac{z}{1}.$$

Ex. 3. *Prove that*

$$5x^2+5y^2+8z^2+8yz+8zx-2xy+12x-12y+6=0$$

represents a cylinder whose cross section is an ellipse of eccentricity $1/\sqrt{2}$ *and find the equations to its axis.*

Solution. Here $a=5, b=5, c=8, f=4, g=4, h=-1,$

$$u=6, v=-6, w=0, d=6.$$

The discriminating cubic is

$$\begin{vmatrix} 5-\lambda & -1 & 4 \\ -1 & 5-\lambda & 4 \\ 4 & 4 & 8-\lambda \end{vmatrix}=0, \quad \text{or} \quad \lambda^3-18\lambda^2+72\lambda=0$$

$$\text{or} \quad \lambda(\lambda-12)(\lambda-6)=0.$$

$$\therefore \quad \lambda=0, 12, 6.$$

The d.c.'s l, m, n of the axis corresponding to $\lambda=0$ are given by

$$\left.\begin{aligned} al+hm+gn=0 \\ hl+bm+fn=0 \\ gl+fm+cn=0 \end{aligned}\right\} \text{ or } \begin{aligned} 5l-m+4n=0 \quad &...(1) \\ -l+5m+4n=0 \quad &..(2) \\ 4l+4m+8n=0. \quad &...(3) \end{aligned}$$

Solving (1) and (2),

$$\frac{l}{-24}=\frac{m}{-24}=\frac{n}{24} \text{ or } \frac{l}{1}=\frac{m}{1}=\frac{n}{-1}=\frac{1}{\sqrt{3}}. \qquad ...(4)$$

$\therefore \quad k=ul+vm+wn=(6-6+0)/\sqrt{3}=0.$

Since $k=0$, the given surface has no unique centre.

It has a line of centres given by any two of the following equations :

$$\tfrac{1}{2}\frac{\partial F}{\partial x}=5x-y+4z+6=0 \qquad ...(5)$$

$$\tfrac{1}{2}\frac{\partial F}{\partial y}=-x+5y+4z-6=0 \qquad ...(6)$$

$$\tfrac{1}{2}\frac{\partial F}{\partial y}=4x+4y+8z=0 \qquad ..(7)$$

The sum of (5) and (6) gives (7). Hence there are only two independent equations.

Assuming $z=0$, from (5) and (6), we get $x=-1, y=1$.

$\therefore$ any centre $(\alpha\ \beta, \gamma)$ on the line of centres is $(-1, 1, 0)$.

$\therefore \quad \mu=-(u\alpha+v\beta+w\gamma+d)=-[6(-1)+(-6).1+0+6]=6.$

Hence the reduced equation is $\lambda_1 x^2+\lambda_2 y^2=\mu$

or $\qquad 6x^2+12y^2=6$ or $\dfrac{x^2}{1}+\dfrac{y^2}{\frac{1}{2}}=1 \qquad ...(8)$

which represents an elliptic cylinder with its generators parallel to z-axis.

The cross section of (8) by the plane $z=0$ is the ellipse

$$\frac{x^2}{1}+\frac{y^2}{\frac{1}{2}}=1,\ z=0.$$

Its eccentricity e is given by

$\tfrac{1}{2}=1\,(1-e^2) \qquad [\because\ b^2=a^2(1-e^2),\ a^2=1,\ b^2=\tfrac{1}{2}]$

or $\qquad e=1/\sqrt{2}.$

The equations of the axis of cylinder are given by

$$\frac{x+1}{1}=\frac{y-1}{1}=\frac{z}{-1}$$

because the axis is a line through any centre $(-1, 1, 0)$ and having its d.c.'s l, m, n given by the equations (4).

Also (as explained to Ex. 1 above) the equations of the axis given by the equations giving the line of centres namely the equations $\qquad 5x-y+4z+6=0=-x+5y+4z-6.$

Ex. 4. *Discuss the nature of the surface*

$$(cy-bz)^2+(az-cx)^2+(bx-ay)^2=1.$$

Solution. The equation of the given surface may be rewritten as

$$x^2(b^2+c^2)+y^2(c^2+a^2)+z^2(a^2+b^2)-2bcyz-2cazx$$
$$-2abxy-1=0. \quad \ldots(1)$$

Here $a=b^2+c^2$, $b=c^2+a^2$, $c=a^2+b^2$, $f=-bc$, $g=-ca$,
$h=-ab$, $u=v=w=0$, $d=-1$.

The discriminating cubic is

$$\begin{vmatrix} (b^2+c^2)-\lambda & -ab & -ca \\ -ab & (c^2+a^2)-\lambda & -bc \\ -ca & -bc & (a^2+b^2)-\lambda \end{vmatrix}=0.$$

Simplifying, we get

$$\lambda\,[\lambda^2-2\lambda\,(a^2+b^2+c^2)+(a^2+b^2+c^2)^2]=0$$

or
$$\lambda\,[\lambda-(a^2+b^2+c^2)]^2=0.$$
$$\therefore\quad \lambda=0,\ (a^2+b^2+c^2),\ (a^2+b^2+c^2).$$

Since two roots of the discriminating cubic are equal, the given quadric is a surface of revolution.

The d.c.'s l, m, n of the axis corresponding to $\lambda=0$ are given by

$$(b^2+c^2)\,l-abm-can=0 \quad \ldots(1)$$
$$-abl+(c^2+a^2)\,m-bcn=0 \quad \ldots(2)$$
$$-cal-bcm+(a^2+b^2)\,n=0. \quad (3)$$

Solving (1) and (2), we get

$$\frac{l}{ab^2c+ca\,(c^2+a^2)}=\frac{m}{a^2bc+bc\,(b^2+c^2)}=\frac{n}{(b^2+c^2)\,(c^2+a^2)-a^2b^2}$$

or
$$\frac{l}{ac\,(b^2+c^2+a^2)}=\frac{m}{bc\,(a^2+b^2+c^2)}=\frac{n}{c^2\,(a^2+b^2+c^2)}$$

or
$$\frac{l}{a}=\frac{m}{b}=\frac{n}{c}=\frac{1}{\sqrt{(a^2+b^2+c^2)}}. \quad \ldots(4)$$

$$\therefore\quad k=ul+vm+wn=0.$$

Since $k=0$, the given surface has no unique centre. It has a line of centres given by any two of the following equations:

$$\tfrac{1}{2}\frac{\partial F}{\partial x}=(b^2+c^2)\,x-aby-caz=0 \quad \ldots(5)$$
$$\tfrac{1}{2}\frac{\partial F}{\partial y}=-abx+(c^2+a^2)\,y-bcz=0 \quad \ldots(6)$$
$$\tfrac{1}{2}\frac{\partial F}{\partial z}=-cax-bcy+(a^2+b^2)\,z=0. \quad \ldots(7)$$

These give only two independent equations.

Assuming $z=0$, (5) and (6) clearly give $x=0$, $y=0$.

$\therefore$ any centre (α, β, γ) on the line of centres is $(0, 0, 0)$.

$\therefore \quad \mu=-(u\alpha+v\beta+w\gamma+d)=-[0+0+0-1]=1.$

Hence the reduced equation is $\lambda_1 x^2+\lambda_2 y^2=\mu$

or $$(a^2+b^2+c^2)(x^2+y^2)=1$$

which represents a right circular cylinder with its generators parallel to z-axis, and having the base radius$=1/\sqrt{(a^2+b^2+c^2)}$.

The equations of the axis of the cylinder (as explained in Ex. 1 above) are $\dfrac{x-0}{a}=\dfrac{y-0}{b}=\dfrac{z-0}{c}$, or $\dfrac{x}{a}=\dfrac{y}{b}=\dfrac{z}{c}$.

Ex. 5. *Prove that the equation*

$$5x^2-4y^2+5z^2+4yz-14zx+4xy+16x+16y-32z+8=0$$

represents a pair of planes which pass through the line $x+3=y=z+1$. *Find also the angle between the planes.*

Solution. Here $a=5$, $b=-4$, $c=5$, $f=2$, $g=-7$, $h=2$,
$u=8$, $v=8$, $w=-16$, $d=8$.

The discriminating cubic is

$$\begin{vmatrix} 5-\lambda & 2 & -7 \\ 2 & -4-\lambda & 2 \\ -7 & 2 & 5-\lambda \end{vmatrix}=0, \text{ or } \lambda^3-6\lambda^2-72\lambda=0$$

or $\lambda(\lambda-12)(\lambda+6)=0$.

$\therefore \lambda=0, 12, -6.$

The d.c.'s l, m, n of the axis corresponding to $\lambda=0$ are given by

$$5l+2m-7n=0 \quad \text{...(1)}$$

$$2l\ \ 4m+2n=0 \quad \text{...(2)}$$

$$-7l+2m+5n=0. \quad \text{...(3)}$$

Solving (1) and (2), $\dfrac{l}{-24}=\dfrac{m}{-24}=\dfrac{n}{-24}$ or $\dfrac{l}{1}=\dfrac{m}{1}=\dfrac{n}{1}=\dfrac{1}{\sqrt{3}}$

$\therefore \quad k=ul+vm+wn=(8+8-16)/\sqrt{3}=0.$

Since $k=0$, the given surface has no unique centre. It has a line of centres given by any two of the following equations:

$$\tfrac{1}{2}\frac{\partial F}{\partial x}=5x+2y-7z+8=0 \quad \text{...(5)}$$

$$\tfrac{1}{2}\frac{\partial F}{\partial y}=2x-4y+2z+8=0 \quad \text{...(6)}$$

$$\tfrac{1}{2}\frac{\partial F}{\partial z}=-7x+2y+5z-16=0$$

or $$7x-2y-5z+16=0. \quad \text{...(7)}$$

Adding (5) and (6), we get (7). Hence there are only two independent equations giving centres.

Assuming $y=0$, (5) and (6) give $x=-3$, $z=-1$.

$\therefore$ any centre (α, β, γ) on the line of centres is $(-3, 0, -1)$.

$\therefore$ $\mu=-(u\alpha+v\beta+w\gamma+d)=-[8(-3)+0-16(-1)+8]=0.$

Hence the reduced equation is $\lambda_1 x^2+\lambda_2 y^2=\mu$

or $$12x^2-6y^2=0 \quad \text{or} \quad y^2=2x^2 \qquad ..(8)$$

which represents a pair of intersecting planes, the line of intersection being $\dfrac{x+3}{1}=\dfrac{y-0}{1}=\dfrac{z+1}{1}$, or $x+3=y=z+1$. ...(9)

Now the equations of the planes represented by (8) are

$$y=\pm\sqrt{2}x$$

or $$\sqrt{2}x+y=0 \text{ and } \sqrt{2}x-y=0.$$

If θ be the angle between these planes, then

$$\cos\theta=\frac{\sqrt{2}.\sqrt{2}+(1)(-1)}{\sqrt{\{(\sqrt{2})^2+(1)^2\}}\sqrt{\{(\sqrt{2})^2+(-1)^2\}}}=\frac{1}{3}.$$

$\therefore$ $$\tan\theta=2\sqrt{2}, \text{ or } \theta=\tan^{-1}(2\sqrt{2}).$$

Some more examples for practice.

1. *Reduce to standard form and find the axis of*
$$26x^2+20y^2+10z^2-4yz-16zx-36xy+52x-36y-16z+25=0.$$
[**Ans.** $\lambda=0, 14, 42$; line of centres passes through $(1, 0, 0)$. Standard form is $14x^2+42y^2=1$ which is an elliptic cylinder. Axis is given by $x+1=y=z$].

2. *Reduce* $x^2-y^2+4yz+4zx-6x-2y-8z+5=0$. *Give the equations of its axis.*

[**Ans.** $\lambda=0, 3, -3$; the line of centres passes through $(1, 1, 1)$. Standard form is $x^2-y^2=1$, which is a hyperbolic cylinder. The axis is $\dfrac{x-1}{-2}=\dfrac{y-1}{2}=\dfrac{z-1}{1}$].

3. *Reduce* $x^2+6y^2-z^2-yz+5xy+2x+5y=0$.

[**Ans.** $\lambda=0, 6\pm\sqrt{(66)}$; the line of centres passes through $(-1, 0, 0)$. The reduced equation is
$$\{3+\sqrt{(33/2)}\}x^2-\{\sqrt{(33/2)}-3\}y^2=1,$$
which is a hyperbolic cylinder.]

4. *Reduce* $3x^2-24y^2+8z^2+16yz-10zx-14xy+22y+?z-4=0$.

[**Ans.** $\lambda=0, 14, -27$; the line of centres passes through $\left(0, \dfrac{5}{10}, \dfrac{-7}{16}\right)$. The reduced equation is $14x^2-27y^2=1$, which is a hyperbolic cylinder.]

5. *Reduce to standard form*

$$4x^2+3y^2+2z^2+4yz-4xy-4x-6y-8z+6=0.$$

Also find the equations to its axis.

[Ans. $\lambda=0, 3, 6$; the line of centres passes through (1, 1, 1).

The reduced equation is $x^2+2y^2=1$, which is an elliptic cylinder.

The equations to its axis are $\frac{x-1}{1}=\frac{y-1}{2}=\frac{z-1}{-2}$]

Case V. When the SECOND DEGREE TERMS in the equation F (x, y, z)=0 form a PERFECT SQUARE.

We have $F(x, y, z)\equiv ax^2+by^2+cz^2+2fyz+2gzx+2hxy$

$$+2ux+2vy+2wz+d=0. \quad ...(1)$$

Since the terms of second degree form a perfect square, therefore $A=B=C=0$ *i.e.* $f^2=bc$, $g^2=ca$ and $h^2=ab$. Hence the equation (1) may be rewritten as

$$F(x, y, z)\equiv(\sqrt{a}x+\sqrt{b}y+\sqrt{c}z)^2+2ux+2vy+2wz+d=0. \quad ...(2)$$

Now there arise the following two cases.

Case (i). If $\frac{u}{\sqrt{a}}=\frac{v}{\sqrt{b}}=\frac{w}{\sqrt{c}}=k$, then the equation (2) becomes

$$(\sqrt{a}x+\sqrt{b}y+\sqrt{c}z)^2+2k(\sqrt{a}x+\sqrt{b}y+\sqrt{c}z)+d=0. \quad ...(3)$$

The equation (3) is a quadratic equation in $(\sqrt{a}x+\sqrt{b}y+\sqrt{c}z)$ and hence represents a pair of parallel planes.

Case (ii). If $\frac{u}{\sqrt{a}}\neq\frac{v}{\sqrt{b}}$, then we rewrite the equation (2) as

$$(\sqrt{a}x+\sqrt{b}y+\sqrt{c}z+\lambda)^2=2x(\lambda\sqrt{a}-u)+2y(\lambda\sqrt{b}-v)$$
$$+2z(\lambda\sqrt{c}-w)+\lambda^2-d. \quad ...(4)$$

Now we choose λ such that the planes

$$\alpha\equiv\sqrt{a}x+\sqrt{b}y+\sqrt{c}z+\lambda=0 \quad ...(5)$$

and $\beta\equiv2x(\lambda\sqrt{a}-u)+2y(\lambda\sqrt{b}-v)+2z(\lambda\sqrt{c}-w)+\lambda^2-d=0$ ...(6)

are at right angles. Hence we have

$$2\sqrt{a}(\lambda\sqrt{a}-v)+2\sqrt{b}(\lambda\sqrt{b}-v)+2\sqrt{c}(\lambda\sqrt{c}-w)=0$$

or $$\lambda=\frac{u\sqrt{a}+v\sqrt{b}+w\sqrt{c}}{a+b+c}.$$

Now we take the rectangular coordinate axes such that the planes $\alpha=0$ and $\beta=0$ become the new coordinate planes $X=0$ and $Y=0$ respectively, so that

$$X=\frac{\alpha}{\sqrt{(a+b+c)}} \text{ and } Y=\frac{\beta}{2\sqrt{[\Sigma(\lambda\sqrt{a}-u)^2]}}.$$

$\therefore$ the equation (4) reduces to

$$X^2(a+b+c)=2Y\sqrt{[\Sigma\{\lambda\sqrt{a}-u\}^2]}. \quad ...(7)$$

But, by Lagrange's identity.

$(a+b+c)\,[\Sigma\,(\lambda\sqrt{a}-u)^2]-[\Sigma\,\{\sqrt{a}(\lambda\sqrt{a}-u)\}]^2=\Sigma\,(v\sqrt{c}-w\sqrt{b})^2.$

∴ The equation (7) reduces to

$$X^2=\frac{2Y\,\{\Sigma\,(v\sqrt{c}-w\sqrt{b})^2\}^{1/2}}{(a+b+c)^{3/2}} \quad \ldots(8)$$

The equation (8) is the required reduced equation.

SOLVED EXAMPLES (F)

Ex. 1. *Show how to reduce the second degree equation in x, y, z when the second degree terms form a perfect square.*

Solution. See Case V above.

Ex. 2. *Reduce the surface*

$$36x^2+4y^2+z^2-4yz-12zx+24xy+4x+16y-26z-3=0$$

to the standard form and find the latus rectum of a normal section.

Solution. Here $a=36,\ b=4,\ c=1,\ f=-2,\ g=-6,\ h=12.$

Clearly $bc=f^2,\ ca=g^2,\ ab=h^2$ *i.e.* $A=B=C=0$. Hence the second degree terms form a perfect square.

The given equation may be rewritten as

$$(6x+2y-z)^2=-4x-16y+26z+3$$

or $(6x+2y-z+\lambda)^2=x\,(12\lambda-4)+y\,(4\lambda-16)+z\,(-2\lambda+26)+3+\lambda^2.$ ...(1)

Now we choose λ such that the two planes

$$6x+2y-z+\lambda=0 \quad \ldots(2)$$

and $x\,(12\lambda-4)+y\,(4\lambda-16)+z\,(-2\lambda+26)+3+\lambda^2=0$ ...(3)

are at right angles. Hence we have

$$6\,(12\lambda-4)+2\,(4\lambda-16)-1.(-2\lambda+26)=0, \quad \text{or } \lambda=1.$$

∴ the given equation *i.e.* the equation (1) becomes

$$(6x+2y-z+1)^2=8x-12y+24z+4$$

or $$\left\{\frac{(6x+2y-z+1)}{\sqrt{(6^2+2^2+1)}}\right\}^2=\frac{4\times 7}{41}\,\frac{(2x-3y+6z+1)}{\sqrt{(2^2+3^2+6^2)}}. \quad \ldots(4)$$

Now taking the rectangular axes with the planes

$$6x+2y-z+1=0 \text{ and } 2x-3y+6z+1=0$$

as the new co-ordinate planes $X=0$ and $Y=0$ respectively, the given equation *i.e.* the equation (4) reduces to

$$X^2=\tfrac{28}{41}Y \quad \ldots(5)$$

which represents a parabolic cylinder with its generators parallel to Z-axis. The normal section of (5) with the plane $Z=0$ is the parabola $X^2=\frac{28}{41}\,Y,\ Z=0.$

The length of the latus rectum of this normal section is $\frac{28}{41}$.

Ex. 3. *Show that the equation*

$$x^2+4y^2+9z^2+12yz+6zx+4xy-54x-52y+62z+113=0$$

represents a parabolic cylinder and that the foci of normal parabolic sections lie on the line

$$x+2y+3z+1=0=x+y-z-5=0.$$

Solution. Here $a=1$, $b=4$, $c=9$, $f=6$, $g=3$, $h=2$.

Clearly $bc=f^2$, $ca=g^2$, $ab=h^2$, *i.e.* $A=B=C=0$. Hence the second degree terms form a perfect square.

The given equation may be rewritten as

$$(x+2y+3z)^2=54x+52y-62z-113$$

or $(x+2y+3z+\lambda)^2=x(54+2\lambda)+y(52+4\lambda)+z(6\lambda-62)+\lambda^2-113.$ ...(1)

Now we choose λ such that the two planes

$$x+2y+3z+\lambda=0 \qquad ...(2)$$

and $\quad x(54+2\lambda)+y(52+4\lambda)+z(6\lambda-62)+\lambda^2-113=0$ ...(3)

are at right angles. Hence we have

$$1.(54+2\lambda)+2.(52+4\lambda)+3.(6\lambda-62)=0, \text{ or } \lambda=1.$$

$\therefore$ the given equation *i.e.* the equation (1) becomes

$$(x+2y+3z+1)^2=56x+56y-56z-112$$

$$=56(x+y-z-2)$$

or $$\left\{\frac{x+2y+3z+1}{\sqrt{(1^2+2^2+3^2)}}\right\}^2=\frac{56\sqrt{3}}{14}\left\{\frac{x+y-z-2}{\sqrt{(1^2+1^2+1^2)}}\right\}. \qquad ...(4)$$

Now taking the rectangular axes with the planes

$$x+2y+3z+1=0 \quad \text{and} \quad x+y-z-2=0$$

as the new co-ordinate planes $Y=0$ and $X=0$ respectively, the given equation *i.e.* the equation (4) reduces to

$$Y^2=4\sqrt{3}\,X \qquad ...(5)$$

which represents a parabolic cylinder. The vertices of the normal parabolic sections of this cylinder lie on the line

$$x+2y+3z+1=0,\ x+y-z-2=0$$

the second plane namely $x+y-z-2=0$ ...(6)

which is given by $X=0$ being the tangent plane touching the cylinder along the vertices.

Now we know that the plane on which lie the foci of the normal parabolic sections of the cylinder is parallel to the tangent plane (6) and is at a distance $\frac{1}{4}\times$(latus rectum) *i.e.*, $\frac{1}{4}\times(4\sqrt{3})$ *i.e.* $\sqrt{3}$ from it.

Therefore, let the plane through the foci *i.e.* parallel to the tangent plane (6) be $\quad x+y-z+k=0.$ ...(7)

Any point on the tangent plane (6) is (0, 2, 0).

$$\therefore\quad -\sqrt{3}=\frac{2+k}{\sqrt{(1^2+1^2+1^2)}}\quad \text{or}\quad k=-5.$$

[Note that the negative sign is taken as both the planes are on the same side of the origin and the constant term is $-$ve in the tangent plane (6)].

Putting this value of k in (7), the line on which lie the foci is given by

$$x+2y+3z+1=0 \text{ (the plane through the axis)}$$

and $$x+y-z-5=0.$$

Ex. 4. *Reduce the equation*

$$4x^2+9y^2+36z^2-36yz+24zx-12xy-10x+15y-30z+6=0.$$

Solution. Here $a=4, b=9, c=36, f=-18, g=12, h=-6$.

Clearly $bc=f^2$, $ca=g^2$, $ab=h^2$ *i.e.* $A=B=C=0$. Hence the terms of second degree form a perfect square.

The given equation may be rewritten as

$$(2x-3y+6z)^2=10x-15y+30z-6$$
$$=5\,(2x-3y+6z)-6$$

or $$(2x-3y+6z)^2-5\,(2x-3y+6z)+6=0 \qquad (1)$$

or $$(2x-3y+6z)^2-2\,(2x-3y+6z)-3\,(2x-3y+6z)+6=0$$

or $$(2x-3y+6z-3)\,(2x-3y+6z-2)=0 \qquad \ldots(2)$$

which represents a pair of parallel planes given by

$$2x-3y+6z-2=0 \qquad \ldots(3)$$

and $$2x-3y+6z-3=0. \qquad \ldots(4)$$

Now choosing $2x-3y+6z=0$ as the new co-ordinate plane $X=0$, the equation (1) becomes

$$49\left\{\frac{2x-3y+6z}{\sqrt{(2^2+3^2+6^2)}}\right\}^2-5\times 7\left\{\frac{2x-3y+6z}{\sqrt{(2^2+3^2+6^2)}}\right\}+6=0$$

or $$49X^2-35X+6=0.$$

This is the required reduced form.

Ex. 5. *Reduce the equation*

$$(3x-4y+z)^2=26\,(x+y+z).$$

Solution. Here the planes $3x-4y+z=0$ and $x+y+z=0$ are at right angles because $3.1+(-4).1+1.1=0$.

Hence taking the planes $3x-4y+z=0$ and $x+y+z=0$ as the planes $Y=0$ and $X=0$, the given equation becomes

$$26\left\{\frac{3x-4y+z}{\sqrt{(3^2+4^2+1^2)}}\right\}^2=26\sqrt{3}\left\{\frac{x+y+z}{\sqrt{(1^2+1^2+1^2)}}\right\}$$

or $$Y^2=\sqrt{3}\,X$$

which represents a parabolic cylinder, the latus rectum of whose normal section is $\sqrt{3}$.

Some more examples for practice.

1. *Reduce the equation*

$$(3x-4y+z)^2+9x-12y+3z-10=0.$$

[**Ans.** Pair of parallel planes.

Write the given equation as

$$(3x-4y+z)^2+3\,(3x-4y+z)-10=0$$

or $$(3x-4y+z-2)\,(3x-4y+z+5)=0.$$

Choose $3x-4y+z=0$ as the plane $X=0$, so that the reduced equation is $26X^2+3\sqrt{(26)}\,X-10=0.$]

2. *Reduce* $(3x+4y+z)^2+16x-27y+18=0.$

[**Ans.** $26Y^2=7X$, which is a parabolic cylinder.]

3. *Reduce*

$$9x^2+4y^2+4z^2+8yz+12zx+12zy+4x+y+10z+1=0.$$

[**Ans.** $Y^2=(7/17)\,X$, which is a parabolic cylinder.]

4. *Reduce* $(2x-2y-3z)^2+19x-34y+50=0.$

[**Ans.** $Y^2=(11/17)\,X$, which is a parabolic cylinder.]

5. *Reduce* $4x^2+y^2+4z^2-4yz+?zx-4xy+2x-4y+5z+1=0.$

[**Ans.** $Y^2=\frac{1}{3}X$, which is a parabolic cylinder. The length of the latus rectum of a normal section is $\frac{1}{3}$].

SURFACE OF REVOLUTION

§ 16. *To find the condition that a general equation of second degree namely $F(x, y, z)=0$, may represent a surface of revolution.*

We have

$$F(x, y, z)\equiv ax^2+by^2+cz^2+2fyz+2gzx+2hxy$$
$$+2ux+2vy+2wz+d=0$$

or $$F(x, y, z)=f(x, y, z)+2ux+2vy+2wz+d=0. \qquad ...(1)$$

We have already seen in Case II (above) that for a surface of revolution two roots of the discriminating cubic should be equal (but different from zero). We know [See § 13 (A)] that by rotation of axes the expression $f\,(x, y, z)$ transforms to $\lambda_1x^2+\lambda_2y^2+\lambda_3z^2$ where $\lambda_1, \lambda_2, \lambda_3$ are the roots of the discriminating cubic.

Again the expression $x^2+y^2+z^2$ remains unchanged by a rotation of the axes through the same origin.

Hence the expression

$$f(x, y, z)-\lambda\,(x^2+y^2+z^2) \qquad ...(2)$$

can be transformed to $\lambda_1x^2+\lambda_1y^2+\lambda_3z^2-\lambda\,(x^2+y^2+z^2)$ ...(3)

because for a surface of revolution two roots of the discriminating cubic are equal.

Clearly (3) becomes a perfect square if $\lambda=\lambda_1$.

Hence it follows that if the equation (1) represents a surface of revolution, then for some suitable value of λ the expression (2) can be made a perfect square. Hence in view of (2), we have

$$ax^2+by^2+cz^2+2fyz+2gzx+2hxy-\lambda(x^2+y^2+z^2)$$
$$\equiv\{\sqrt{(a-\lambda)}\,x+\sqrt{(b-\lambda)}\,y+\sqrt{(c-\lambda)}\,z\}^2 \text{ (say).}$$

Comparing the coefficients of like powers on either side, we have

$$\left.\begin{array}{l}\sqrt{(b-\lambda)}\sqrt{(c-\lambda)}=f\\ \sqrt{(c-\lambda)}\sqrt{(a-\lambda)}=g\\ \sqrt{(a-\lambda)}\sqrt{(b-\lambda)}=h\end{array}\right\}. \qquad \ldots(4)$$

Now if none of f, g, h is zero, the equations give

$$a-\lambda=\frac{gh}{f},\ b-\lambda=\frac{hf}{g},\ c-\lambda=\frac{fg}{h}$$

or $$a-\frac{gh}{f}=b-\frac{hf}{g}=c-\frac{fg}{h}\ (=\lambda). \qquad \ldots(5)$$

These are the required conditions.

Now if one of the quantities f, g, h is zero, say f is zero, then from the first of the equations (4), we get $\lambda=b$ or $\lambda=c$.

If $\lambda=b$, then $g=\sqrt{(b-b)}\sqrt{(c-b)}=0$.

If $\lambda=c$, then $h=\sqrt{(a-b)}\sqrt{(b-b)}=0$.

So we see that one of the three quantities f, g, h is zero then another quantity must be zero.

Hence the required conditions are

$$\left.\begin{array}{ll} & \lambda=a,\ g=0,\ h=0,\ (b-a)(c-a)=f^2\\ \text{or} & \lambda=b,\ h=0,\ f=0,\ (c-b)(a-b)=g^2\\ \text{or} & \lambda=c,\ f=0,\ g=0,\ (a-c)(b-c)=h^2\end{array}\right]. \qquad \ldots(6)$$

So if the equation (1) represents a surface of revolution then (5) and (6) give the conditions and the value of equal roots in each case.

SOLVED EXAMPLES (G)

Ex. 1. *If $f(x, y, z)=1$ represents an ellipsoid formed by the revolution of an ellipse about its major axis, show that the eccentricity of the generating ellipse is given by*

$$\frac{a+b+c}{3-e^2}=a-\frac{g-h}{f}.$$

Solution. Since $f(x, y, z) = 1$ represents an ellipsoid of revolution, it will reduce to an equation of the form

$$\lambda_1 x^2 + \lambda_2 y^2 + \lambda_2 z^2 = 1.$$

or $$\lambda_1 x^2 + \lambda_2 (y^2 + z^2) = 1. \qquad ...(1)$$

Here two roots of the discriminating cubic are equal (λ_2 and λ_3 are equal) and the third (*i.e.* λ_1) is non-zero so that the axis of revolution is x-axis (which is major axis of the ellipse). We have

[See § 16] $$a - gh/f = b - hf/g = c - fg/h = \lambda_2. \qquad ...(2)$$

The discriminating cubic is

$$\lambda^3 - (a + b + c)\,\lambda^2 + \lambda\,(A + B + C) - D = 0.$$

The sum of roots *i.e.* $\lambda_1 + \lambda_2 + \lambda_3 = (a + b + c)$

or $$\lambda_1 + 2\lambda_2 = a + b + c. \qquad ...(3)$$

Now the equations of the generating ellipse of the ellipsoid (1) are

$$\lambda_1 x^2 + \lambda_2 y^2 = 1, \quad z = 0$$

or $$\frac{x^2}{1/\lambda_1} + \frac{y^2}{1/\lambda_2} = 1, \quad z = 0$$

The eccentricity e of the ellipse is given by

$$\frac{1}{\lambda_2} = \frac{1}{\lambda_1}(1 - e^2) \qquad [\because b^2 = a^2(1 - e^2)]$$

or $$\frac{\lambda_1}{\lambda_2} = 1 - e^2 \quad \text{or} \quad \frac{\lambda_1}{\lambda_2} + 2 + 2 + 1 - e^2$$

or $$\frac{\lambda_1 + 2\lambda_2}{\lambda_2} = 3 - e^2 \quad \text{or} \quad (\lambda_1 - 2\lambda_2) = (3 - e^2)\,\lambda_2$$

or $$(a + b + c) = (3 - e^2)\,(a - gh/f) \qquad \text{[using (2) and (3)]}$$

or $$\frac{a + b + c}{3 - e^2} = a - \frac{gh}{f}.$$

Ex. 2. *If $f(x, y, z) = 0$ represents a right cone of semi-vertical angle α, then show that*

$$\frac{gh}{f} - a = \frac{hf}{g} - b = \frac{fg}{h} - c = \left(\frac{gh}{f} + \frac{hf}{g} + \frac{fg}{h}\right)\cos^2\alpha.$$

Solution. Since $f(x, y, z) = 0$ represents a right cone, the two roots of the discriminating cubic should be equal so that the given equation reduces to

$$\lambda_1 x^2 + \lambda_2 (y^2 + z^2) = 0$$

or $$y^2 + z^2 = -(\lambda_1/\lambda_2)\,x^2.$$

Let α be the semi-vertical angle of the cone. Then we have

$$\therefore \qquad \sec^2\alpha = 1 + \tan^2\alpha = 1 - \lambda_1/\lambda_2 = (\lambda_2 - \lambda_1)/\lambda_2$$

or
$$\frac{1}{\cos^2\alpha} = \frac{3\lambda_2 - (\lambda_1 + 2\lambda_2)}{\lambda_2}$$

or
$$\cos^2\alpha\,[3\lambda_2 - (\lambda_1 + 2\lambda_2)] = \lambda_2$$

or
$$\cos^2\alpha\left[\left(a - \frac{gh}{f}\right) + \left(b - \frac{hf}{g}\right) + \left(c - \frac{fg}{h}\right) - (a+b+c)\right]$$
$$= a - \frac{gh}{f} = b - \frac{hf}{g} = c - \frac{fg}{h}$$

[using the results (2) and (3) of Ex. 1 above]

or
$$\cos^2\alpha\left(\frac{gh}{f} + \frac{hf}{g} + \frac{fg}{h}\right) = \frac{gh}{f} - a = \frac{hf}{g} - b = \frac{fg}{h} - c.$$

Ex. 3. *Prove that if* $F(x, y, z) = 0$ *represents a paraboloid of revolution, then*

$$\frac{a}{f} + \frac{h}{g} + \frac{g}{h} = 0, \frac{h}{f} + \frac{b}{g} + \frac{f}{h} = 0, \frac{g}{f} + \frac{f}{g} + \frac{c}{h} = 0$$

and that if it represents a right circular cylinder, then there is also an additional condition $u/f + v/g + w/h = 0$.

Left as an exercise for practice.